Swithland Wood

A Study of its History and Vegetation

by

S. F. Woodward

B. Sc.,
Advanced Certificate in Ecology and
Environmental Management (Leicester).

Leicestershire Museums, Arts and Records Service

1992

Contents

List of Tables

List of Figures

Conventions and Abbreviations

Scientific and English names of plants

Ecologists conventionally use the scientific ('Latin') names of plants, but it is appreciated that readers without a biological background would find their exclusive use in this report irksome. On the other hand, the English names of many plants are imprecise, ambiguous, or in common usage by neither biologists nor laymen. A compromise has been adopted. Scientific names are always used on tables and diagrams within the biological chapters (5, 6 and 7), and in the text directly relating to them. Elsewhere, species that are very familiar to all readers, such as bracken, bramble and alder, are referred to by their English names if those names are well-established and unambiguous. The two common kinds of oak are distinguished, where necessary, by their scientific names *Quercus robur* and *Q. petraea*. When a species is first mentioned, both English and scientific names are given. For convenience, a cross-reference table for all species mentioned more than once in the main text is printed inside the back cover. Further details regarding nomenclature are given in chapter 5.

Measurements

Modern units of distance (metres, m) and area (hectares, ha) are used, except where reference or comparison is made to historical sources, which of course use the imperial system. In such cases, areas are given as acres, roods and perches in the traditional format a:r:p. The pre-decimal pound (£) contained twenty shillings (s), and each shilling was worth twelve pence (d).

1 m = 3.281 feet	1 acre = 4 roods
1 ha = 10000 square metres	1 rood = 40 perches
1 ha = 2.471 acres	

Bibliographical references

The first part of the References section (page 221) comprises published material of the kind that is available through most libraries. These items are called up in the main part of the text by author and year, for example (Mitchell 1974). The second part (page 226) lists manuscripts and old printed material that is accessible only in public or private archives. The main text (mainly chapter 3) cross-references this list by means of the numbers preceding each entry, for example (ref. 10).

Miscellaneous

Compartment numbers are those that have been defined for this project, and are shown on figure 2.2. Compartment is sometimes abbreviated to 'cmpt'. Numbers with the prefix SK, which appear in photograph captions and elsewhere, are grid references. Those that relate to the study area may be located on figure 2.3. Occasionally, years before Christ are given as b.c. rather than B.C., to distinguish radiocarbon years from calendar years.

Chapter 1

Introduction

Situated in attractive countryside, and less than ten miles from Loughborough and Leicester, Swithland Wood is one of Leicestershire's most popular public open spaces (figure 1.1). It is a varied wood in which the visitor will find magnificent oak, lime and holly trees, bracken glades, flower-rich meadows, marshes, rocky knolls and spectacular water-filled quarries. The wood is large enough to warrant many visits before all of its paths have been explored, and all of its corners discovered. There are few local woods that can rival the spring-time display of bluebells and wood anemones. Indeed, on one particular Sunday each spring, a 'bluebell service' is traditionally held in the wood.

The place has fascinated the writer from an early age. I recall, as a small child, clambering over the outcrops and skidding down the quarry spoil heaps; making dens beneath the bracken; and catching hapless creatures such as beetles and slow-worms. Even the least observant adult cannot fail to notice the animal life - the antics of the grey squirrels, the drumming of woodpeckers, or the caterpillar 'plagues' of green tortrix moth. Those with a more discerning eye for wild flowers soon discover that this is good hunting ground for common and rare species alike. Indeed, from the naturalists' point of view it is the rich variety of wildlife that is the principal attraction of Swithland Wood. Some consider it to be the finest wood in the county (Squires 1990). Along with nearby Bradgate Park, these two sites preserve aspects of Charnwood's natural heritage which, elsewhere, have not survived the twentieth century. This is not to say that the wood is 'natural' in the sense of being undisturbed by man; there is in fact a long history of exploitation. Students of landscape history and industrial history will find plenty to interest them here.

Despite its popularity with both naturalists and the general public, very little published information is available on Swithland Wood. Brief accounts of its wildlife are included in publications of somewhat wider geographical scope (NCC 1975, Ratcliffe 1977, Peterken 1981, Horwood & Gainsborough 1933, Primavesi & Evans 1988), but the more detailed accounts are not easily accessible (Gamble 1965, Loughborough Naturalists' Club 1970). None of these discusses the history of the site in any depth, although Ramsey (1986) has published a paper on the old slate quarries within the wood. My intention is to go some way towards filling this gap. I have attempted to cover three principal subjects: physical geography, history and botany. The geographical description (chapter 2) is based on original survey and addresses both natural and man-made features. The historical account (chapter 3) includes the results of original research on the woodlands belonging to the Bradgate Estate, the property of the Grey family. Indeed, Swithland Wood's history cannot be told except in the context of the estate to which it belonged. Consequently, chapter 3 is essentially a history of woodland on the Bradgate Estate. The botanical description has been approached in two complementary ways. The account of the *flora* (chapter 5) comprises a list of species together with information on the distribution and status of each. The list has been compiled from published records and from my own survey. The *vegetation* chapters (6 & 7), on the other hand, consider which species grow together in particular places, and in what quantity, and how these plant communities are physically structured. Representative samples were surveyed for this purpose using

Figure 1.1 The footpath from the ancient farmstead of Hallgates crosses some fields called 'Alblaster Hay', and enters the wood at a foot-bridge. (Compartment 80, SK53901187, November 1984.)

scientific (ecological) techniques. One of my personal interests is the relationships between vegetation and site history, so discussions with this theme will be found in several places. The animal life is unquestionably very diverse and interesting, but I have left the daunting task of cataloguing the fauna of Swithland Wood to future authors.

The plan of this book and the style of presentation reflect my scientific training: generally the facts are presented first, then their significance is discussed. Statements are supported, where appropriate, with bibliographical references. Where scientific methods of survey have been adopted, I have endeavoured to describe them in sufficient detail for the survey to be replicated. This has necessarily filled a few pages in the vegetation chapters with rather tedious explanations and definitions, which many readers will wish to skip over. I do hope that readers who may be accustomed to a more narrative style of natural history will appreciate why these details must be included. For the benefit of those who are unfamiliar with ecological methods and terminology, I have included a short chapter (4) to serve as an introduction to the ecological survey chapters. Finally, the findings are reviewed in chapter 8.

No project of this kind can claim to be comprehensive. Even within the subject areas I have outlined, there are certainly other aspects that need to be addressed. One of these is nature conservation. In 1988 Swithland Wood was at the centre of a well-publicised dispute over the suitability of its management for nature conservation. It is not my intention here to evaluate the ecological importance of the site, nor to argue for or against particular management operations. By and large, I have confined myself to presenting the results of my investigations along with an attempt at their interpretation. Hopefully, these may prove to be of value to those who will formulate future management plans. As one of the county's richest, most interesting and best-loved woods it is surely beyond dispute that every effort should be made to safeguard its beauty and fascination for future generations.

Chapter 2

Geography

2.1 General Site Information

2.1.1 Location

Swithland Wood lies approximately mid-way between Leicester and Loughborough, in west Leicestershire (figure 2.1). It straddles the parish boundary between Swithland and Newtown Linford, the latter parish containing most of the wood. The nearest villages are Swithland (0.5 km), Woodhouse Eaves (1 km), Cropston (2 km) and Newtown Linford (3 km). A permanent caravan and chalet site at Swithland Wood Farm abuts the wood on the west side, and the ancient farmstead of Hallgates lies some 300 m south of the eastern-most corner of the wood. The national grid reference is SK5312. Latitude is 52 degrees 42 minutes north, and longitude 1 degree 12 minutes west.

2.1.2 Definition and area

Swithland Wood is a complex site, and its precise extent requires some clarification (figure 2.2). The Ordnance Survey regard the whole of the continuous block of woodland here as Swithland Wood, i.e. both the larger portion in Newtown Linford, and the two compartments (labelled 1 and 2) in Swithland parish. The scope of this project is somewhat different. Essentially, it is the part of Swithland Wood that lies within Newtown Linford parish; i.e. all except compartments 1 and 2. The eastern boundary of the study area is the fence which delimits these two compartments. The parish boundary does not follow the fence precisely, but takes a parallel course a few metres within (and in some places beyond) the fence. Thus the study area actually includes some thin strips of Swithland parish.

Contained within the woodland are two disused water-filled quarries and some grassland. Table 2.1 gives the areas of the various categories. The woodland rides, including one about 15 m wide which follows the course of a water main, have been included with the woodland areas. In order to avoid tiresome qualification each time, the name *Swithland Wood* will be used henceforth to refer to the study area only, as detailed in table 2.1, unless otherwise noted.

2. Geography

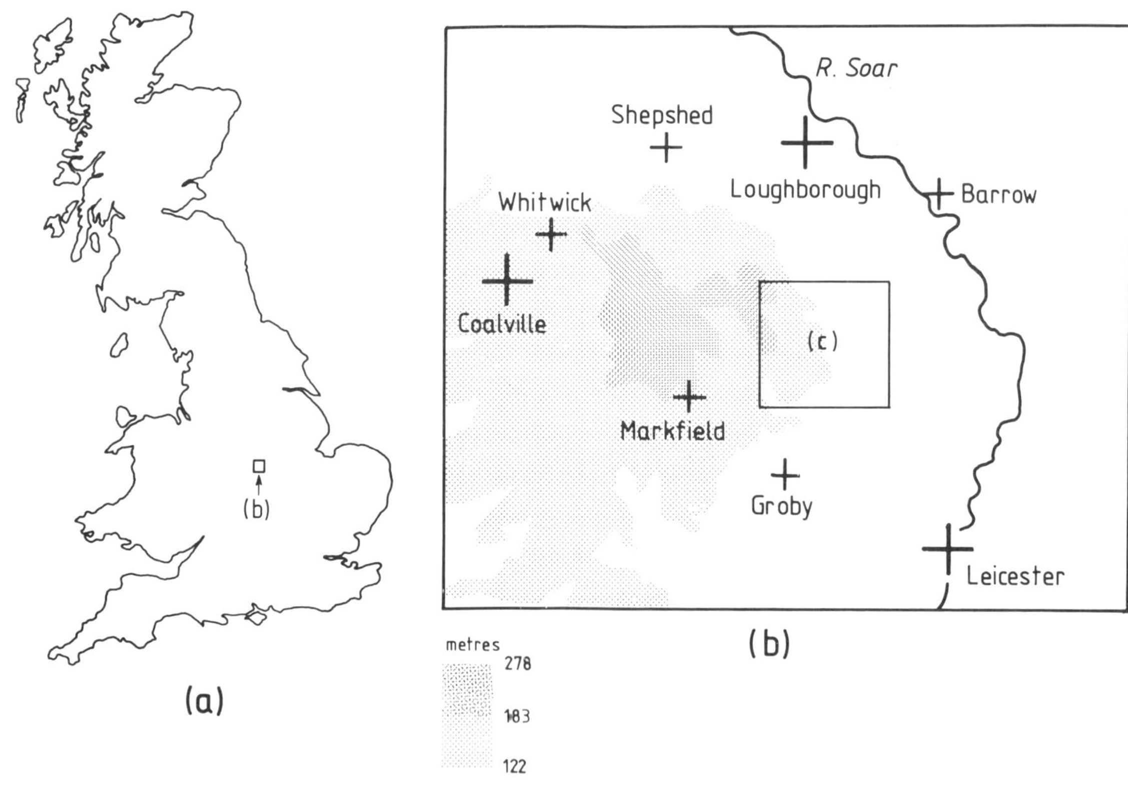

(b)

(a)

R. Soar
Shepshed
Loughborough
Barrow
Whitwick
Coalville
(c)
Markfield
Groby
Leicester
metres
278
183
122

(b)

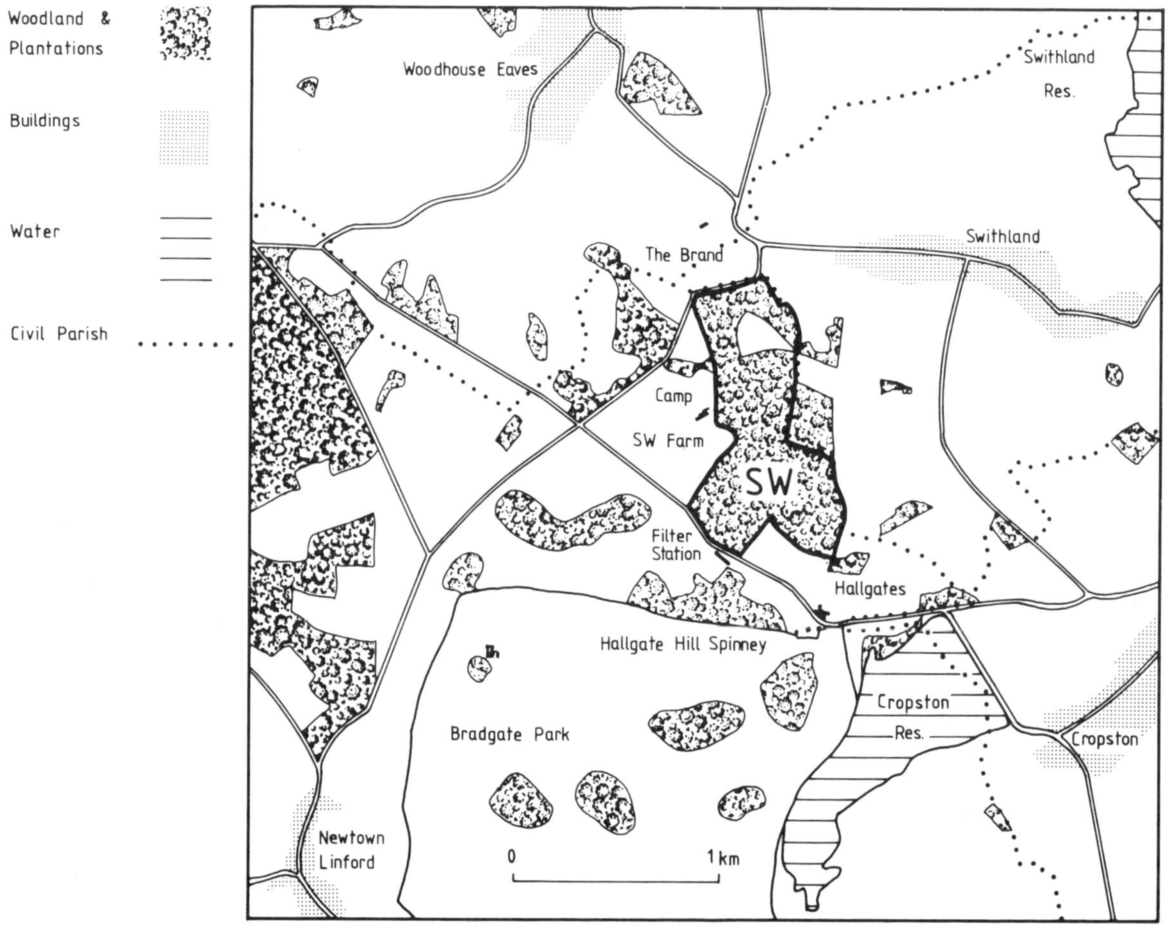

Woodland & Plantations
Buildings
Water
Civil Parish
Woodhouse Eaves
Swithland Res.
Swithland
The Brand
Camp
SW Farm
SW
Filter Station
Hallgates
Hallgate Hill Spinney
Bradgate Park
Cropston Res.
Cropston
Newtown Linford
0
1 km

(c)

2.1.3 Compartments

The wood has been subdivided into a number of *compartments* for the purposes of recording and reference. Their boundaries and numbers are also marked on figure 2.2. As far as possible, they are defined by features which are easily identified on the ground: earthworks, main rides and fences (compare with figure 2.3). Apart from the practicality of finding compartment boundaries in the wood, there were other reasons for using these features. One of the aims of the project was to investigate the historical development and past management of the site. It will be shown in later sections that in past centuries the wood was regarded as a number of separate units, and that these were very probably delimited by earthworks and other topographical features. It has been presumed that their origins and management histories are different. In an attempt to bring out any biological differences between them, compartment boundaries follow those features which were thought to be historical boundaries.

Table 2.1. Constituent parts of Swithland Wood, listing all the parts shown by the Ordnance Survey as belonging to 'Swithland Wood'; the area of each part (author's calculation); the extent of public access in 1986; and the area covered by this project. Compartment numbers are those shown in figure 2.2.

Description	Area (ha)	Public access	Study area
Newtown Linford parish			
Woodland	54.00	*	*
Quarry enclosures: water	0.47		*
: rock/spoil	1.07		*
Large field (cmpt 21)	1.92		*
Small field (cmpt 23)	0.61	*	*
Plantation (cmpt 22)	0.82		*
Swithland parish (all woodland)			
Compartment 1	4.58		
Compartment 2	6.13		
Strips between parish boundary and fence	0.21	*	*
TOTALS			
Woodland and plantation	65.74		55.03
Water and Quarries	1.54		1.54
Grassland	2.53		2.53
GRAND TOTAL	69.81 (172.5 acres)		59.10 (146.0 acres)

< **Figure 2.1.** Location of Swithland Wood within (a) Great Britain; (b) West Leicestershire; (c) parishes and adjacent settlements.

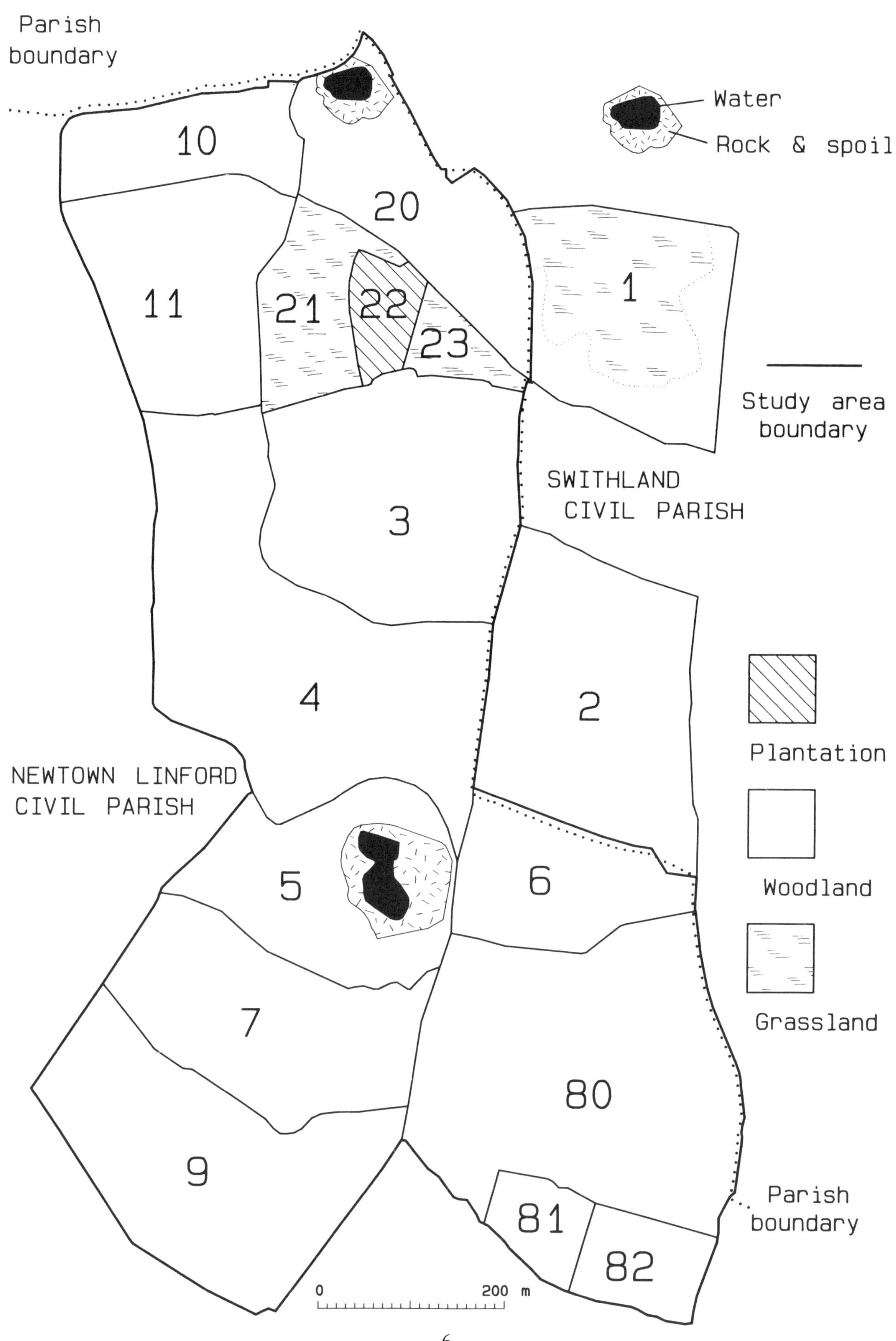
Parish
boundary
Water
Rock & spoil
10
20
1
11
21
22
23
Study area
boundary
SWITHLAND
CIVIL PARISH
3
4
2
Plantation
NEWTOWN LINFORD
CIVIL PARISH
5
6
Woodland
7
Grassland
80
9
81
82
Parish
boundary
0
200 m

Fortuitously, all of the historical boundaries coincided almost exactly with the compartment boundaries used in the Loughborough Naturalists' Club survey (LNC 1970). The LNC used main tracks to split off two extra compartments; numbers 3 and 6. These have been retained for this project even though there was no historical justification for them. This allowed maximum use to be made of LNC records, and reduced the size of what would otherwise have been very large compartments. Where the LNC compartments coincide, their reference numbers have been adopted, i.e. numbers 3, 4, 5, 6, 7 and 9. LNC compartment 1 has been split for this project into 10 and 11, likewise 2 into 20, 21, 22 and 23 and 8 into 80, 81 and 82. Table 2.2 gives some details for each compartment.

Table 2.2. Numbered compartments within Swithland Wood, as adopted for this project.

Compartment number	Area (ha)	(acres)	Notes
3	6.30	15.57	
4	8.87	21.92	
5	4.63	11.44	Contains quarry enclosure (1.16 ha)
6	2.79	6.89	
7	4.91	12.13	
9	6.43	15.89	Contains car-park
10	2.29	5.65	Contains car-park
11	4.31	10.64	
20	4.05	10.01	Contains quarry enclosure (0.38 ha)
21	1.92	4.74	Grazed field with scrub
22	0.82	2.03	Mixed plantation
23	0.61	1.51	Mown grass with about 50% scrub
80	9.05	22.36	
81	0.82	2.03	
82	1.30	3.21	

2.1.4 Ownership

Swithland Wood is owned by the Bradgate Park Trust. The Trust was established in 1929 to look after nearby Bradgate Park, a gift to the people of Leicester from a local benefactor. Swithland Wood was acquired in 1931, also as a charitable donation (see section 3.9). The Trust is administered through Leicestershire County Council, who employ full-time keepers. Compartments 1 and 2 are privately owned.

2.1.5 Access

Most of Bradgate Park Trust's property is Public Open Space, and both Swithland Wood and Bradgate Park are open to the public at all times. Several public footpaths and bridleways lead through the wood, and visitors' car-parks have been provided. Visitors are

< **Figure 2.2.** Swithland Wood; the study area and adjacent woodland, showing the 1978 civil parish boundary and the compartment numbers adopted for this study. Compartments 1 and 2 (in Swithland parish) are outside the study area.

not permitted to take their vehicles beyond the car-parks, but there are gravel tracks for the use of the keepers' Land-rovers. Restricted access to one of the water-filled quarries is available to a skin-diving club, otherwise both quarries are securely enclosed in the interests of public safety. The larger of the fields (cmpt 21) and the adjacent plantation (cmpt 22) are closed to the public. The ease of access by car from both Loughborough and Leicester ensures that Swithland Wood is a very busy place on fine Sunday afternoons. Accurate figures are not available, but the Department of Planning and Transportation at County Hall estimates that the annual number of visitors is 150,000 (excluding dogs!).

2.1.6 Nature conservation status and management

The wood has been scheduled by the Nature Conservancy Council (NCC) as a Site of Special Scientific Interest (SSSI) grade 2 (Ratcliffe 1977), and re-scheduled following the Wildlife and Countryside Act (1981). The emphasis of management has been on public amenity rather than nature conservation. Recently, there has been a well-publicised disagreement between the owners and the NCC regarding management (see ref. 68).

The whole of the area occupied by compartments 21, 22 and 23 used to be divided into two enclosures known as the Wood Meadows. Some time in the late 1960s, a mixed (but mainly coniferous) plantation was planted up in part of the larger meadow (cmpt 22). The trees in the plantation were set in rows and are treated as a forestry crop. Thinning was carried out in 1986. The remainder of the large meadow (cmpt 21) has been grazed and the smaller meadow (cmpt 23) has been mown. Both areas of grassland now contain large thorn bushes, and small trees of birch and oak, indicating that grazing intensity in the past has been low. A few cattle are grazed on compartment 21 intermittently throughout the year. In compartment 23, shrub encroachment from the woodland margins is well advanced and affects about half the area (figure 2.3). What remains of the grassland is mown once in summer.

Active management in the semi-natural woodland entails the maintenance of tracks, fences and ditches, and the occasional removal of fallen and sometimes standing trees. About 20 saplings were planted in various places throughout the wood in 1986, but planting has not been a regular practice. The quarry enclosures are unmanaged and largely undisturbed. The spoil heaps are sometimes used as a source of material to repair tracks.

2.2 Situation

2.2.1 Charnwood Forest

That part of north-west Leicestershire between Leicester, Loughborough and Coalville is occupied by a region known as Charnwood Forest. Since 1974 the name Charnwood has been attached to an administrative borough (Evans 1976), but its extent is somewhat different from the true Forest, which is a topographically and historically distinct tract of countryside. The Charnwood landscape has an upland character, with its rugged scarps, slate walls, and fragments of heathland and sessile oak-wood (i.e. predominantly *Quercus petraea*). Of the numerous woods within Charnwood Forest, none is bigger than one hundred hectares and most are set within a mixed farming landscape. The proportion of woodland of various sorts in Charnwood is about 12% (Crocker 1981), compared with 2% for the county (NCC 1983) and 9.4% for Great Britain (Locke 1987). The history of land-use on the Forest is reviewed in section 3.4.

2.2.2 Geology

Much of western Leicestershire lies on *Keuper Marl*, a soft, brick-red material that was laid down in the Triassic period (about 200 million years ago). It is more accurately described as a mudstone, comprising clay and silt particles. Generally, it gives rise to a somewhat flat landscape, but in Charnwood Forest, a series of very much older and harder rocks reach the surface and protrude through the Keuper Marl as craggy hills. These older rocks were originally laid down in the late Precambrian period (650-700 million years ago), as volcanic material settled out below water. Major upheavals shortly afterwards compressed, heated and distorted these sedimentary rocks, to form the tilted layers of metamorphic rocks that we can find today. In Charnwood Forest, the Precambrian rocks occur as an *anticline*, or upward fold. The top of the fold has been worn down to expose older rocks; these are found towards the centre of the Forest. The youngest of the Precambrian rocks, which sit directly below the Keuper Marl, are to be found at the edges of the Forest. Between the Precambrian and Triassic periods, these old rocks would have been buried and re-exposed several times. In more recent times (less than a million years ago), relatively thin layers of material associated with the 'ice-age' have been deposited. These include *boulder clay* (dumped by glaciers) and *alluvium* (dumped by meltwater).

For further information on Leicestershire and Charnwood geology, readers are referred to Hains & Horton 1969, Martin 1988, Ford 1975 and Sutherland *et al.* 1987. Details of the geology within Swithland Wood itself are given in section 2.3.3.

2.2.3 Climate

Meteorological Office statistics are available for a station in Newtown Linford, at the same altitude as the wood. A brief summary of the observations made between 1960 and 1983 is given in table 2.3 (Met. Office 1960-1983). These figures are intended to give a general description of the local climate. The flora of the site is, of course, strongly influenced by climate but it should not be assumed that the parameters given in the table correspond with limiting factors for any particular species. From an ecological point of view, the selection presented in table 2.3 is unavoidably arbitrary.

Table 2.3. Summary of meteorological data for Newtown Linford (altitude 119 metres) for the period 1960-1983.

Air temperature (Celsius)		
(a) Mean of daily maxima	12.8	
(b) Mean of daily minima	4.9	
Mean of (a)+(b)	8.8	
Highest maximum	33.1	(1975)
Lowest minimum	-16.1	(1963)
Rainfall (mm)		
Average annual total	672	
Maximum annual total	909	(1960)
Minimum annual total	494	(1975)
Average number of days with frost		
Air frost	60	
Ground frost	113	
Average duration of bright sunshine		
(hours per day)	3.52	

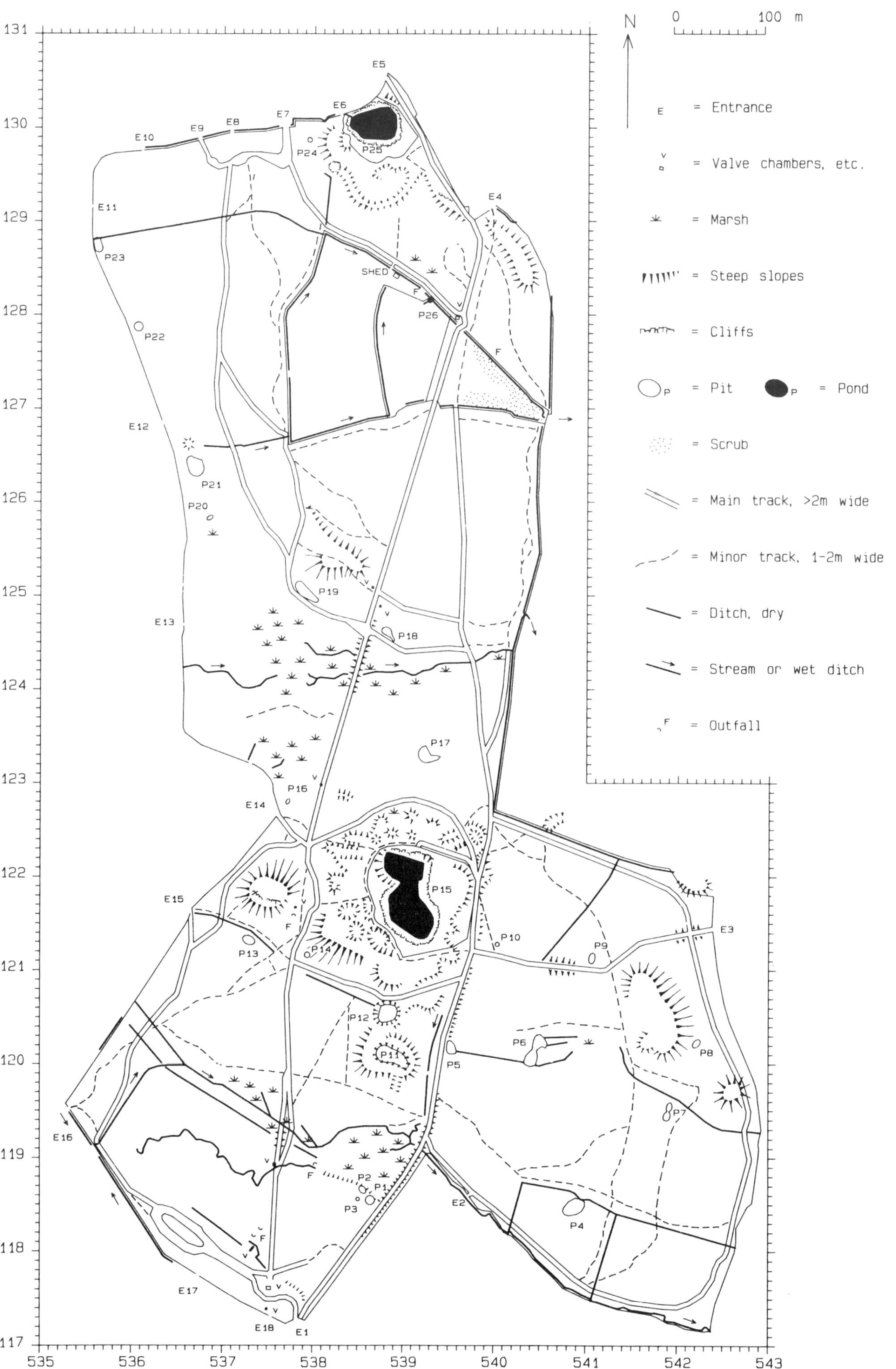
N
0
100 m
E = Entrance
v = Valve chambers, etc.
= Marsh
= Steep slopes
= Cliffs
P = Pit
P = Pond
= Scrub
= Main track, >2m wide
= Minor track, 1-2m wide
= Ditch, dry
= Stream or wet ditch
F = Outfall
E1
E2
E3
E4
E5
E6
E7
E8
E9
E10
E11
E12
E13
E14
E15
E16
E17
E18
P1
P2
P3
P4
P5
P6
P7
P8
P9
P10
P11
P12
P13
P14
P15
P16
P17
P18
P19
P20
P21
P22
P23
P24
P25
P26
SHED
131
130
129
128
127
126
125
124
123
122
121
120
119
118
117
535
536
537
538
539
540
541
542
543

2.3 Site Description

2.3.1 The survey

The most detailed Ordnance Survey plan (1:2500 or 25 inches to the mile) gives the boundaries of woodland, quarries and grassland, and shows such internal features as principal tracks and streams. Some of these features (particularly tracks) are not accurately represented. Moreover, the project is concerned with minor features that the OS did not attempt to map; marshes, pits, outcrops, etc. The first year of fieldwork (1982-3) was devoted to revising and adding the details to the OS plan. The result was a base map showing all principal man-made and natural topographical features in the wood (a copy is held on file at the museum). Figures 2.3 and 2.10 present the results of this survey.

It was necessary to locate both major and minor tracks reasonably accurately within the wood because they would be used later for reference, particularly in parts of the wood distant from any other landmarks. Other features including distinctive trees, pits, outcrops, valve chambers and inspection covers associated with the water main, were mapped principally for their value as landmarks. The survey was accomplished with the aid of a compass and a calibrated pace. Some key distances were measured with a surveyor's tape. It is estimated that the inaccuracy inherent in this method may have displaced some features on the map by, at worst, 30 m from their true position. Despite this, eight figure grid references have been used to locate small features on the map to a resolution of 10 m.

Special efforts were made to locate those man-made features which reflect the history of the site. In addition to the quarries,various types of earthwork are to be found in Swithland Wood. They include banks and ditches which appear to relate to old boundaries, and 'ridge-and-furrow'. The latter term describes the regular undulations in land that was ploughed by methods prevalent in the Middle Ages, and which has since remained relatively undisturbed (Taylor 1975).

2.3.2 Rides and tracks

Rides and tracks have been represented on figure 2.3 by two symbols, according to their importance. Major rides and tracks are those greater than two metres in width. These include the made-up roads regularly used by horses or vehicles, which appear to derive from the occupation roads in use when the quarries were being worked in the nineteenth century. A substantial embankment beneath the road at grid reference SK538118, and lesser examples elsewhere, suggests that the natural topography of the wood proved something of a hindrance to the heavy stone-laden carts. Also shown are minor unmade tracks of between one and two metres average width. These tracks are well defined and did not change their course noticeably over the four years of fieldwork. A lower class of path (less than one metre wide) was surveyed for the base map, and was found to be useful for the purposes of location. However, these paths have not been included on figure 2.3, firstly to avoid cluttering the map, and secondly because they will have wandered significantly in the space of a few years.

Some of the wider tracks in the wood have been designated as bridle-ways by means of marker posts, but have not been distinguished as such on the map. Likewise, official

---

< **Figure 2.3.** Principal topographical features of Swithland Wood. Based on the Ordnance Survey, amended and with details added from the author's own survey (mainly 1982-3). The margin shows the national grid with references for 100 metre squares. The entrances marked are the 'official' ones; there are, in addition, many gaps in the stone wall between E11 and E14. Vehicular access to the car-parks is through E1, E7 and E9. The main track between E18 and E4 follows the line of a water main along which there are access covers for air valves and valve chambers.

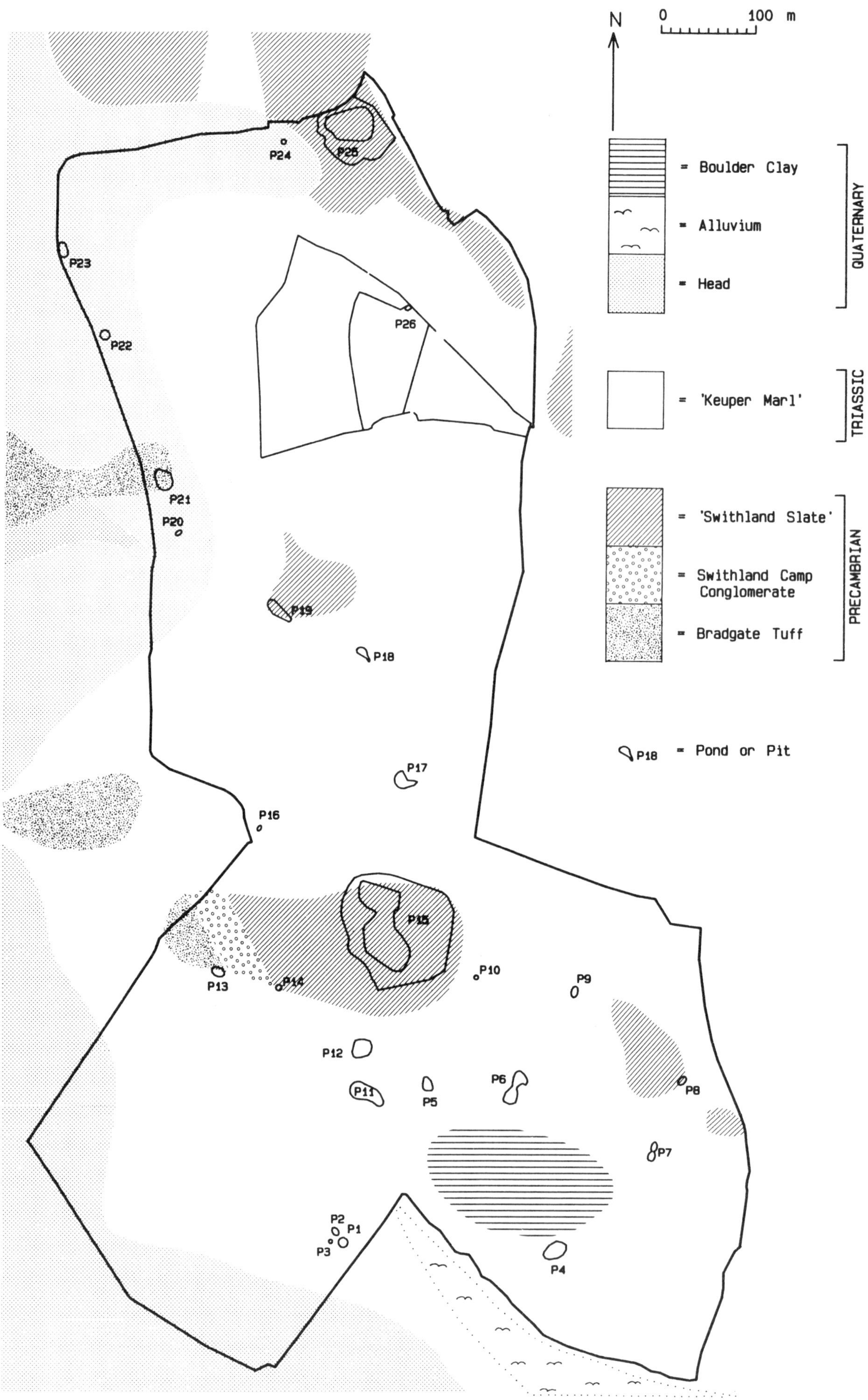

N
0
100 m
= Boulder Clay
= Alluvium
= Head
QUATERNARY
= 'Keuper Marl'
TRIASSIC
= 'Swithland Slate'
= Swithland Camp Conglomerate
= Bradgate Tuff
PRECAMBRIAN
P18 = Pond or Pit
P1
P2
P3
P4
P5
P6
P7
P8
P9
P10
P11
P12
P13
P14
P15
P16
P17
P18
P19
P20
P21
P22
P23
P24
P25
P26

public rights of way have not been separately indicated (these can be found on any OS map). The conspicuous ride from the southern tip to the north-east of the wood follows the course of a water main. It is raised above the marsh in compartment 4 by a large embankment.

2.3.3 Geology and relief

Swithland Wood lies at the eastern edge of Charnwood Forest, where the youngest of the Precambrian rocks plunge eastwards below the Keuper Marl (figure 2.4.) These Precambrian rocks are popularly known as *Swithland Slate*; technically they belong to the *Swithland Greywacke Formation*. The bedding plane dips to the north-east at an angle of roughly 40 degrees to the horizontal, although it is the cleavage plane that is most conspicuous at the outcrops. There are slate outcrops in several areas. The north-eastern boundary of the wood, in compartment 20, is formed by a ridge of slate, now quarried away at the extreme north (P25). A second prominent outcrop of slate is found in compartment 3 (beside P18). The quarry in compartment 5 (P15) exploits the largest exposure. Two smaller outcrops lie to its east in compartment 80. The knoll to the west of the quarry in compartment 5 is composed of rocks older than the slate; namely *Swithland Camp Conglomerate* and *Bradgate Tuff*. The latter also occurs at the western boundary of compartment 3 (by P21).

During the last glaciation (*Devensian*) the alternate freezing and thawing of moisture at the surface of the outcrops caused fragments to break loose and accumulate as a superficial deposit known as *head*. It surrounds many outcrops in Charnwood Forest, and occurs in parts of Swithland Wood; notably compartment 10, the western edge of compartment 11, and the southern and eastern parts of compartment 9. Beneath the root-plates of windthrown trees and in the stream beds one can find these fragments of various sizes. The mapping of boulder clay is not consistent over the whole wood (see caption to figure 2.4), and its true distribution is imperfectly known.

Original work on relief was confined to marking steep slopes and cliffs on the base map (figure 2.3) - the contours provided by the OS show the basic pattern of hills and valleys in the wood (figure 2.5). The relief is varied, with a wide range of slopes and aspects. The underlying trend is that of a eastward facing slope, but this is modified by three valleys (V1-3) and four ridges (R1-4). This is shown by the vertical section. All the valleys run east or south-eastwards. Ridge R1 corresponds with the slate exposure at the north-eastern corner of the wood. It is an extension of a ridge running through adjacent estate known as The Brand. R2 and R3 are most prominent at the western side of the wood, both of them petering out before reaching the eastern boundary. R2 is the weaker of the two, and expresses itself most conspicuously as the knoll in compartment 3. R3 raises Swithland Wood to its summit of about 120 m and extends all the way across compartment 5 where it has been extensively quarried. The outcrops in compartment 80 represent the fragmented extremity of this ridge. South of valley V3, the rising ground labelled R4 continues to rise beyond the limit of the section through Hallgate Hill Spinney and into Bradgate Park. There are no rocky crags associated with this ridge within Swithland Wood, but they do occur in Hallgate Hill Spinney. Away from the outcrops, slopes in the wood are generally less than five degrees.

< **Figure 2.4.** Geology within Swithland Wood, based in part on the Geological Survey of Great Britain. The disposition of the Precambrian outcrops has been corrected to agree with the author's more detailed survey. The quaternary deposits have not been mapped by the author, and are taken from the Geological Survey. However, these should be regarded as approximate. The eastern part of the wood was covered by different surveyors to the western part (sheets 155 & 156 respectively). When the two maps are juxtaposed it is clear that the interpretation of drift deposits is inconsistent; consequently the author has been obliged to smooth out the discontinuities.

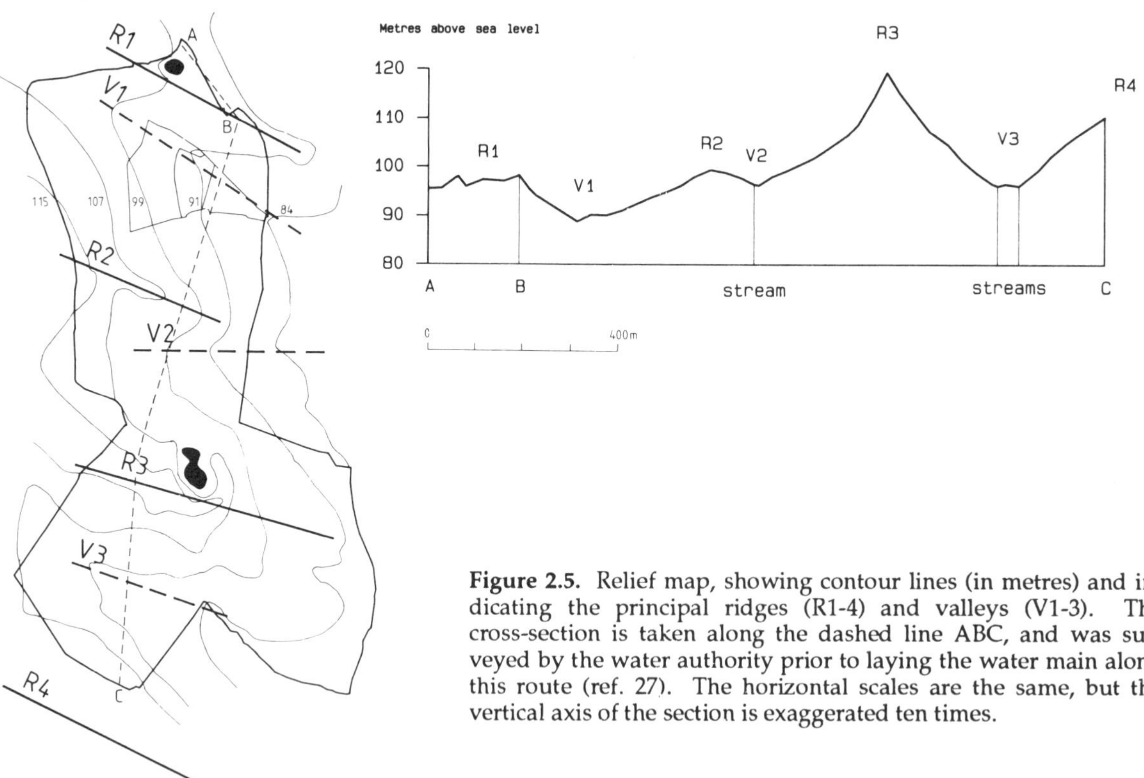

Figure 2.5. Relief map, showing contour lines (in metres) and indicating the principal ridges (R1-4) and valleys (V1-3). The cross-section is taken along the dashed line ABC, and was surveyed by the water authority prior to laying the water main along this route (ref. 27). The horizontal scales are the same, but the vertical axis of the section is exaggerated ten times.

2.3.4 Drainage

None of the streams in Swithland Wood (figure 2.3) carries a great deal of water. They frequently dry up altogether, even in winter. The stream in valley V1 follows a wholly artificial course, from the ditches around the Wood Meadows, along their northern edge via a tiny pond (P26), then out of the wood. The ditch at the southern edge of the meadows is usually dry.

Much of valley V2 is poorly drained, and has become marshy and dominated by alders. The water main embankment has apparently divided what used to be a continuous marsh into three smaller ones. One is supplied by a trickle of water which emerges from beneath the track to Swithland Wood Farm at SK53651242. A spring at SK53751231 feeds another. Both of them drain through a culvert below the embankment into the third marsh. The stream follows a natural meandering course towards the east side of the wood. Here it encounters a large artificial bank (see section AK on figure 2.11), apparently contrived to force the flow northwards along a deep ditch for some 400 m before releasing it into the private part of the wood.

The drainage in valley V3 has been modified significantly. The sinuous stream shown by the OS is now quite dry and, judging by the profusion of ash saplings in its bed, has not carried any water for some years. The presence of old alders nearby demonstrates that wetter conditions once prevailed here. Extensive disturbance is evident between the old stream bed and the south car-park. A complex system of gulleys and embankments occupies the area indicated in figure 2.3. Six earthen dams had been made across the former stream, with pools excavated behind each. Prior to 1984, this section of the wood had been fenced off for many years; one reason why it has not been surveyed in detail. These features are connected with Severn Trent Water Authority's filter station at Hallgates, just to the south of the wood. A fuller account of the earthworks will be found in section 3.8, in relation to the history and operation of the filter station. The result of the disturbance is that the stream which enters the south-western corner of compartment 9, and which once meandered eastwards, is now channelled north-eastwards. This channel cuts through an older ditch as it turns through 90 degrees to the right, to form the compartment's northern boundary. A minor stream entering this compartment's northern corner is also captured by the diverted stream. Two marshy areas, in compartments 7 and 9 respectively, flank the stream as it flows towards the embanked occupation road. It is culverted beneath the embankment, whence it continues along an apparently natural course to define the southern edge of compartments 80, 81 and 82.

A small marshy area is to be found at the northern extremity of compartment 5. It appears to be the result of seepage from the water-filled quarry (P15) about 50 m to the south. After leaving the wood, all streams eventually merge in Swithland village prior to discharging into Swithland Reservoir.

2.3.5 Soils

Soil is a mixture of mineral particles, organic matter, water and air (Jarman 1984). The mineral component derives from the *parent material*, which may be either solid rock or else superficial drift deposits such as boulder clay. Even minor drift layers, too small in thickness or extent to warrant representation on the geological map, may give rise to different kinds of soil over a distance of a few metres, as Rackham (1980) has described for some East Anglian woods. Consequently, a soil map would be far more useful than a regular geological map in understanding plant distribution. Unfortunately, a detailed soil survey has not been possible. In the first place, the writer is not qualified in this specialist field, and secondly, to map such a large and varied site as Swithland Wood at a useful level of detail would be a major project in itself. The treatment of soils here is confined to two aspects. Firstly *soil reaction* or acidity (pH) was measured at various sites throughout the wood; and secondly *soil profiles* (including simple texture assessments) were recorded at rather fewer sites.

Soil reaction

The samples taken for pH analysis were located at the centre of each of 74 field layer samples (see section 6.2.2) and two other places (figure 2.6). One of the reasons for measuring soil reaction was to relate it to field layer vegetation, therefore the samples were extracted at the depth of most roots (usually about five centimetres). Samples were collected on 14 September 1986, sealed in polythene bags, then taken to Leicester University (Department of Botany) the following day. Each sample was mixed with de-ionised water into a slurry and tested with a glass electrode pH meter (EIL model 3050). The meter was periodically checked against buffer solutions of pH 7.0 and 4.0.

A value of pH 7 is neutral, lower values are acidic and higher values are alkaline. The results are shown in figure 2.6. The soils are predominantly acidic; 54% of the samples lie in the range pH 4.3 to 4.8. Only twelve samples measured pH 5.5 or greater. Most of these were from marshes, or else from compartment 9, where recent disturbance and effluent associated with Hallgates Filter Station (see section 3.8) would seem to have modified the soils. Some readings from slate spoil heaps gave higher readings than expected: 4.9, 5.0 and even 6.5 at the far north. Outcrops of hard rocks such as slate normally give rise to acid soils because bases are released so slowly relative to the leaching effect of rain-water. Perhaps basic minerals are released in greater abundance from small rock fragments, as occurs on mountain screes (Pearsall 1971, page 58).

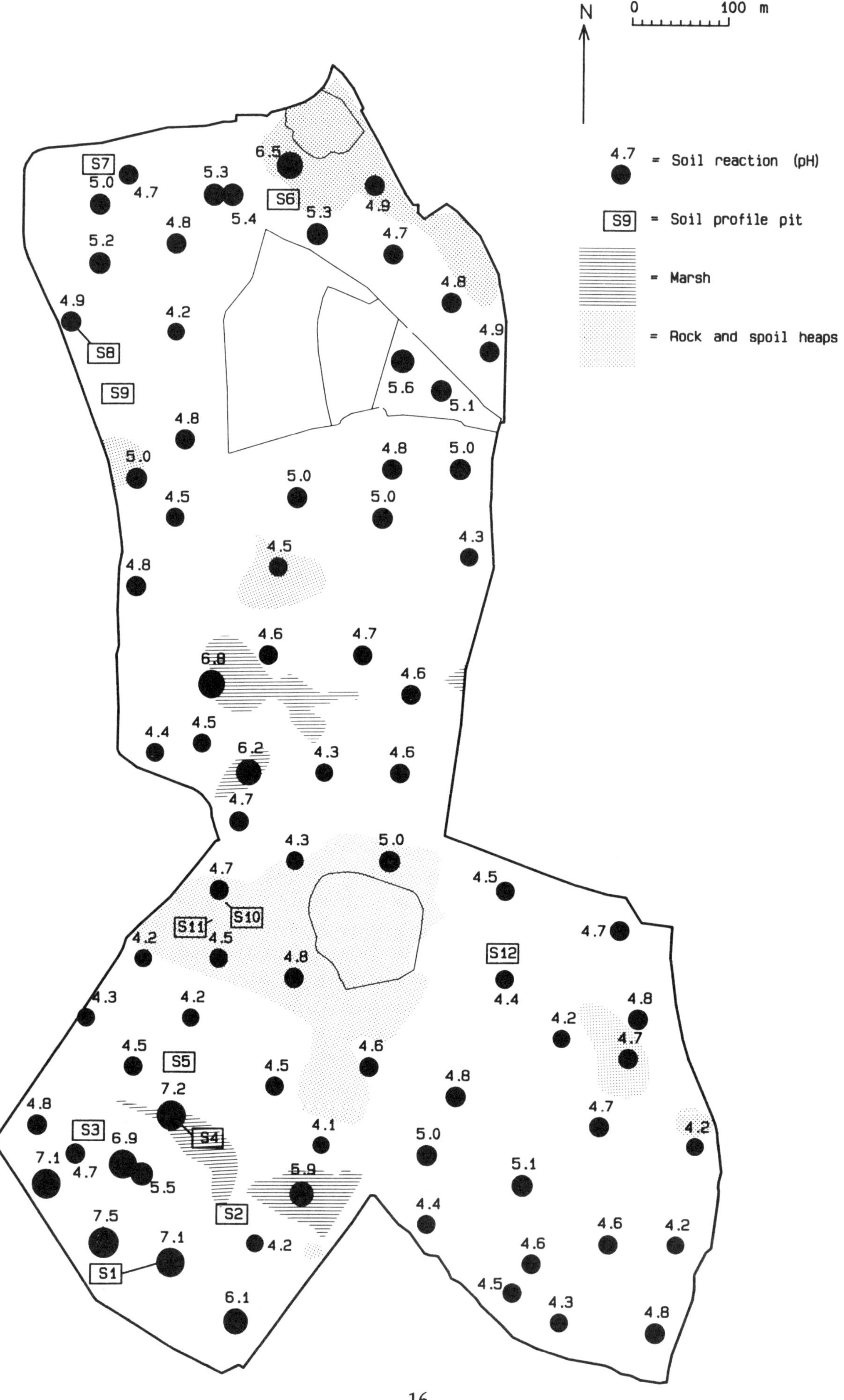

N
0
100 m
4.7 = Soil reaction (pH)
S9 = Soil profile pit
= Marsh
= Rock and spoil heaps

Soil profiles

From the ground's surface down to the bedrock, soil generally varies in colour, texture and composition. In woodland, the proportion of organic material, for example, is greatest near the surface. More or less distinct horizontal layers known as *soil horizons* can usually be discerned. In Swithland Wood twelve pits were excavated with a trowel to reveal vertical sections or *soil profiles*. This technique did not reach any great depth, of course, but from the ecological point of view it is the upper horizons which are most relevant. The soil pits (S1-S12) were sited so as to cover the range of variation in soil types, as expressed in the vegetation and other surface attributes. The profiles were measured and sketched, and are presented as figure 2.7. In these sketches, an attempt has been made to assign letters to the horizons according to the scheme used by soil scientists (Trudgill 1989). Typically, three horizons of purely organic material (L, F and H) are present at the top of the profile. Uppermost are fallen leaves and twigs that have hardly begun to decay, which comprise the litter or *L* horizon. Then there is a layer of decomposing litter, known as the *F* or fermentation horizon. Below this is the *H* horizon, made up of humus in which plant remains are no longer recognisable. The F and H horizons are often too thin or else insufficiently distinct to be shown separately on the figure. In Swithland Wood, the horizons containing minerals derived from the parent rock are generally designated *A* and *B*. The A horizon is the uppermost layer of mineral matter into which organic material has been washed down (or pulled down by earthworms) to give it a brown colour. Below this is the B horizon, which lacks humus and differs in texture and colour. B horizons also differ from the parent rock in that weathering has displaced certain minerals. None of the profiles in this study was deep enough to expose little-altered parent rock - the *C* horizon. Some profiles exhibit a pale layer called an *E* horizon. This mineral horizon has been weathered to the extent that iron and aluminium salts and/or clay particles have been washed out and deposited lower down in the profile. Figure 2.7 includes notes on colours, and descriptions of the B horizon texture. The terms used to describe texture have particular meanings in soil science. They refer to the relative proportions of clay, silt and sand particles. The procedure used to determine texture is that of Burnham (1980), which is a simple field test in which moistened soil is manipulated between the fingers.

Most of the profiles from Swithland Wood have a well developed A horizon, in which organic and mineral matter are well mixed and form a 'crumb' structure, often inhabited by worms and moles. Such a topsoil is described as a *mull*. In a few profiles, however, litter has evidently not decomposed readily and persists as a thin blackish layer (with a characteristic smell), directly above the mineral horizons. This kind of topsoil, without a clear A horizon, is called a *mor*.

Some of the B horizons are dark greyish in colour, and contain orange mottling. Under waterlogged conditions, iron salts exist in the reduced (ferrous) state, which are grey in colour. Where atmospheric oxygen is able to penetrate, down cracks or root channels, then the salts become oxidised (ferric) and turn rusty orange. Hence, this pattern of coloration in a soil shows that it is periodically waterlogged, and is described as a *gley*. The suffix *g* is used to identify gleyed horizons.

Conclusions

The range of soils is perhaps not surprising in view of the varied geology and topography of the site. Profiles S2, S3, and S4 are gley soils; they are typical of marshy ground and valley bottoms where the water table is seasonally close the surface. Profile S12, near the top

< **Figure 2.6.** Soil sampling sites and pH values. The circle diameter is proportional to the pH value. The high values tend to come from marshes and from the south-west (compartment 9). In compartment 21 (the large pasture) the pH is reported to vary between 5.6 and 7.0 (Primavesi & Evans 1988).

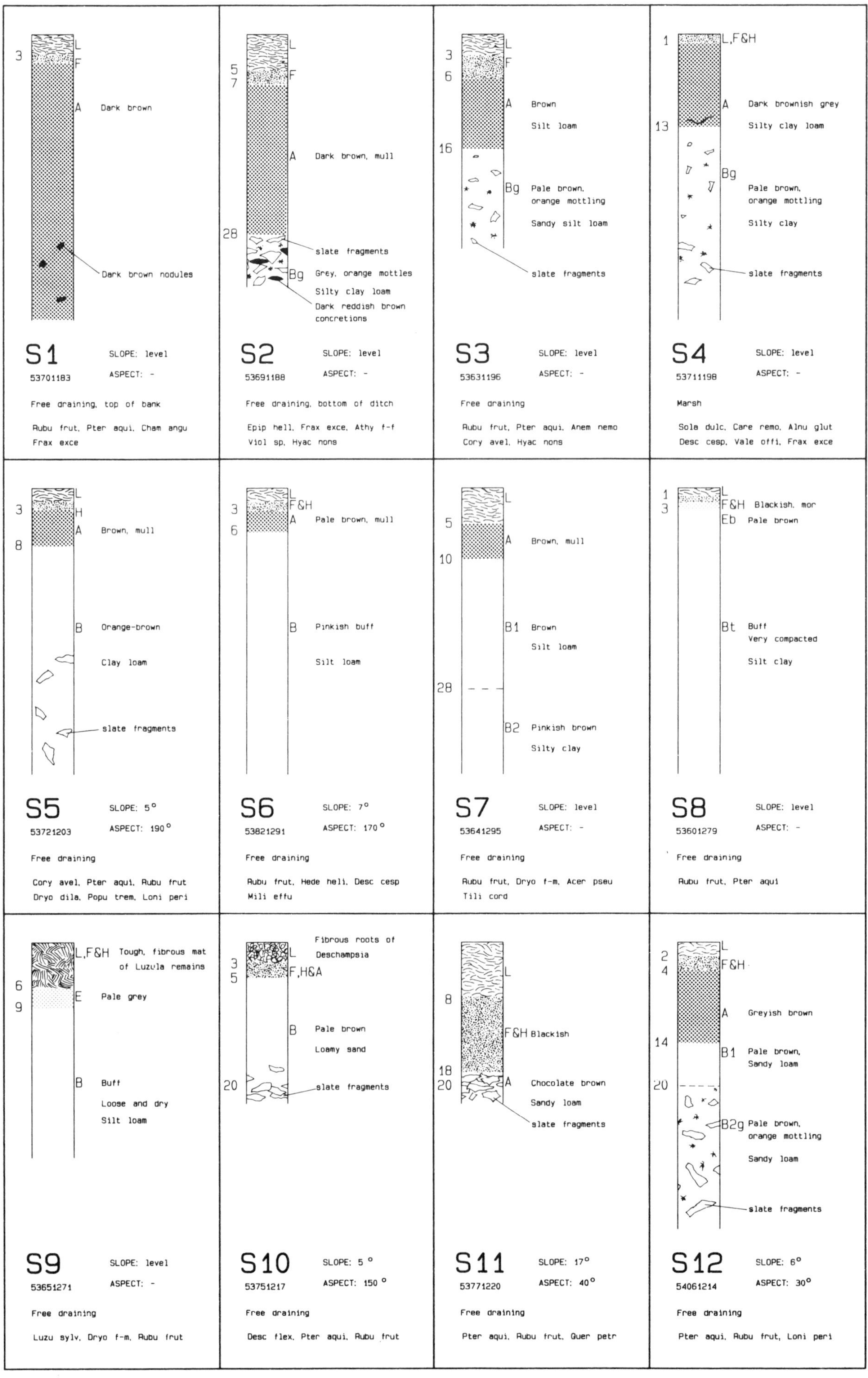

S1
SLOPE: level
ASPECT: -
53701183
3
L
F
A Dark brown
Dark brown nodules
Free draining, top of bank
Rubu frut, Pter aqui, Cham angu
Frax exce
S2
SLOPE: level
ASPECT: -
53691188
5
7
28
L
F
A Dark brown, mull
slate fragments
Bg Grey, orange mottles
Silty clay loam
Dark reddish brown concretions
Free draining, bottom of ditch
Epip hell, Frax exce, Athy f-f
Viol sp, Hyac nons
S3
SLOPE: level
ASPECT: -
53631196
3
6
16
L
F
A Brown
Silt loam
Bg Pale brown, orange mottling
Sandy silt loam
slate fragments
Free draining
Rubu frut, Pter aqui, Anem nemo
Cory avel, Hyac nons
S4
SLOPE: level
ASPECT: -
53711198
1
13
L,F&H
A Dark brownish grey
Silty clay loam
Bg Pale brown, orange mottling
Silty clay
slate fragments
Marsh
Sola dulc, Care remo, Alnu glut
Desc cesp, Vale offi, Frax exce
S5
SLOPE: 5°
ASPECT: 190°
53721203
3
8
L
H
A Brown, mull
B Orange-brown
Clay loam
slate fragments
Free draining
Cory avel, Pter aqui, Rubu frut
Dryo dila, Popu trem, Loni peri
S6
SLOPE: 7°
ASPECT: 170°
53821291
3
6
L
F&H
A Pale brown, mull
B Pinkish buff
Silt loam
Free draining
Rubu frut, Hede heli, Desc cesp
Mili effu
S7
SLOPE: level
ASPECT: -
53641295
5
10
28
L
A Brown, mull
B1 Brown
Silt loam
B2 Pinkish brown
Silty clay
Free draining
Rubu frut, Dryo f-m, Acer pseu
Tili cord
S8
SLOPE: level
ASPECT: -
53601279
1
3
L
F&H Blackish, mor
Eb Pale brown
Bt Buff
Very compacted
Silt clay
Free draining
Rubu frut, Pter aqui
S9
SLOPE: level
ASPECT: -
53651271
6
9
L,F&H Tough, fibrous mat of Luzula remains
E Pale grey
B Buff
Loose and dry
Silt loam
Free draining
Luzu sylv, Dryo f-m, Rubu frut
S10
SLOPE: 5°
ASPECT: 150°
53751217
3
5
20
Fibrous roots of Deschampsia
L
F,H&A
B Pale brown
Loamy sand
slate fragments
Free draining
Desc flex, Pter aqui, Rubu frut
S11
SLOPE: 17°
ASPECT: 40°
53771220
8
18
20
L
F&H Blackish
A Chocolate brown
Sandy loam
slate fragments
Free draining
Pter aqui, Rubu frut, Quer petr
S12
SLOPE: 6°
ASPECT: 30°
54061214
2
4
14
20
L
F&H
A Greyish brown
B1 Pale brown, Sandy loam
B2g Pale brown, orange mottling
Sandy loam
slate fragments
Free draining
Pter aqui, Rubu frut, Loni peri

of a ridge, demonstrates that waterlogging is not confined to these situations. Although most of the wood appears to be well-drained at the surface, this is not necessarily the case 20 cm down. The behaviour of ground water might well have ecological effects on the deeper rooted plants. Profiles S8 and S9 are unusual in that they have a pale E horizon and no A horizon. S8, with its mor humus, looks like the upper levels of a *podzol* profile, a soil type common in upland Britain and under heathland. To confirm this identification would require a deeper pit, to check for the diagnostic iron-rich horizon. Most other profiles may be described as *brown earths*.

Comparison with figure 2.10 will confirm that profiles S6-S9 and S12 are on formerly ploughed soil. The degree to which these soils have 'matured' into their respective profiles doubtless reflects the period of time since cultivation lapsed - it presumably takes a ploughed soil centuries to sort itself out into well defined horizons. Profile S1 is from an area that is known to have been disturbed - certainly this century and perhaps as recently as 20 years ago. The deep horizon labelled 'A' is very rich in humus, and has the consistency of potting compost. The bank from which the profile was taken appears to be where material dredged from the bottom of a pond has been dumped (see section 3.8).

This somewhat cursory look at soils has perhaps raised more questions than it has answered. The possibility of podzolic soils at the western edge of the wood (S8) is interesting, for it may indicate a heathland phase in the development of the site (Peterken 1969, page 20).

2.3.6 Quarries and pits

The two water-filled quarries within the wood (P15 and P25 on figure 2.3) are tiny by modern standards, but spectacular nonetheless in their woodland setting (figure 2.8). The precipitous rock-faces plunging into the dark waters have induced suicide attempts (Dare 1925, page 101). I am informed by a member of a local diving club that the water in the large central quarry (P15) is 55-60 m deep. The workings were surveyed by the OS shortly before they were abandoned in the 1880s, and are consequently represented accurately on the modern map. The spoil heaps associated with them, however, have certainly been disturbed, indeed material is still taken for repairing tracks. The present survey attempted to map the extent of the spoil heaps, but not the fine detail, which was of neither ecological nor historical importance. The history of slate quarrying will be presented in section 3.7.

There are about 24 smaller pits throughout the wood, not shown by the OS. Most of them are quite dry in the summer, but a few are seasonally wet. The large pit in compartment 80 (P6) is steep-sided and about two metres deep, with a flat bottom. It is associated with a curious system of ditches. Some pits (e.g. P7) cut through ridge-and-furrow and must therefore be medieval or later (cf. figure 2.10). In every case there is no spoil heap nearby, implying that the pits were quarries rather than saw-pits or charcoal burning pits. A few of them are obviously small slate quarries (e.g. P11, 12, 14, 21), but this explanation is unconvincing for all of them. Exposures of slate are generally not visible, and in fact many pits do not seem to relate to outcrops at all, judging by the geological map. Furthermore,

---

< **Figure 2.7.** Soil profiles, recorded in August 1986. Below each profile is its identity and an eight figure map reference. The slope of the sample site was measured with a clinometer; less than five degrees is deemed to be 'level'. Steeper slopes are given in degrees, along with the aspect i.e. which direction with respect to north the slope faces. Comments on drainage relate to observations at the surface. The abbreviations at the bottom give the plants growing on this soil, refer to table 5.10. To the left of each profile are the depths of the horizon boundaries in cm; pits were dug only to the depth shown, usually 40 cm. To the right, the conventional letters used by soil scientists have been tentatively assigned - refer to text for further details.

Figure 2.8. The water-filled slate pit (P15), disused since 1887. (Compartment 5, SK53881223, October 1983).

if slate was being sought, then the quarrymen would surely have worked places where material was available at the surface. One possibility is that superficial clay deposits have been excavated. The fact that the pits do not coincide with boulder clay shown on the geological map may be due to the inadequacy of the map - the survey did not attempt to resolve this level of detail. Local clay has, in fact, been used for brick making. A brick kiln or 'clamp' site, some 1.5 km to the south of the Wood (SK543102), has been described by Ramsey (1987). It appears to have supplied the bricks for Bradgate House, built in the late fifteenth century.

2.3.7 Banks and ditches

Banks and ditches in the countryside have generally been made for two purposes. In the first place, ditches were dug for drainage, their banks being nothing more than by-products. Drainage ditches and gullies (or 'grips') are few in number because the majority of Swithland Wood is naturally dry. Secondly, banks and ditches were made along property or land-use boundaries. When combined with a fence or hedge, such earthworks help to make the boundary stockproof - particularly from the ditch side of the boundary towards the bank side (Rackham 1976). Furthermore, once dug, an earthwork is a lasting feature in the landscape: an unscrupulous neighbour cannot easily annex land by surreptitiously moving the boundary. In an age before accurate maps, this was an important consideration. Boundary ditches may serve for drainage at the same time, of course.

In figure 2.10, ditches that perform only the drainage function have been excluded. Those ditches that are shown are either natural water-courses or boundary features. Dry ditches which are clearly boundary earthworks are shown by a thick line. Wet ditches and natural water-courses, which were probably also used to define boundaries, are shown by a thinner line. Often these earthworks coincide with boundaries which are still meaningful, for

Figure 2.9. Ridge-and-furrow in Swithland Wood, emphasised by the shadows of trees in the foreground. (Compartment 80, SK542120, February 1982.)

example those along the present margins of the wood. Others, such as those around compartments 81 and 82 have outlived their usefulness. There are a few examples in the wood of banks without obvious ditches. Figure 2.11 shows cross-sections of the various banks, ditches and artificial changes in ground level. These were surveyed by stretching a string horizontally between two rods with the aid of a spirit level. The string had been marked at 0.5 metre intervals and the vertical drop to the ground was measured from every mark. Once a piece of landscape is covered by trees it cannot be ploughed, so earthworks tend to be preserved in woodland. They may span several centuries, and some features may relate to a previous land-use. The chronology and interpretation of woodland earthworks is an interesting exercise (Rackham 1980); this will be attempted in chapter 8.

2.3.8 Ridge-and-furrow

A further important class of earthwork is evidence of former cultivation in the form of ridge-and-furrow. It is commonly seen in the pasture-lands of the Midlands, but is of course much less conspicuous in woods (figure 2.9). The discovery of extensive ridge-and-furrow in Swithland Wood (figure 2.10) clearly has far-reaching implications with regard to site history.

Surveying earthworks accurately in woods is a difficult and time-consuming business. Features tend to disappear beneath vegetation, and shrubs invariably block the line of sight to crucial reference points. A properly measured survey of all the ridge-and-furrow was not feasible, and the representation on figure 2.10 should be regarded as an accurate sketch. The extent of ridge-and-furrow has been carefully mapped and no great liberties have been taken in joining up ridges on the map where none could be seen on site. This cautious approach has doubtless resulted in blanks appearing on the distribution map where the brambles were particularly aggressive, for example. Compass bearings were

N
0 100 m
= No earthwork
= Parish boundary in 1888
= Boundary stones
= Bank (no ditch)
= Dry ditch
= Stream or wet ditch
= Ridge-and-furrow
= Disturbed areas (post 1900)
= Pond or pit
= Marsh
= Outcrops & thin soil
AK = Earthwork sections
AA
AB
AC
A
AH
C
AI
F
E
D
AJ
AD
AF
AE
AG
AK
AL
AM
AN
Q
R
S
P
G
J
K
H
L
M
O
N

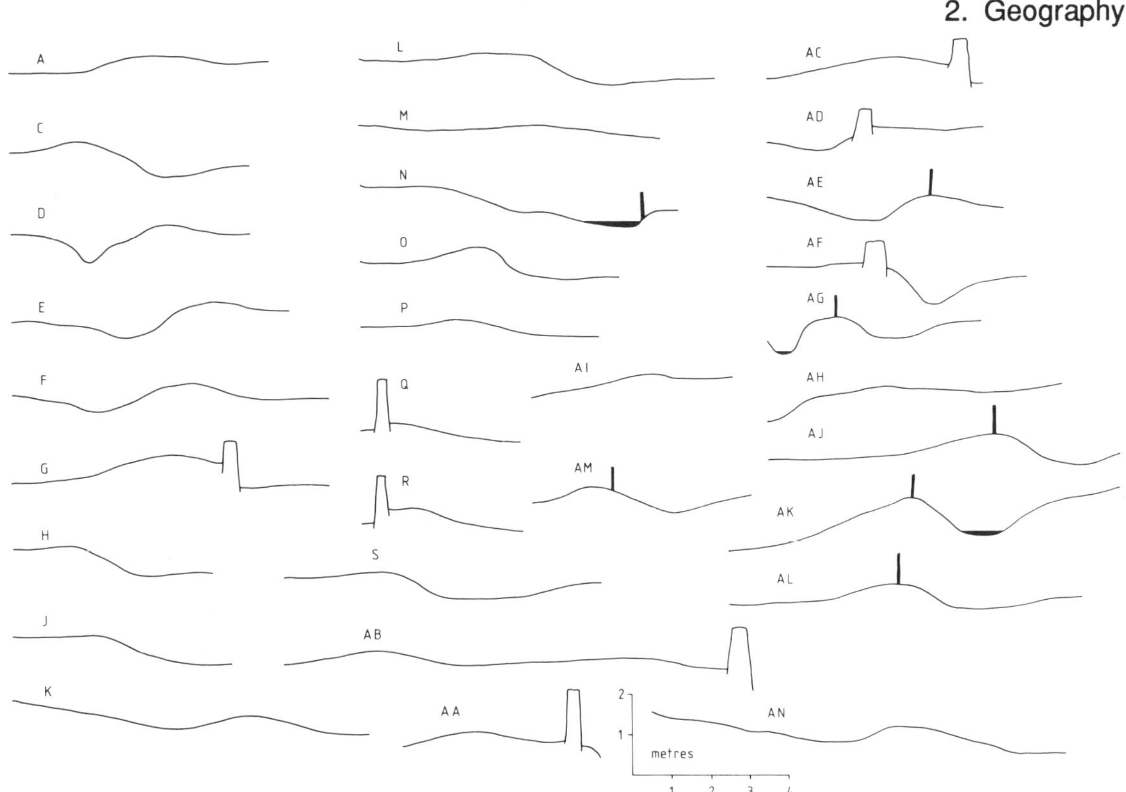

Figure 2.11. Earthwork sections, whose locations are shown in figure 2.10.

taken of the ridges, so their indicated directions should be accurate to within two degrees. Generally, the distance between adjacent furrows is about six metres. This is similar to the wavelength found in abandoned arable known to be cultivated in medieval times, for example in Groby (Woodward 1984, page 23), but there is no direct way of dating ridge-and-furrow on morphological grounds. It is generally assumed that broad, curving ridges (in a reverse S-shape) are medieval in origin (Aston & Rowley 1974, page 144). In woodland, though, the curvature is impossible to determine without an accurate survey.

Ridge-and-furrow underlies most of Swithland Wood. In many cases the blanks on the map may be caused by loss of evidence - former ploughland might have been quarried or buried by spoil. It looks as though some areas that are presently marshy were once ploughed. Some short ridges run north to south between the marsh and the larger outcrop in compartment 4. Had the marsh been contemporary with cultivation, then the farmer would surely not have chosen to plough in that direction; the strips would have been impracticably short and the ploughteam would become bogged down whilst trying to turn. Some of the pits (e.g. P4, 5, 6 & 7 on figure 2.3 and described in section 2.3.6) and their drainage ditches are demonstrably younger than the ploughing. In contrast, the boundary earthworks (with the exception of the ditch at the west of cmpt 21) are all respected by ridge-and-furrow, showing that they were in place during the period of cultivation. At the north of compartment 81, where a ditch appears to cut ridge-and-furrow, a drop in level of 0.5 m (section J on figure 2.11) shows that, in fact, ploughs were turned at this boundary. At the north of the north-south ridges in the east of compartment 80, is a 'headland', a bank (without a ditch) formed where ploughs were turned around.

< **Figure 2.10.** Earthworks and boundary features. Minor earthworks such as drainage grips are not shown. The representation of ridge-and-furrow is symbolic, since it is impossible to resolve individual ridges at this scale. However, its extent and direction have been carefully plotted. The locations of the measured cross-sections are shown by lines, with arrows that indicate the direction of viewing. These sections are given in figure 2.11. See also figures 3.3 and 8.1.

When consideration is given to the area occupied by slate outcrops, which could never have been ploughed, and to the quarries, spoil heaps and marshes where ridge-and-furrow (if it ever existed) would no longer be evident, then it would appear that the ploughmen tackled most of the land available on this site. The only ploughable parts of Swithland Wood apparently uncultivated are compartments 9, most of 7 and parts of the Wood Meadows. In view of the poor quality of the soil, it is remarkable that farmers grew crops here, and indeed brought their ploughs right up to the very edges of the outcrops.

2.3.9 Boundary stones

An unusual feature along the east of the wood is the series of old stones which still define the parish boundary. They are all of Swithland slate, but of two forms. The six stones at the north of compartment 6 are more or less square in section. A well-preserved example is shown on the left half of figure 2.12. It is 45 cm high, 14 cm wide and 15 cm deep. The Newtown Linford side of each stone bears a deeply engraved 'S' and the Swithland side bears the letter 'D'. Two further stones were found just beyond the fence to the east. The line of the parish boundary here is up to seven metres inside the physical boundary. The latter comprises a ditch on the Newtown Linford side with a bank on the Swithland side surmounted by a wire fence. The other kind of boundary stone is found from the western corner of compartment 6 northwards, alongside compartments 3, 4 and 20. These are flat, like small headstones. The example shown on the right of figure 2.12 is 56 cm high, 30 cm wide and 6 cm thick. All ten are marked 'S' on both sides, and sit either at the bottom of the internal ditch, or on the near slope of the bank. The age of these stones is unknown but they pre-date the Ordnance Survey of 1883. Had all the stones been engraved with 'S' and 'D', then the most likely interpretation would be Stamford and Danvers, the names of former owners (see chapter 3). Alas, this is not the case and the true meaning of these letters remains a puzzle.

Figure 2.12. Two types of boundary stone. On the left are two views of the 'square' type and on the right are two views of the 'headstone' type. In each case the left and right figures are viewed from Newtown Linford and Swithland parishes, respectively.

Chapter 3

History

3.1 The Historical Approach

People and woods have interacted with one another for several thousand years. Even seemingly 'natural' woods in remote places will, upon closer inspection, be found to contain evidence of human interference, such as the effects of browsing by farmers' sheep. The characteristics of a wood cannot be fully explained by geographical factors alone; the actions of woodmen, foresters, farmers and gamekeepers must be taken into account. It is *management*, past and present, that generally explains why woods on comparable sites each possess an individual character and atmosphere (Peterken 1981). Woodland management today is usually directed towards timber production or shooting, and sometimes nature conservation or amenity. When trying to account for the vegetation of a wood, we must bear in mind that the present management regime may be relatively recent compared with the age of the oldest trees. The aims and methods of woodland management at a particular site 100 or 200 years ago may have been quite different, and need to be ascertained. In more remote times, the management of a particular site may not have related to woodland at all - many woods have developed on former grassland, ploughland or even settlements (Rackham 1980). The mode of origin and subsequent development of a site as a piece of woodland are generally reflected in the earthworks and the distribution of certain plant species. In order to understand such features, we need to trace back the land-use history as far as possible.

Where should we look for this kind of historical information? Owners or managers had no reason to publish detailed descriptions of their woods and how they were managed. Eighteenth and nineteenth century antiquaries mention in passing the more important woods in their county histories, but for details of one particular wood or group of woods the enquirer must be prepared to search through unpublished manuscripts and the more obscure printed sources. With respect to the present project, it is fortunate that some contemporary working documents, including estate plans, account books and title deeds have been preserved in public and private archives. Hardly any of this material, however, deals specifically with Swithland Wood in any detail. The relevant information is thinly scattered around many documents - for example, the felling regime became clear only after searching through 130 years of newspapers for wood sale advertisements! The archival material (manuscript and printed) used in this study is listed at the end of the references section where each item is numbered sequentially. In the text that follows these numbers are quoted thus: (ref. 10).

In some of the following sections, historical evidence is used in conjunction with the topographical survey presented in the previous chapter. In particular, boundary features and quarries are related to documentary sources. The most important problem which historical research might be expected to resolve is how and when woodland became established on the site. Unfortunately, the origin of Swithland Wood, as woodland, pre-dates detailed records, so it will be necessary to bring all available resources - historical, archaeological and ecological - to bear on this particular problem. Consequently, a full discussion on the origin of the wood must be deferred to chapter 8. The present chapter mainly confines itself to the factual evidence from historical sources. First, some important terms relating to types of woodland are defined. We then consider certain aspects of woodland history at various levels of detail; namely Great Britain, Charnwood Forest, and the Bradgate Estate; before focusing on the study area itself.

3.2 Types of Woodland

During the twentieth century, we have become accustomed to the practice of making new woods by planting trees on previously open ground. By this method, the Forestry Commission claims to be increasing the area of woodland in Britain (Locke 1987). It is often assumed that the older woods, which are those that generally merit greater attention from naturalists, were established in the same way in earlier centuries. In some cases this is so, but Dr Oliver Rackham (1976, 1980) has shown us that many of the more interesting woods are certainly not old plantations. On the contrary, they are the results of centuries of human exploitation and management of what was originally *natural* woodland. A useful distinction can, in fact, be drawn between plantations and woods. A *plantation* is made by someone who plants seeds or saplings on ground that was previously used for some other purpose, such as grazing. Plantations are artificial, and typically contain a few tree species (often exotic) and a meagre selection of woodland herbs. In contrast, *woods* are demonstrably or implicitly natural in origin, and typically comprise many native tree, shrub and herb species. It seems that plantations (other than orchards) were rarely made before the year 1600 AD. Many sites do not, in practice, fit comfortably into either category. People certainly planted trees in pre-existing woods and, given enough time, nature will reclaim a neglected plantation. Most woods may be placed towards the middle of a scale, in which untouched, natural woodland lies at one end, and wholly artificial plantations at the other. They are best described as *semi-natural* (Peterken 1981). A small part of the present study area is a plantation, the rest is semi-natural woodland in which some planting has undoubtedly taken place.

The history of many woods can be traced back far beyond the age of their oldest trees. Those that greet their visitors with a profusion of bluebells, primroses and other select woodland plants are generally on sites which have been continuously wooded for many centuries. Indeed, some woods are thought to be directly descended from original natural woodland, and must be thousands of years old. In such *primary* woods, as they are called, ecological continuity has been maintained, in the sense that they have never been converted to any other land-use. Yet, as we have noted, all woods in Britain whether primary or otherwise have been actively managed or otherwise disturbed by man. There is little doubt that no truly natural woodland survives in its original form today, and we must travel to remote parts of Eastern Europe to find anything resembling Britain's original natural woodland in both composition and structure (Peterken 1981). Woods which have grown anew on previously cleared ground (with or without the assistance of man) are called *secondary* woods. To identify a wood as secondary, simply requires evidence of a former alternative land-use, such as the ridge-and-furrow of former arable land. To show that a wood is primary is much more difficult - lack of evidence to the contrary is hardly conclusive. This problem is avoided by the use of an alternative classification which has been widely adopted. This is to distinguish between *ancient* and *recent* woods, according to whether they originated before or after 1600 AD (Peterken 1981). Thus, woods may be ancient primary, ancient secondary or recent secondary. Rackham (1980) has studied critically many aspects of ancient woods, and has concluded that many of them are, in fact, primary.

3.3 The History of Woodland in Britain

The story of our *native* trees and shrubs, and their associated plant communities, begins about 12,000 years ago (Pennington 1969). Previously, the landscape had been in the grip of the Devensian glaciation, the most recent of several major ice-advances. As the climate ameliorated, ice gave way to a tundra type of vegetation. This was followed by woodland dominated by the more hardy species, such as birch and hazel, that had taken refuge in warmer parts of Europe (Britain was not yet an island). The more warmth-demanding trees like ash, lime and maple moved in later, so that our full complement of native species had become established some 7500 years ago. From that time onwards, permanent inundation by the North Sea and English Channel ensured that few, if any, further additions to our flora would arrive without the intervention of man.

In the absence of any major climatic disturbances over the next two and a half millennia, the various species jostled with each other for dominance, culminating in a series of so-called *climax* forests (see page 62). The composition of the primeval forest is of great interest from the point of view of comparison with existing primary woods, but this will not concern us in the present chapter. There can be little doubt that Leicestershire, in common with practically all of lowland Britain, was clothed by a more or less continuous mantle of trees. The decline of woodland from about 3000 b.c. onwards has little to do with climate, but heralds the dawn of agriculture; the start of man's ever-increasing hunger for land.

One of the more significant advances in the study of landscape history over the last 30 years concerns the chronology of forest clearance. Hoskins, writing in 1955, regarded clearance as principally the work of Saxon and Medieval farmers, and even by the fifteenth century: 'from rising ground England must have seemed one great forest'. More recent writers have been able to draw upon new archaeological evidence, particularly of the high density of Roman settlement, implying an intensively farmed landscape. Rackham (1980) places the most active period of forest destruction in the late Iron Age and Roman period, whereas Taylor (1983) ventures to suggest that 'by 1000 BC there was probably less woodland in England than there is now'. Authorities may differ with regard to which period of prehistory witnessed the greatest clearance, but all would now agree that it was well advanced before the lapse of Roman control (410 AD).

3.4 Charnwood Forest and its Landscape

The landscape history of Charnwood Forest has been researched in depth by Squires (1981). In summary, he found that early settlers chose to avoid this agriculturally inferior part of the county, and thousands of acres remained unenclosed and more or less wild, until the 1820s. Settlement and land-use history impinge directly on the survival of woodlands in general, and Swithland Wood in particular, and what follows is a review of these topics in relation to Charnwood Forest.

3.4.1 Archaeology

Archaeological signs of prehistoric activity are sparse, and hardly constitute sufficient data for an account of land-use at this time (figure 3.1). The earliest evidence of man's presence is provided by neolithic polished axes fashioned from local igneous rock (Shotton 1959). It is tempting to interpret these axes as evidence for local felling, but their production for a wider market is equally possible, particularly as Charnwood stone axes have been found as far afield as Norfolk and the Peak District. It has been suggested that such axes may in any case have been used for purposes other than forest clearance (Megaw & Simpson 1979, page 111). The summit of Beacon Hill, 4 km to the north-west of Swithland Wood, is partly enclosed by a rampart considered by Liddle (1982) to be late Bronze Age in date.

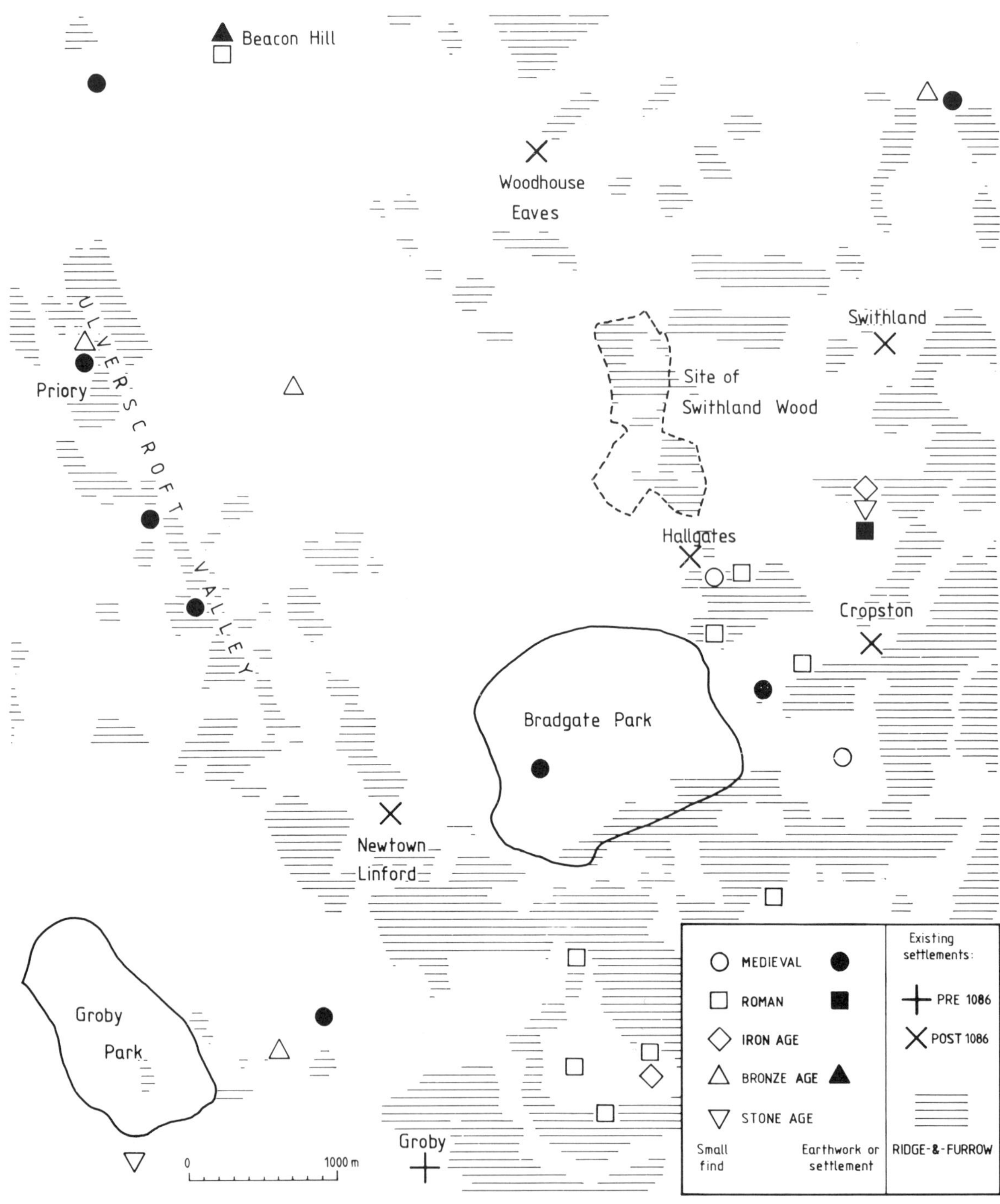

Figure 3.1. Archaeology in the southern part of Charnwood Forest. Based on the Sites and Monuments Record held at the Jewry Wall Museum, Leicester, and supplemented by personal observations. Solid symbols denote earthworks or other evidence of former settlement. Existing settlements are shown by one of two symbols according to whether they are named in Domesday Book. The park outlines are those considered by Squires & Humphrey (1986) to be the original medieval deer-park boundaries. Shading shows the approximate extent of medieval cultivation based on ridge-and-furrow, visible either on the ground or in aerial photographs.

Defensive sites on hills only make sense if an approaching enemy could be seen at a distance, which would imply local woodland clearance by approximately 600 BC. Among the small finds from this period also are a number of axes.

The Romans in Leicester, and further afield, found uses for Charnwood stone (including Swithland Slate) in their building projects, although the precise location of their quarries and the scale of operations are not known (McWhirr 1988). Except for a few coins found at Beacon Hill, the only traces of Roman activity are on the margins of, rather than within Charnwood Forest: to the east and south of what was to become Bradgate Park. Some Romano-British pottery and corn-grinding stones have been found near Hallgates (Sites and Monuments Record, Jewry Wall Museum). The latter are heavy items and are unlikely to have been moved far from where they were last used.

Thus, traces of early man are very thin on the ground, and it appears that the area was more or less deserted in prehistoric times. We ought to reflect on the nature of the evidence before reaching a firm conclusion, however. Casual finds tend to be made during ploughing or construction work, and it is only since the last war that these activities have been commonplace in the area. Evidence may await discovery in the soil. Although systematic archaeological survey of the area is very far from complete, the general dearth of early finds on ploughed fields, compared with ancient farmland elsewhere, supports the notion that people did largely avoid Charnwood Forest prior to the Middle Ages (Groby Archaeology Society records held at Jewry Wall Museum).

3.4.2 Domesday Book

The Conqueror's great survey of 1086 records for the first time the names of settlements surrounding Charnwood, including Groby to the south, Anstey and Thurcaston to the east (Morgan 1979). The names are predominantly Saxon and Danish in origin (Bourne 1981), though we should recognise the possibility that these were new names for older settlements. Taylor (1983) stresses that names which now refer to villages may then have been applied to farmsteads, hamlets or even dispersed settlements. Whatever the actual form of settlement at this time, it is clear that by the ninth century farmers were working the land around Charnwood. Considerable areas of woodland were associated with these settlements, whereas deforestation was more or less complete throughout most of the county. Newtown Linford, Hallgates and Swithland, all places on the margin of the forest, are not mentioned in Domesday Book; it appears they were later settlements, though they might have been included anonymously as minor dependants of other settlements.

The entries show that Charnwood was very sparsely populated in 1086: less than three persons per square mile according to Darby & Terrett (1971). Reading between the lines of the Domesday folios, Charnwood was a rocky wilderness, still containing much primary woodland. It was used for rough grazing. Other early medieval sources corroborate this view, and show that its resources were shared among the neighbouring manors of Groby, Shepshed, Barrow and Whitwick (Farnham 1930).

Much of the unenclosed forest in the eleventh century would have been what is now called *wood-pasture*, a landscape where trees and grassland are intimately mixed (Rackham 1980). This ancient tradition of land-use is ecologically unstable, for too little grazing allows the growth of scrub and eventually woodland, whereas excessive grazing suppresses saplings and ultimately destroys the tree cover. It is because of this precarious balance, and the careful continuity of management needed to maintain it, that rather few good examples of wood-pasture have survived to the present day (Harding & Rose 1986). With the notable exception of Bradgate Park, Charnwood Forest retains hardly a vestige of its former wood-pasture aspect. Trees in wood-pasture were harvested in a particular way. Their branches were cut off at about three metres above the ground, so that the regrowth could not be nibbled back by stock. Trees regularly treated in this way ('lopped') developed a characteristic growth-form and are known as *pollards*. (A later but interesting account of local pollarding is listed as ref. 3.)

3.4.3 Middle Ages

A strong influence on the development of Charnwood's landscape has been the taste of the upper classes for hunting. From an early date, possibly back to Saxon times, special enclosed areas were set aside for beasts of the chase. At least nine deer parks had been created in and around Charnwood by about 1300 AD (Squires & Humphrey 1986). The open forest was also certainly hunted, but landowners who were powerful enough to enclose a few hundred acres from the waste and obtain a licence from the Crown were able to enjoy both the convenience of having the quarry close at hand and the prestige of private ownership. Swithland Wood happens to be very close to Bradgate Park, the only deer park to have survived in anything like its medieval state. Following its extension in the sixteenth century, further changes were relatively minor, so the park has survived as a remarkable relic of medieval landscape.

Confusion may arise over the meaning of the word *forest*. Nowadays, an extensive woodland or plantation is called a forest, so we speak of primeval forest, or of Kielder Forest. This is not what our ancestors had in mind when they alluded to Charnwood as a Forest - we shall see later that it has not been thickly wooded for a very long time. Tracts of country which were subject to special laws concerned with preserving deer (or other game) were known as Forests, whether or not they were wooded (Rackham 1976). Royal Forests were under the direct control of the Crown, with the original function of providing the King with venison, recreation, timber, and so on. Charnwood was never a Royal Forest; it was owned and controlled by the lords of the adjacent manors for their own use, although commoners enjoyed certain grazing rights (Squires & Humphrey 1986, page 10). Charnwood was sometimes called a *chase*; an alternative name for a Non-Royal Forest.

An important aspect of Charnwood's medieval landscape history was the gradual encroachment of agriculture. Wider studies have demonstrated the general 'land hunger' of the thirteenth and early fourteenth centuries, attributable to rising population (Hoskins 1957). There are numerous references in the documents of that period to *assarting* in Charnwood Forest, the term used to describe the process of bringing portions of the *waste* into a more formal regime of land-management. In favourable seasons, when perhaps they had a few weeks to spare, the peasants of the marginal settlements would add to their acres by grubbing adjacent woodland, or enclosing common pasture, legally or otherwise. We first read of Swithland and Newtown Linford in the early and late thirteenth centuries respectively, in contexts that imply substantial assarting (Victoria County History, vol. 2). The settlement of Hallgates is first mentioned in 1268 (Farnham 1930, page 92). In addition to those working inwards, were others who established new farmsteads in the heart of Charnwood and worked outwards. Among the earliest of these pioneers were the inmates of monastic foundations, notably Ulverscroft Priory, founded 1134 (figure 3.1). The place-name 'hay' or 'hays', of which there are many examples in Charnwood, seems to be a reliable pointer to such an assart. Squires has estimated that the area of woodland decreased by 40% between 1086 and 1289. Thousands of acres of the less attractive ground remained as unenclosed woodland or rough grazing for commoners' sheep and cattle (figure 3.2).

By the fourteenth century, it is clear from contemporary documents that the original woodland cover was very fragmented. Individual woods were identified by name, many of which are familiar today. We cannot be sure of their precise shape and size at that time, but we may reasonably suppose that named medieval woods can be equated, at least approximately, with those of the same name on the earliest maps. Swithland Wood, alas, is not among them. Timber on the forest was no longer an abundant resource that could be

Figure 3.2. Rough grazing land, as much of Charnwood Forest would have appeared prior to 1800. (Charnwood Lodge Nature Reserve, SK463155, September 1982.)

Figure 3.3. Woodbank surmounted by a wall. See section G on figure 2.11. (Compartment 9, SK53621180, February 1991.)

plundered indiscriminately, and the archives record numerous legal proceedings against those accused of stealing trees (Farnham 1933, page 364 *et seq.*). Woods became discrete and well-defined because it was necessary to fence them securely against grazing animals. Post-medieval records show that stone walls were then used extensively for that purpose, and there is no reason to suppose that this was not so in earlier times. Walls or other sorts of fence were often combined with a bank and ditch for extra security, the bank being on the wood side of the boundary. The combination of a substantial woodbank and slate wall can be seen at the south of Swithland Wood, see figure 3.3. This was not simply a woodbank, but the boundary of the open forest in 1780, as can be seen in figure 3.13.

The expansion of farming was severely checked during the fourteenth century by a series of famines and epidemics, most notably the Black Death of 1349. Charnwood seems to have been affected as severely as elsewhere and perhaps one person in three fell victim to the plague. Two and a half centuries would elapse before the population recovered (Taylor 1975, page 107). Arable farming was neither economic nor necessary on the old scale, and substantial areas of marginal land dropped out of cultivation. Hoskins (1957, page 27) attributes the falling value of land in Groby Manor to this cause. On the other hand, pastoral farming required little labour and was now more profitable, so that grazing in Charnwood may actually have increased (Squires 1981). Abandoned medieval ploughland that has been little disturbed usually contains ridge-and-furrow. The distribution of ridge-and-furrow (figure 3.1) gives an approximate indication of the extent of arable farming at that time. Cultivation was widespread beyond the forest, i.e. to the east and south of Bradgate Park. Ploughland associated with Hallgates (including the site of Swithland Wood), Newtown Linford, and the Ulverscroft Valley evidently represented the limit of cultivation. The core of the forest, from Bradgate Park north-westwards, was unworkable.

3.4.4 Post-medieval history

By the seventeenth century, owners found themselves under economic pressure to sacrifice their deer parks in order to meet the demand for agricultural produce. Of the eleven medieval parks around Charnwood, Squires and Humphrey estimate that four survived to 1600, and all but Bradgate were disparked by 1700. On the unenclosed forest, the stocking levels of commoners' cattle and sheep increased to the point where their depredations overpowered the capacity of the trees to reproduce themselves. The wood-pasture had degenerated towards a treeless, wind-swept heath by the time the first topographical descriptions were published. Burton (1622) alludes to the 'vast and decayed forest of Charnwood'. Marshall (1790) reported that 'Charnwood Forest has not, figuratively speaking, a stick left in it'. There was, of course, plenty of woodland that was enclosed, especially towards the south of the forest.

The character of the open forest is perhaps best appreciated by the kinds of wildlife that it supported. Records from the mid eighteenth century onwards demonstrate the widespread occurrence of plant species that are tolerant of grazing and poor soils; notably ling *Calluna vulgaris*, gorse *Ulex* spp., bracken *Pteridium aquilinum* and mat-grass *Nardus stricta*. Of particular interest are records for species which we now associate with the uplands of northern and western Britain, and are now extinct or very rare on the forest. These include the heathland species cowberry *Vaccinium vitis-idaea* and crowberry *Empetrum nigrum*, and plants of acid bogs such as sundew *Drosera* spp., cotton-grass *Eriophorum angustifolium*, and butterwort *Pinguicula vulgaris*. Breeding birds formerly included both red and black grouse, ring ouzel, hen harrier and raven (Squires 1981, NCC 1975).

> **Figure 3.4.** The Swithland Wood area in 1883/4, as depicted by the Ordnance Survey six inch series (ref. 66).

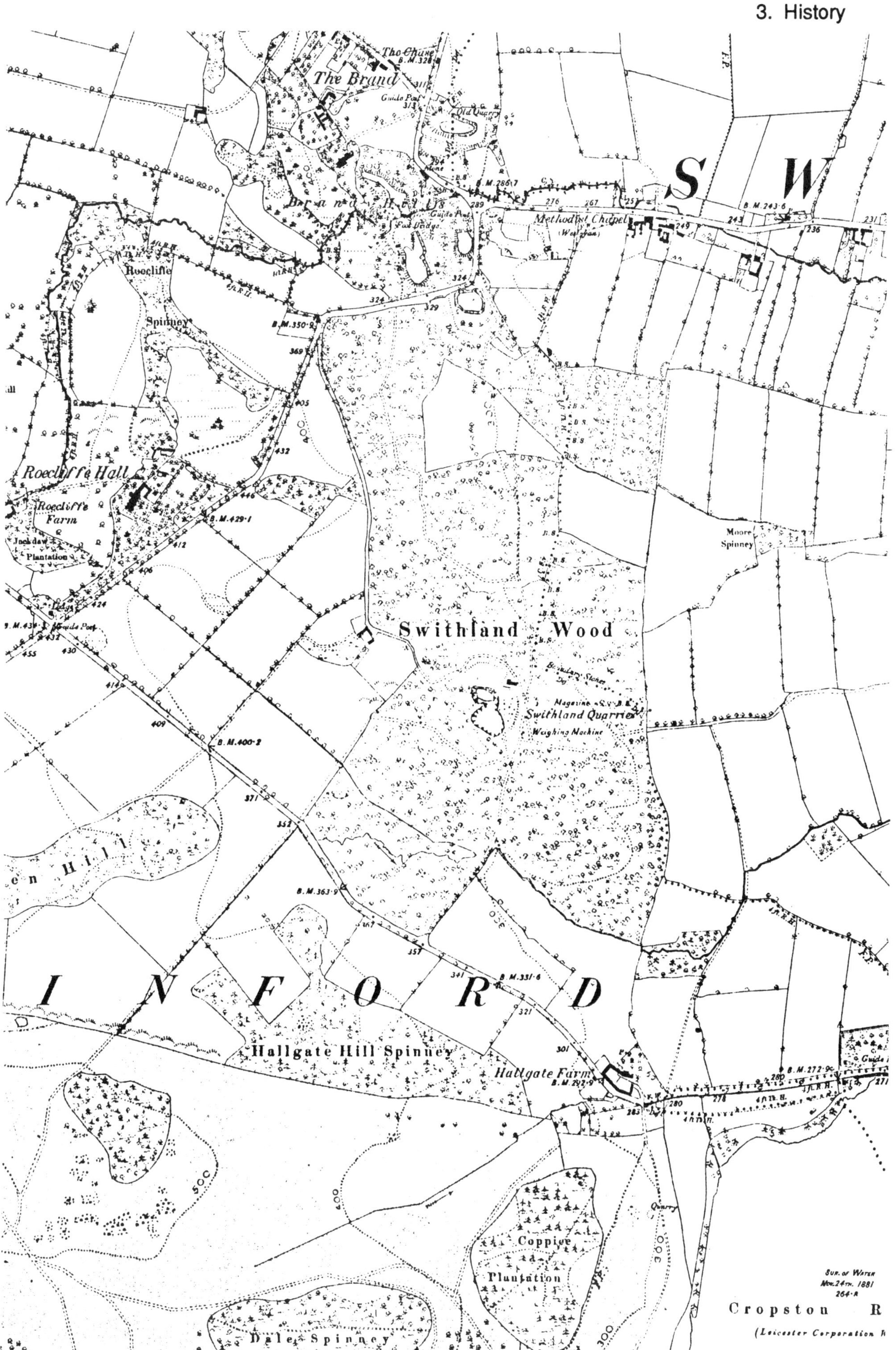
The Chase
The Brand
Old Quarry
S W
Methodist Chapel
(Wesleyan)
Roecliffe
Spinney
Roecliffe Hall
Roecliffe Farm
Jackdaw Plantation
Swithland Wood
Moore Spinney
Swithland Quarries
Magazine
Weighing Machine
I N F O R D
Hallgate Hill Spinney
Hallgate Farm
Coppice Plantation
Dale Spinney
Quarry
Cropston R
(Leicester Corporation

The latter half of the eighteenth century saw great advancements in agricultural technology and dramatic population increases in towns such as Leicester. A Board of Agriculture and Internal Improvement report (Pitt 1809) concluded that the productivity of the open forest could be greatly enhanced by means of draining and enclosing. Such an investment would only be worthwhile if land could first be re-distributed among the various landowners into more economically viable units. The Parliamentary Enclosure Act that was required to do this was passed in 1808, having been sponsored by the principal landowners. The complex legalities were all finalised by 1829 (ref. 8), and the early decades of the nineteenth century were to witness a profound transformation of the wild, open landscape. The common grazing and other rights enjoyed by the adjacent parishes were abolished, in return for allotments of land from the 16,000 acres of open forest. These new privately owned areas were freed from the restrictions associated with common land, so that owners were at liberty to subdivide, improve and manage them as they saw fit. The new landscape was one of long, straight roads and of regular fields bounded by stone walls and hedges. Great energy was expended in draining the mires, and in ploughing, liming and clearing stones from the more fertile parts. New farmsteads were erected and numerous plantations were made, particularly around the crags. The resulting landscape, shown beautifully on the Ordnance Survey maps of the 1880s (figure 3.4), differs only in detail from that of today.

3.5 The Bradgate Estate

Until the 1920s, Swithland Wood was part of the extensive *Bradgate Estate*, which originated as the medieval *Manor of Groby*. The history of the wood is inseparable from that of the estate to which it belonged, and indeed its management makes little sense except in the context of the estate woodlands as a whole. A brief introduction to the manor or estate in the present section will set the scene for a more detailed examination of its woodlands.

3.5.1 Origin and ownership

In 1086, the manor of Groby was one of the many Leicestershire properties of Hugh Grentemaisnil, one of the Conqueror's most favoured supporters (Phythian-Adams 1986). It descended through the Beaumont Earls of Leicester and Earls of Winchester, into the hands of the Ferrers family in the thirteenth century. In 1445 the estate passed by marriage to Sir Edward Grey (Nichols 1811). The Greys were destined to become one of the most powerful noble families in England. In 1553, Henry Grey, Duke of Suffolk, successfully contrived with others to place his daughter Jane on the English throne, albeit for just nine days (Stevenson 1974). The repercussions of this ill-fated venture cannot be detailed here, but following its confiscation by the Crown, the manor was eventually returned to a member of the family who had escaped the gallows. The title 'Earl of Stamford' was created in 1628 for Thomas, Lord Grey, a celebrated parliamentary general (Burke's Peerage 1938, Richards 1988). Successive earls retained the property until the death of the seventh earl in 1883, when it was inherited by his niece, Mrs Katherine Henrietta Venezia Duncombe (latterly Grey).

The family ran into financial difficulties in the late nineteenth century, said to be largely due to the seventh earl's expensive hobbies, which included racehorses, fox-hunting and entertaining on a grand scale (Ellis 1951). Mrs Grey eventually sold the estate in the 1920s, thereby breaking up one of the county's most extensive and long-established landholdings. The history of Swithland Wood under subsequent owners will be related in section 3.9.

3.5.2 Extent

The medieval manor included Groby, Swithland, Ulverscroft, Newtown Linford, Hallgates and parts of Ratby, together with the deer parks of Groby and Bradgate, numerous woods and a large portion of the waste in Charnwood Forest. The precise extent of the manor is imperfectly known, but must have amounted to 5,000 - 10,000 acres. The manorial rights for the Swithland portion appear to have been granted to the family of Waleys in the thirteenth century. Their estate was split between two sisters in the mid fourteenth century, but was re-united in 1629 when the Danvers branch of the family acquired the portion which had descended to the Kendalls (Farnham 1930, page 93). Groby manor was to become the core of the Bradgate Estate, as it was later known under the Earls of Stamford. The extent of the estate was 9,428 acres in 1857 (ref. 47). A further 2,217 acres, comprising the Breedon Estate in north-west Leicestershire, were sold off in 1873, but following the sale, Stamford was still the county's largest landowner (Parker 1976). He then possessed land in eight English counties totalling 30,962 acres, of which 9,012 were in Leicestershire (Bateman 1883).

3.5.3 Land-use

Groby manor is poorly represented in the archives of the medieval period, and little detail can be added to what has already been said about Charnwood Forest in general. The varied terrain within the manor is reflected in the range of land-uses. The more fertile parts, such as Groby itself on the margin of the forest, were tilled in the open field tradition (Woodward 1984), but such systems never developed within the forest proper. There is good documentary and field evidence that Newtown Linford, Hallgates, and other isolated holdings including Ulverscroft Priory did cultivate some land (figure 3.1); but their farmers were primarily pastoralists. At least 120 acres of arable land were lost at the expansion of Bradgate Park in 1499 (Squires & Humphrey 1986). Although evidence is rather thin, there are grounds for linking at least some of this land with the 'lost' settlement of Bradgate (the medieval settlement between Cropston and Bradgate Park in figure 3.1).

Tenants in the manor of Groby shared with other manors the right of common grazing for sheep and cattle on the unenclosed core of Charnwood Forest. The property known as The Brand, immediately north of Swithland Wood (figure 2.1(c)), is a reminder of the necessity for commoners to mark their cattle prior to turning them out into the open forest (Turner 1985). The extent of the open forest is shown on figure 3.13. Timber trees belonged to the lord of the manor, but commoners had the right to take firewood from the forest, for which they each paid yearly one hen, known as a wood-hen (Farnham 1930). Nearly all of the outcrops of good quality slate on Charnwood Forest fell within Groby manor, and its lords must have enjoyed a virtual monopoly for the supply of this locally important material (see section 3.7). The manor also derived income from various fish ponds, mills and other minor enterprises.

Whereas the pursuit of 'beasts of the chase' was the preferred pastime of medieval noblemen, shooting and fox-hunting were to occupy the leisure time of their descendants. Although for much of the eighteenth and nineteenth centuries, the Earls of Stamford lived away from Leicestershire, they frequently returned to entertain guests on the estate. Revenue was not the only consideration bearing on estate management; the provision of pleasing vistas and good sport were also regarded as worthy objectives (Robinson 1988). Gamekeepers were employed from the late eighteenth century onwards to ensure that shooting parties encountered plenty of pheasants, partridges, woodcock, wildfowl, rabbits and hares. The seventh earl in particular was passionate about shooting and there can be little doubt that he valued both the old woods and the new plantations as much for sport as for potential financial return.

3.6 Woodland on the Bradgate Estate

3.6.1 The identity of Swithland Wood

Before we can assess Swithland Wood's role in the estate's woodlands, it is necessary to address the troublesome matter of its identity in the records. It was noted above that Swithland was not among the woods named in fourteenth century records, and indeed that name was rarely used before the 1800s. In the early stages of the research this was a little puzzling, since there were strong ecological indications that the wood was much older than 200 years. A closer scrutiny of the archives confirmed initial suspicions that woodland indeed existed here, but was not known by its present name.

Former names

Among the archives of the Bradgate Estate are a number of schedules which list its woods (refs. 11, 40, 41, 43, 44, 46). The earliest of them is dated 1677 and the latest 1791. Nearly all of the woods can be identified using old maps, and a high proportion of them are still to be found in today's landscape. Four of the names, alas, appear on no map that is known to the author. Their areas remain fairly constant from one schedule to the next, although there are several versions of their names; see table 3.1. They are listed one after another in each schedule. Furthermore, the schedule of 1765 (ref. 41) shows the four woods, together with a fifth called 'Slate Pit Hill or Intake' of 5:0:00 (acres:roods:perches), sub-totalled as 114:3:34. Conspicuous by its absence from these same schedules is Swithland Wood. According to an undated map of about 1800 (figure 3.5, ref. 54) its area was reckoned to be 116:1:16. Samuel Wylde's map of 1754 (figure 3.6, ref. 39) is the earliest to show what we now call Swithland Wood, and around the large central quarry he has drawn a rectangular piece labelled 'Old Slate Pit Intake'. Nichols (1811) mentions that the 'Old Slate Pits Hill' was enclosed or 'taken in' from the open forest in the mid eighteenth century to become part of Swithland Wood. Moreover, wood sale advertisements (refs. 55 & 56) confirm that Great Dunham Linns and Slate Pit Hay were parts of Swithland Wood. All these pieces of evidence together leave little doubt that the four woods listed in table 3.1, along with Slate Pit Wood, were parts of Swithland Wood in about 1800.

Table 3.1. Names of some woods found in seventeenth and eighteenth century schedules. Their areas are quoted in the traditional format of acres:roods:perches.

Name	Area
Great Lynns or Great Dunham Linns	46:1:34
Little Lynns or Little Dunham Linns	6:0:29
Dunham Lynns or Dunham Linns Spring or Slate Pit Wood	30:2:04
Slate Pit Hay or Old Slate Pit Wood	26:3:07

For reference purposes figure 3.8 is provided, which shows the compartments and their numbers defined for this project, along with some information on how these relate to the task in hand.

To these five names we must add three others which can legitimately claim to be part of our study area. The 1800 map (figure 3.5) identifies 'Slate Pit Wood' of area 6:3:24. It occupies the area labelled 20- in figure 3.8. This is not the same 'Slate Pit Wood', mentioned previously, with an area of 30:2:04, nor is one part of the other. The sequence of schedules reveals the curious fact that there were in operation, simultaneously, two schemes for naming the various parts of our study area. For this reason, the larger of the two 'Slate Pit Woods' will be referred to in this section by its alternative name of Dunham Lynns. The same map also shows compartment 10 sketched in at a later date with a note 'Bought of Mr. Danvers in 1816 by Lord Stamford', but gives no area. My estimate is 6 acres. Compartment 81 is similarly marked, along with a block of land at Hallgates known as Alblaster Hay (figure 1.1). A title deed which apparently deals with this transaction (ref. 38) alludes to 'Smith Ayres Wood', of 5 acres 'by estimation'. The date of the transaction was actually 1819, but the location of the wood described in the deeds ('in Newtown Linford and adjoining the High Road from Newtown Linford to Swithland') can only refer to compartment 10 of Swithland Wood. Compartment 81 is included with the Alblaster Hay part, and is not specifically named. The third extra name appears on the Charnwood Forest Enclosure map of 1828 (figure 3.7). 'Holgate Wood' appears where the south margin of compartment 9 abuts the open forest at Holgate Nook. Holgate is a spelling variant of Hallgates. Unfortunately, the map does not show how far to the north Holgate Wood extended. 'Hall Gates Wood' is also mentioned in the Swithland Enclosure Award of 1799 (ref. 7, folio 3) as the property of A. R. B. Danvers, the proprietor of Swithland lordship. The award refers to the woodland outside the study area (compartment 2) as Whites Wood. This and all other adjacent property in Swithland parish, although in Groby manor, never belonged to the Bradgate Estate, as far back as detailed records go.

Having established the former names of Swithland Wood, we are now in a position to search back through the records for them. The earliest reference is in the minister's accounts for 1512 (ref. 2). The sum of £8 6s 7d was received for 'divers polls sold to divers persons out of the wood of the lord there called Magna Lyndes' (Farnham's translation). Clearly, trees must have been established in Great Lynns at the end of the fifteenth century. A similar document from 1540 (ref. 14), under the heading Swithland, accounts for rent from 'a pasture called Litell Lynds in the tenure of John Smyth' and 'eight acres of pasture called Sclatepitthey'. The account of John Somerfield, seller of woods, in the same document includes '£12 13s 4d for divers trees called *pollis* sold this year in Sclatpitt Hey...' and '64s for 16 cart-loads of bark [*carrect cortic*] at 4s per cart-load sold from the said wood this year'. Evidently, Slate Pit Hay combined grassland and trees - it was wood-pasture (see section 3.4.2). In the abbreviated latin of the sixteenth century *pollis* may have referred to pollards. In view of the entry for Slate Pit Hay, we cannot assume that Little Lynns was without trees despite its description as 'pasture'. By 1656, it is described as a 'spring-wood' (see below), and was in the hands of the Danvers family (ref. 11). Slate Pit Hill is also mentioned in 1540, but with no clue as to what extent it was wooded. In 1574-5 a list of woods in the Manor of Groby was drawn up by Henry Skipwith, which included 'Great Lynes, 34 acres' (ref. 42).

To summarise: the earliest mention of a piece of woodland was Great Lynns, in 1512. Although Little Lynns first appears in 1540, we cannot be sure that it was woodland until 1656. Slate Pit Hay seems to have been wood-pasture in 1540. These three, together with Dunham Lynns, were certainly woodland by 1677. It has to be emphasised that records prior to the mid seventeenth century are very sparse; their contents cannot be cross-checked against other documents. The risk of misinterpretation, or of being deceived by minor clerical errors or simplifications, is fully acknowledged and any conclusions about this period must be qualified as tentative.

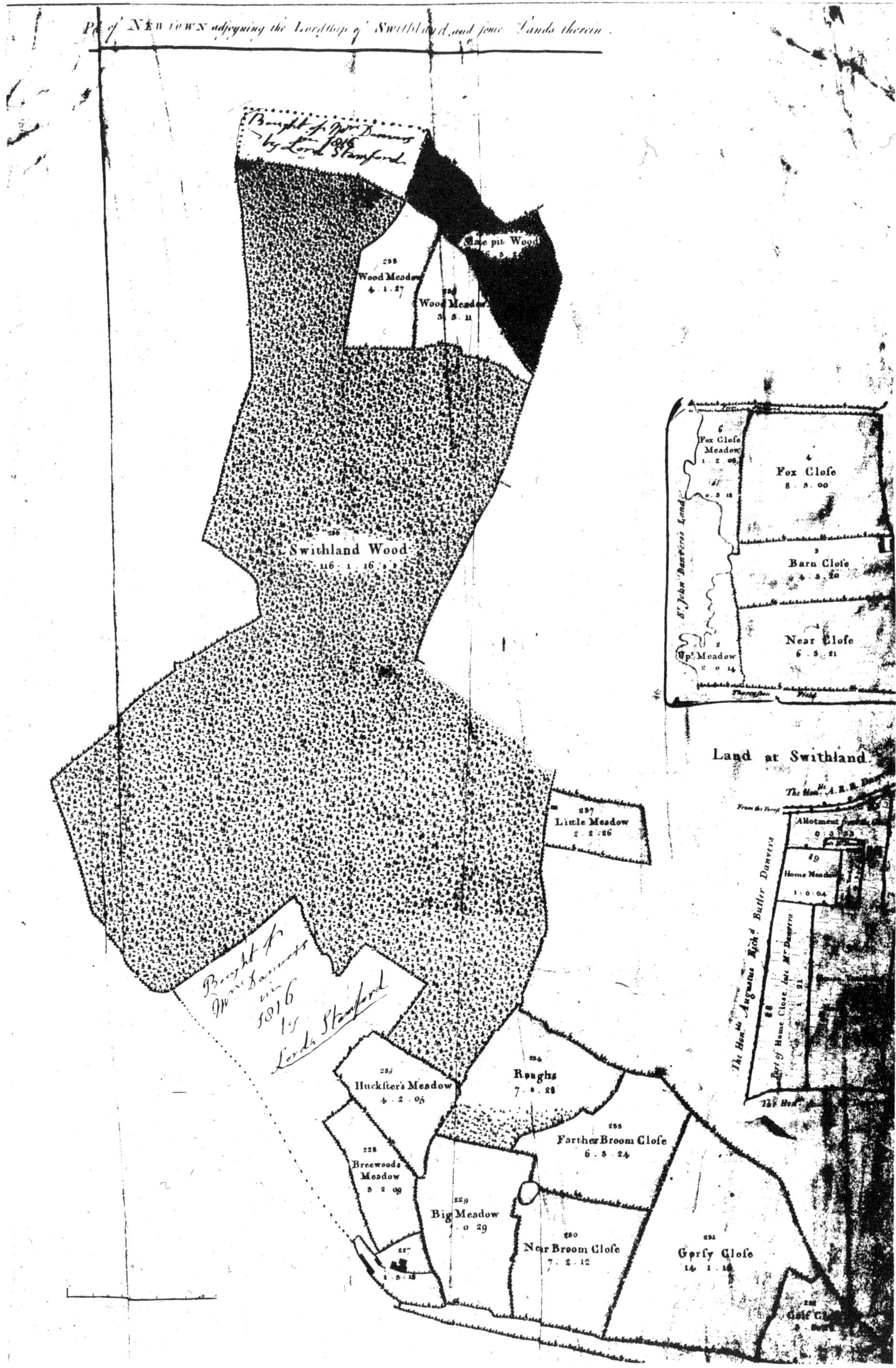

Figure 3.5. Extract from a map of *c.* 1800 (ref. 54).

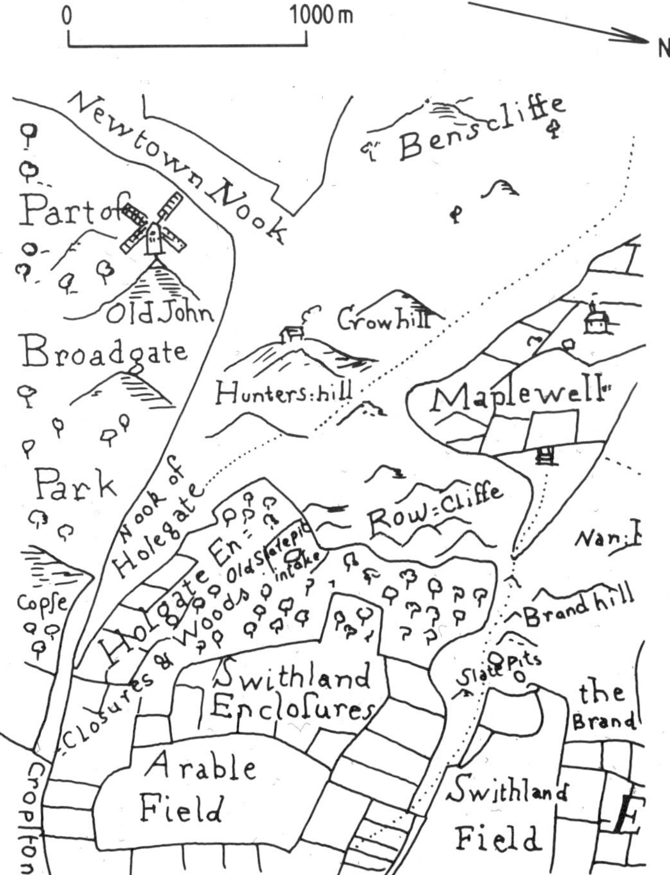

Figure 3.6. Extract from Wylde's map of 1754. Swithland Wood is between 'Row-Cliffe' and 'Swithland Enclosures'. The scale of this map is not sufficient to show much detail, but the northern, southern and western margins of the wood appear to be as they are on later maps. The 'Old Slate Pit' and 'Intake' abut the open forest. Wylde chose to represent enclosures symbolically rather than accurately, so the eastern margin is unclear; it is also partly obscured by the words 'Holgate Enclosures and Woods'. The square, westerly extension of the Swithland Enclosures apparently occupies the space between compartments 1 and 2, and was itself at least partially wooded at this time. There are two contemporary copies of the original map which are slightly different. One is damaged in the area of interest; this tracing is a composite of the two (ref. 39).

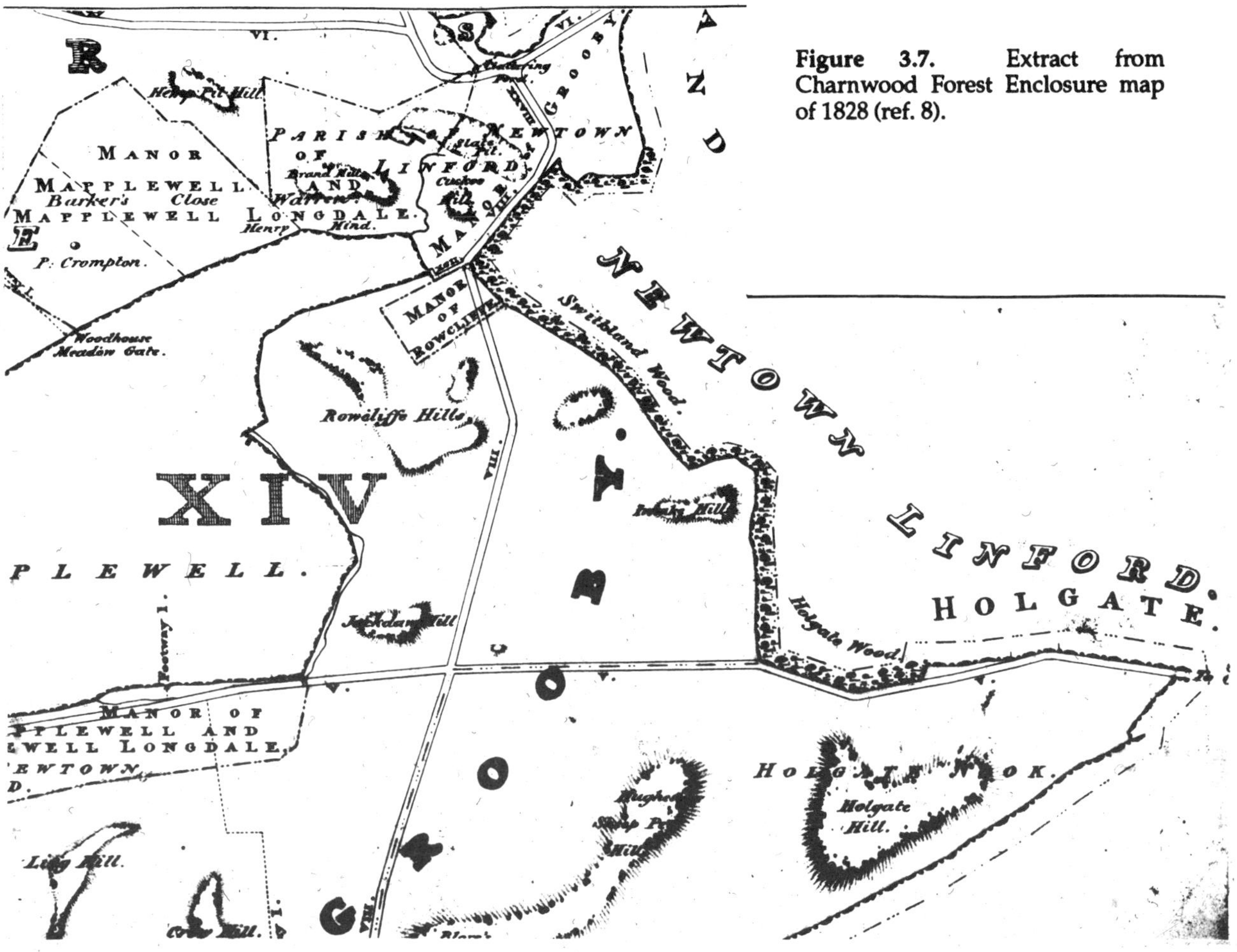

Figure 3.7. Extract from Charnwood Forest Enclosure map of 1828 (ref. 8).

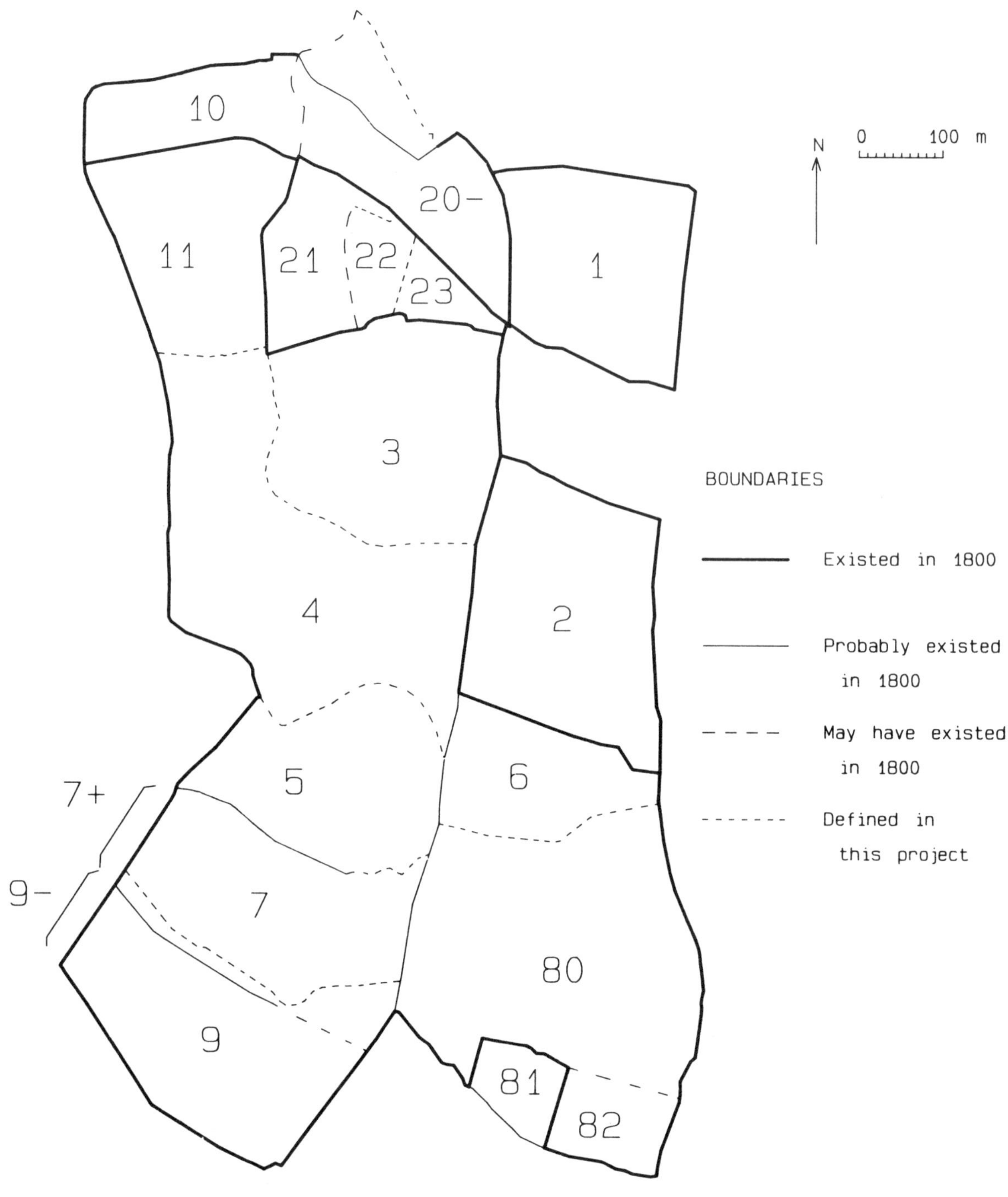

Figure 3.8. Compartment numbers defined in chapter 2 of this report, and some derivatives of them. Prior to the late nineteenth century, the quarry in compartment 20 and a small enclosure to its south-east were considered to be outside Swithland Wood. The remainder of compartment 20 has been labelled 20- here. The 1858 and 1907 maps (refs. 6, 27) show this boundary, although it is now mostly obscured by quarry spoil. The edge of the enclosure (described as a garden in 1907) is picked out by a low bank. Compartments 9- and 7+ arise from an adjustment of the mutual boundary between 9 and 7 (see text). Compartments 1 and 2 are outside the study area.

Boundaries

Let us now attempt to work out the disposition of the named woods within the study area in, say, 1800 (figure 3.9). This year has been chosen so that we may refer to the earliest large scale map (figure 3.5), and make use of the schedules and wood sale records that are available from around this date. Slate Pit Wood (6:3:24) is the only one that is accurately and unambiguously shown on any map (figure 3.5). We also have a good idea where Holgate Wood was (figure 3.7), and probably Slate Pit Hill (figure 3.6).

In addition to the documentary sources, we have the features in the wood itself to guide us. Topographical features such as streams, banks and ditches are likely to have been used as boundaries. These have been identified in the previous chapter, and used where appropriate to define the numbered compartments used for recording in this project. As a starting point, it will be presumed that the named woods can be allocated, by and large, in terms of these numbered compartments (figure 3.8).

Although not actually named on a map, it has already been argued that Smith Ayres Wood corresponds with compartment 10. Its eastern boundary must have been indistinct here since the quarry was opened up; this is probably why it was given as 5 acres 'by estimation' in 1819. We know, from the 1800 map, that the Wood Meadows were extant at this time, so it would seem that there are five woods: Great Lynns, Little Lynns, Dunham Linns, Slate Pit Hay and Slate Pit Hill, to fit into 'Swithland Wood' as delimited on that map.

Whether or not Holgates Wood should be added to that list is questionable. By comparing with figure 3.7, it will be found that 'Swithland Wood' of 116:1:16 in figure 3.5 must have included Holgates Wood. No boundary is delineated. Yet the whole of this area is assigned to 'Swithland Wood' in a schedule of the Earl of Stamford's woods in about 1772 (ref. 10). Did Holgate Wood belong to Danvers, as the Swithland Enclosure Award states; or to Stamford, as his records imply? There is no doubt that it belonged to Stamford in the later nineteenth century, yet there are no references to it by name in any estate records. With some hesitation, I shall regard Holgate Wood as an alternative name for one of the others, and assume that it was Stamford property in which Danvers had some interest in 1799.

The acquisition of compartment 81, by my estimation two and a quarter acres, in 1819 provides a clue to the location of Dunham Linns. This wood is known to have increased in area from 30:2:4 in 1791 (ref. 40) to 32:3:33 in 1829 (ref. 45), a difference of slightly over two and a quarter acres. The whole of the eastern portion of Swithland Wood, i.e. compartments 6, 80, 81 and 82 was regarded as one unit in 1858 (ref. 6, not illustrated), and reckoned to be 33:2:03. The sub-rectangular shape of this part of Swithland Wood and its relationship to the remainder make it a good candidate for a separately named wood. I believe we can be confident that compartments 6, 80 and 82 comprised Dunham Linns, to which 81 was added in 1819.

Compartments 11, 3 and 4 have been separated for the purposes of biological recording, rather than for compelling topographical reasons. Their combined area, by my estimation, is 48:0:24, using the occupation road north of the quarry as an arbitrary southern boundary (arbitrary because this road probably did not exist in 1800). Great Lynns, at 46:1:34 approaches this area. In 1658, under the heading 'Swithland', Danvers is recorded as owning '... a parcel of wood lying on the east side of Great Lyns called Little Moore, or Lane Hey, sometimes White's Land' (ref. 11). It is difficult to see where else Great Lynns could be, given that woodland belonging to Danvers, in Swithland parish, lay to the east.

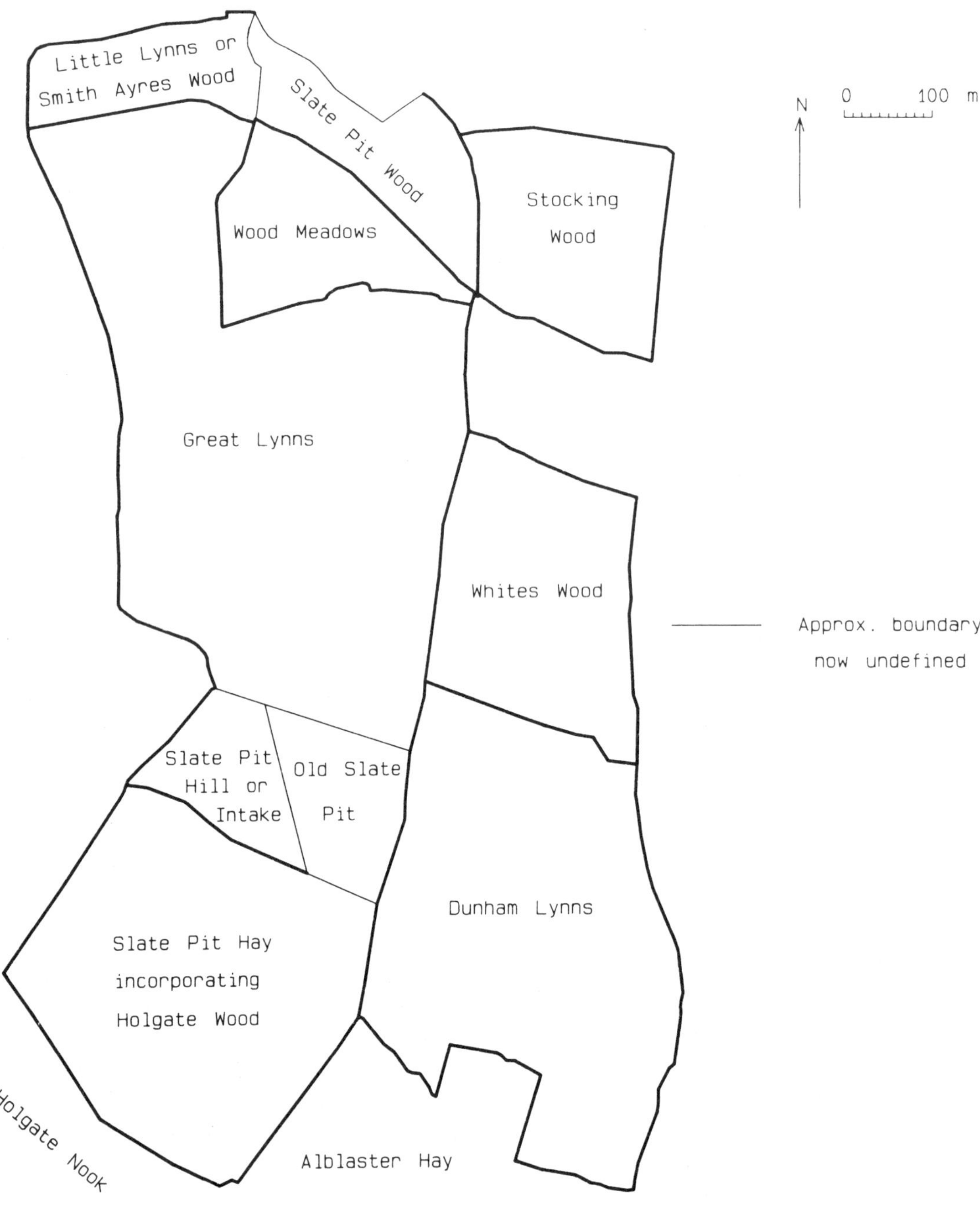

Figure 3.9. Provisional allocation of the old names for the various parts of Swithland Wood.

We have now placed all but Little Lynns, Slate Pit Hill and Slate Pit Hay. The last time Slate Pit Hay appears in a schedule, in 1791, it was 26:3:07 in area. The wood sale advertisement for 1796, however, quotes 37 acres (ref. 59). Unfortunately, there are no other sources to confirm this larger area. If correct, we would then have 48:0:29 of woods to fit into the remaining space (according to the 1858 map) of 39:0:38 (=39.235) acres. This is too large a discrepancy to dismiss as surveying error. Let us assume that the 37 acres is either an error, or that it included additional unidentified woodland. We then have 37:3:36 which, on the face of it, should fit.

Wylde's map, although drawn at a small scale and not very accurately, shows that 'Old Slate Pit Intake' (which Nichols implies is Slate Pit Hill) was roughly equivalent to compartment 5. We should not expect the correspondence to be very good, however, because compartment 5 is only partially delimited by features which are likely to have existed in 1754 - for the most part it follows later quarry features. Any old boundary banks would have been engulfed by spoil heaps. In fact, the areas are significantly different: compartment 5 measures 11:1:08 whereas Slate Pit Hill was only 5:0:00. Various attempts by the writer to re-align the boundaries of compartment 5 so as (a) to include the quarry, (b) to obtain an area of five acres, (c) to incorporate the bank and ditch between 5 and 7 and (d) to define a shape similar to that depicted by Wylde; were all unconvincing. A second approach to this problem was then explored, prompted by the 1858 map (not illustrated). This shows a boundary around the quarry in the eastern part of compartment 5 enclosing 4:3:32 (=4.950) acres. Perhaps the statement in Nichols is misleading: the eastern part may have been Slate Pit Hill and the western part was Slate Pit Intake, each of about 5 acres. Wylde chose to combine the two areas for the sake of simplicity, perhaps. The justification for this assumption is weak, but at least we are in a position to proceed.

Compartments 7 and 9 together contain 28:0:30. After the decision was made to use the stream as their mutual boundary, a weak earthwork was discovered running parallel to it, a little to the south. This feature is much more likely to have been an ancient boundary than the present stream. Adopting this revised boundary, let us define compartments 7+ and 9-, of areas 14:3:27 and 13:1:03 respectively (figure 3.8). Clearly, there is no way of fitting Little Lynns (6:0:29) and Slate Pit Hay (26:3:07) into these two. In fact the latter wood is fairly close in area to 7+ and 9- combined, which leaves us with Little Lynns left over!

Much time has been spent by the writer in re-allocating the named woods, trying to make them fit into the numbered compartments. Although a solution seems to be tantalisingly close, a totally satisfactory answer which squares with all the evidence has proved elusive. The 'best fit' solution is the one previously described, but with both Little Lynns and Smith Ayres Wood assigned to compartment 10; in other words they were alternative names for the same place (figure 3.9). This proposition is not without foundation. Firstly, the traditional practice of naming parcels of land (whether they be pasture, arable, woods etc.) included the habit of using 'Great' and 'Little' as prefixes for adjacent plots, according to their relative areas. So we would expect Little Lynns to lie next to Great Lynns. Secondly, the area of this part of the wood could easily have been 6:0:29 before expansion of the quarry obscured its eastern margin. Thirdly, the 1540 accounts state that the tenant of Little Lynns was called Smyth (although no link with Ayres has been traced). Finally, we noted that Smith Ayres Wood belonged to Danvers prior to 1819. Little Lynns is also recorded as being held freehold by that family in 1677 (ref. 11). The most serious objection to this provisional solution is that Little Lynns appears in the eighteenth century Stamford schedules, and indeed its produce was being sold by Stamford as early as 1766 (ref. 60). This is difficult to explain if Stamford acquired it (as Smith Ayres Wood) in 1819. Yet, other solutions raise equally discomforting inconsistencies.

Among the Bradgate woods, Swithland Wood is uniquely complex with regard to its identity. We have found that different names were used for the same part of the wood, and the same name for different parts. The names are confusingly similar to one another, and there is no doubt that some records have the names mixed up. Some of the schedules are of uncertain date, and it is not always clear whether or not the areas quoted in them include the quarries. In these difficult circumstances, we can only hope that clearer evidence, ideally a detailed contemporary map of the site, will be discovered by the next researcher.

Although the name Swithland Wood first appears in a schedule of 1772 (ref. 10), when it is listed alongside Slate Pit Wood (6:3:24), the alternative set of old names continued in use until 1850. The old names seem to have been abandoned in the latter part of the nineteenth century, and it will be shown later that a change in management practice may have diminished the importance of distinguishing the various component parts.

3.6.2 Woodland management

Coppicing, underwood and timber

In the 1990s, commercial management of woods is almost exclusively geared towards the production of *timber* - large trees with tall, straight trunks, suitable for conversion by machine into building timber, telegraph poles, planks, plywood and so on. This has not always been so. Prior to the early nineteenth century, local records show that timber came mainly from hedgerows, rather than woods. Hedgerow timber would have been shorter, and often crooked, but carpenters were highly skilled at turning the natural shape of their raw material to their advantage (Hewett 1980). The principal function of woodland was to produce *underwood* (or simply *wood*), the regrowth from the stumps of the previous felling. The regrowth was known as the *spring*, and these woods were called *spring-woods*. Although the term *coppice* very rarely appears in local records, spring-woods are now better known as coppices or coppice-woods.

Nearly all native kinds of tree and shrub will, if healthy and not too shaded, send up vigorous new stems if cut to ground level. After a few years, when the stems have reached a useful diameter, they too can be felled or *coppiced* (figure 3.10). An individual tree may be repeatedly coppiced for hundreds of years, and its stump becomes a large *stool*. The fundamental difference between this and modern forestry practice is that the trees are not killed, but actually rejuvenated by the harvesting process. Replanting is rarely necessary, and a well-managed spring-wood was a self-renewing resource. So long as the young shoots are protected from grazing animals, a wood will continue to yield a regular crop of underwood for little investment on the part of its owner.

Naturally, spring-wood owners preferred a more or less regular yield of underwood and an annual income, so woods were typically subdivided into compartments, one (or more) of which would be felled each year. Thus, a single wood managed on a ten year coppice cycle might be divided into ten parts, and would be in ten different stages of regrowth. The reality was usually more complicated, since an owner might possess more than one wood; or local markets might demand underwood of different ages or in irregular quantities from year to year (Rackham 1976). It was common practice to leave a few single stems or spontaneous saplings uncut, to grow on for two or more cycles of the underwood. These became the timber or *standard* trees of the *coppice-with-standards* system, but they were deliberately maintained at a low density so as not to suppress the underwood (figure 3.10).

Timber was required for large structures such as buildings and wagons, but smaller material was preferable for smaller products, to avoid the waste of cutting it to size. In our age of machinery and abundant energy, it is easy to forget the toil involved in manually shifting and cutting up large trees. Thus, underwood supplied communities

Figure 3.10. A short-rotation coppice at Etherley Copse, Surrey (May 1984). Here, the underwood is pure hazel, which is still used to make traditional hurdles. In the preceding winter, the section in the foreground was felled. The section beyond was last cut about two years ago. The hazel is cut again before it attains any great height, so that the standard trees in the background have been able to develop spreading crowns.

with fuel, furniture, clogs, bowls, punnets and countless other domestic items (Edlin 1949). It was used in large quantities by farmers for fences, gates and other agricultural equipment. Wooden rods found many applications in buildings, for example in thatching and in wattle panels. Coppice-woods and their associated specialist trades were very much part of the fabric of traditional rural life (Fitzrandolph & Hay 1926).

Coppicing on the Bradgate Estate

A survey of Groby manor for 1677 survives in the form of an eighteenth century copy (ref. 11). With reference to spring-woods it carefully differentiates between 'timber ... of the age of 40 years or more' and 'wood ... under the age of 40 years'. This implies that spring-woods did contain both timber and underwood (but see *Planting and felling* below). If timber was regarded as stems left uncut for two or more coppice cycles, then we may deduce that the underwood was cut every 20 years. This is, in fact, the scheme that emerges in the middle of the following century, when detailed information becomes available. Under the Earls of Stamford, all the woods were retained 'in hand'; under the direct control of the estate. Every year, the forthcoming sale of underwood was advertised in the *Leicester Journal* along with particulars of which woods were to be felled (figure 3.11). This information, supplemented where necessary from Stamford manuscripts, is summarised in figure 3.12. To help relate these records to the landscape, a map has been compiled (figure 3.13) which attempts to show all woods as they were in about 1780. This figure should be examined in conjunction with table 3.2, which gives the contemporary name and area.

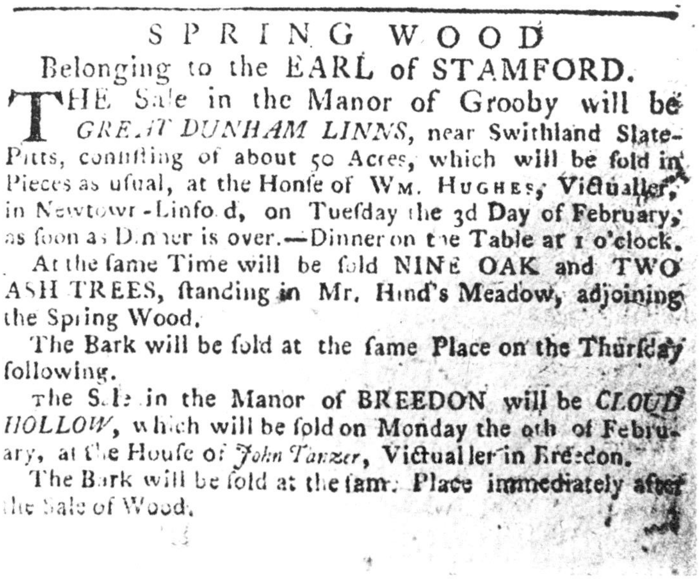

SPRING WOOD

Belonging to the EARL of STAMFORD.

THE Sale in the Manor of Grooby will be *GREAT DUNHAM LINNS*, near Swithland Slate-Pitts, consisting of about 50 Acres, which will be sold in Pieces as usual, at the House of WM. HUGHES, Victualler, in Newtown-Linford, on Tuesday the 3d Day of February, as soon as Dinner is over.—Dinner on the Table at 1 o'clock.

At the same Time will be sold NINE OAK and TWO ASH TREES, standing in Mr. Hind's Meadow, adjoining the Spring Wood.

The Bark will be sold at the same Place on the Thursday following.

The Sale in the Manor of BREEDON will be *CLOUD HOLLOW*, which will be sold on Monday the 9th of February, at the House of *John Tanzer*, Victualler in Breedon.

The Bark will be sold at the same Place immediately after the Sale of Wood.

Figure 3.11. The spring wood sale advertisement from the *Leicester Journal*, 24 January 1784.

The woods were not managed individually, but all were integrated into one scheme for the whole estate. Figure 3.12 demonstrates the striking regularity of the fellings over nearly a hundred years, which may well extend back into less well documented centuries. With few exceptions, woods were cut every 19 years prior to 1786, every 20 years between then and 1816, and every 21 years thereafter. In total, there were about 1000 acres of woodland. Therefore, about 50 acres could be felled annually without depleting the resource. Individual woods that were smaller than this were clear-felled every 20 years whereas those larger than 50 acres were visited by the woodcutters in two or more consecutive years in that period. A conspicuous exception is Foxley Hay, a small wood in which fellings additional to the normal rotation took place. The singular reference to 'oak and ash timber of large dimensions and very superior quality' in 1810, implies that part of this wood was devoted to timber rather than underwood.

During the period covered by figure 3.12, neither the sale advertisements nor the surviving estate records ever mention the species of underwood being sold, as if this were irrelevant to potential buyers. In fact, the underwood was sold standing in lots. Lots, in turn, were subdivided into *furlongs*, of variable area (ref. 45). Buyers inspected the lots before the sale and selected those which contained the kinds of wood best suited to their requirements. The auction took place at a local hostelry after the traditional 'wood-dinner' provided by the earl. Unfortunately, this procedure, in conjunction with the later practice of selling through a firm of auctioneers, has left little record of which underwood species were being sold, and for what purpose. The annual spring-wood sale, which usually took place in January, was followed a few weeks later by a bark sale. This implies that oak was a major constituent of the underwood, since it was oak bark that was valued for tanning leather (see page 53).

Seventeenth and eighteenth century writers commented on the scarcity of trees in Leicestershire. Marshall (1790) thought that the county possessed sufficient timber, but that more coppice-woods could be usefully planted. Stamford evidently shared these views, for some 283 extra acres were 'laid down for wood' between 1751 and 1759, mostly at Old Wood, Lawn Wood and Blakes Hay (ref. 41). More detail on the economic influences on the woods will be presented shortly.

```
                                 1                                               1
                                 7                                               8
                                 6666 66666 77777 77777 88888 88888 99999 99999  00000 00000 11111 11111 22222 22222 33333 33333 44444 44444 55555 55555
No. Name                         1234 56789 01234 56789 01234 56789 01234 56789  01234 56789 01234 56789 01234 56789 01234 56789 01234 56789 01234 56789

29  Sheet Hedges Wood            ◆◆◆. ..... ..... ..... ◆◆◆.. ..... ..... .....  ◆◆◆.. ..... ..... ..... .◆◆◆. ..... ..... ..... ..◆◆◆ ..... ..... .....
33  Choices Rough                .... ..... ..... ..... ..... ..... ..... .....  .◆... ..... ..... ..... ..◆.. ..... ..... ..... ...◆. ..... ..... .....
36  Ratby Burrough               ..◆. ..... ..... ..... ..◆.. ..... ..... .....  ..◆.. ..... ..... ..... ...◆. ..... ..... ..... ..... ..... ..... .....
08  Great Lee Wood               ...◆ ..... ..... ..... ...◆. ..... ..... .....  ...◆. ..... ..... ..... ....◆ ..... ..... ..... ..... ◆.... ..... .....
01  Great Dunham Linns           .... ◆.... ..... ..... ....◆ ..... ..... .....  ....◆ ..... ..... ..... ..... ◆.... ..... ..... ..... .◆... ..... .....
13  New Hay Wood                 .... .◆... ..... ..... ..... ◆.... ..... .....  ..... ◆.... ..... ..... ..... .◆... ..... ..... ..... ..◆.. ..... .....
22  Lawn Wood                    .... ..... ..... ..... ..... ◆◆◆.. ..... .....  ..... ◆◆◆.. ..... ..... ..... .◆◆◆. ..... ..... ..... ..◆.◆ ..... .....
11  Foxley Hay                   .... .◆... ..... ..... ..... ◆.... ..... .....  ◆◆... ◆...◆ ◆◆◆◆◆ ◆.... ..◆.. .◆... ...◆◆ ..... ..... ..◆.. ...◆. .....
01  Little Dunham Linns          .... .◆... ..... ..... ..... ◆.... ..... .....  ..... ◆.... ..... ..... ..... .◆... ..... ..... ..... ..◆.. ..... .....
09  Little Lee Wood              .... .◆... ..... ..... ..... .◆... ..... .....  ..... .◆... ..... ..... ..... ..◆.. ..... ..... ..... ...◆. ..... .....
16  Browns Hay Wood Spring       .... ..◆.. ..... ..... ..... .◆... ..... .....  ..... .◆... ..... ..... ◆.... ..◆.. ..... ..... ..... ...◆. ..... ....◆
38  Change Wood                  .... ..◆.. ..... ..... ..... .◆... ..... .....  ..... .◆... ..... ..... ..... ..◆.. ..... ..... ..... ...◆. ..... .....
20  Cover Cloud Wood             .... ..... ..... ..... ..... ..◆.. ..... .....  ..... ..◆.. ..... ..... ..... ...◆. ..... ..... ..... ....◆ ..... .....
21  Heyday Hey Wood              .... ..◆.. ..... ..... ..... ..... ..... .....  ..... ..◆.. ..... ..... ..... ...◆. ..... ..... ..... ....◆ ..... .....
01  Slate Pit Wood               .... ...◆. ◆.... ..... ..... ...◆. ..... .....  ..... ...◆. ..... ..... ..... ....◆ ..... ..... ..... ..... ..... .....
24  Horse Close Rough            .... ..... ..... ..... ..... ...◆. ..... .....  ..... ...◆. ..... ..... ..... ....◆ ..... ..... ..... ..... ..... .....
14  Sandhills Wood (Rough)       .... ....◆ ..... ..... ..... ...◆. ..... .....  ..... ...◆. ..... ..... ..... ....◆ ..... ..... ..... ..... ◆.... .....
10  Bench Cliff Hay              .... ....◆ ..... ..... ..... ....◆ ..... .....  ..... ....◆ ..... ..... ..... ..... ◆.... ..... ..... ..... .◆.◆. .....
35  Marten Shaw Wood             .... ..... .◆◆◆◆ ◆.... ..... ....◆ ◆◆◆◆◆ ◆....  ..... ....◆ ◆◆◆◆◆ ◆◆... ..... ..... ◆◆◆◆◆ ◆◆◆.. ..... ..... .◆◆◆◆ ◆◆◆◆.
37  Somerfields Borough          .... ....◆ ..... ..... ..... ..... ◆.... .....  ..... ..... ◆.... ..... ..... ..... .◆... ..... ..... ..... ..◆.. .....
12  Blakehay                     .... ..... ..◆.. ..... ..... ..... ...◆◆ .....  ..... ..... ...◆◆ ..... ..... ..... ....◆ ◆.... ..... ..... ..... ◆....
15  Sandhills (Spring) Wood      .... ..... ..... .◆... ..... ..... ..... ◆....  ..... ..... ..... ◆.... ..... ..... ..... .◆... ..... ..... ..... ..◆..
25  Carter's Rough               .... ..... ..... ◆.... ..... ..... ..... ◆....  ..... ..... ..... .◆... ..... ..... ..... ..◆.. ..... ..... ..... ..◆..
01  Slate Pit Hay                .... ..... ..... .◆... ..... ..... ..... .◆...  ..... ..... ..... .◆◆.. ..... ..... ..... ..◆◆. ..... ..... ◆.... .....
23  Old Wood                     .... ..... ..... ..◆◆. ..... ..... ..... .◆◆◆◆  ..... ..... ..... ..◆◆◆ ◆.... ..... ..... ...◆◆ ◆◆... ..... ....◆ ◆...◆
26  Stewards Hay Spring Wood     .... ..... ..... ..◆◆. ..... ..... ..... ..◆◆◆  ..... ..... ..... ...◆◆ ◆.... ..... ..... ....◆ ◆◆... ..... ..... ...◆.
27  Lady Hay Wood                .... ..... ..... ..... ..... ..◆.. ..... .....  ..... ..... ..... ..... .◆... ..... ..... ..... ..◆.. ..... ..... .....
```

Figure 3.12. Fellings in the Bradgate Estate woods, 1761-1859. The years are shown across the top, to be read vertically. The symbol ◆ shows which woods were felled in each year. The reference numbers of the woods are those of table 3.2. Based mainly on advertisements in the *Leicester Journal* and estate accounts at Enville Hall, Staffordshire.

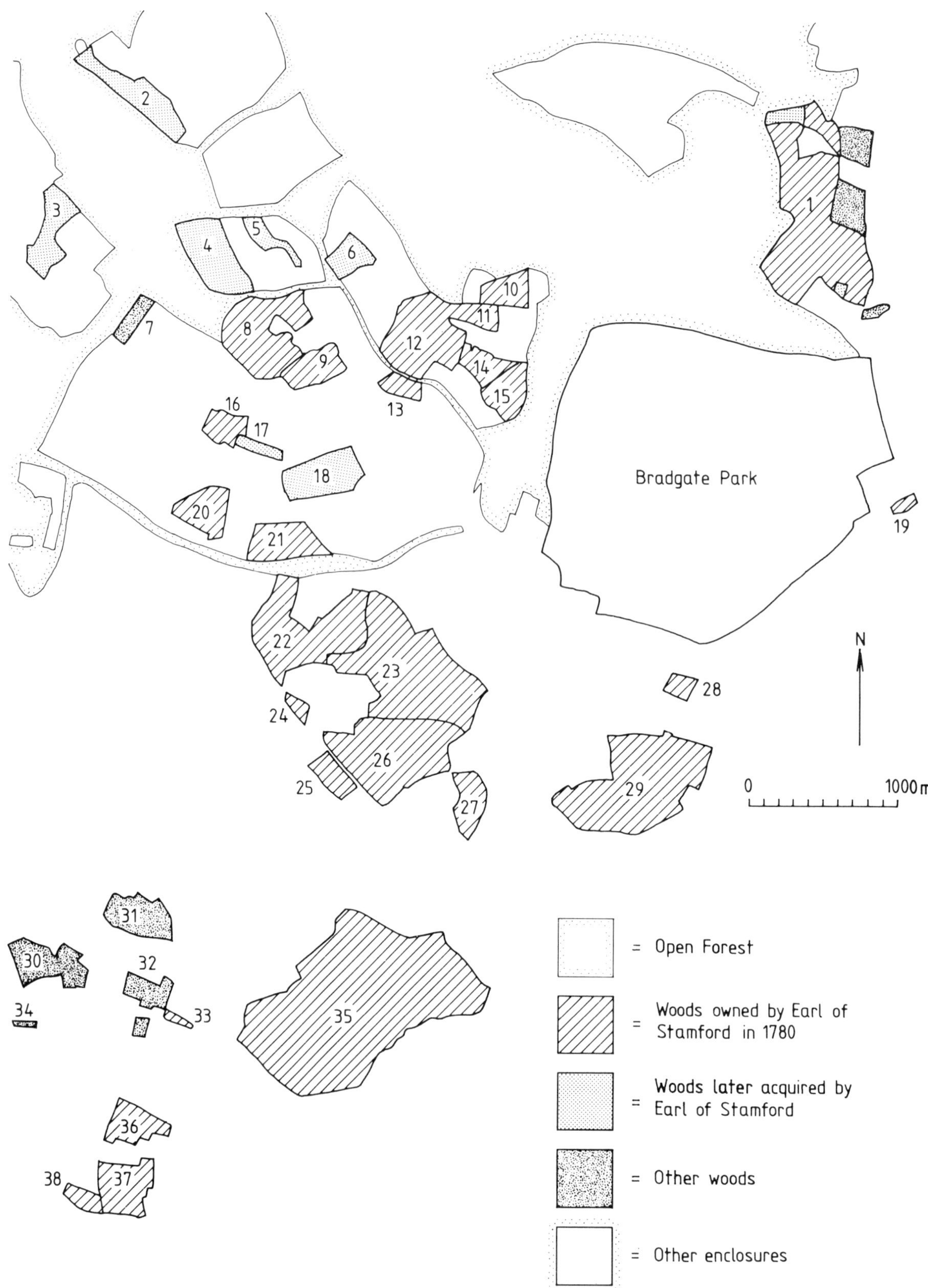

Figure 3.13. Woods on or near the Bradgate Estate in 1780 (see also table 3.2). This is a reconstruction rather than a copy of a contemporary map, although three late eighteenth century maps have been the main sources (refs. 52, 53, 58). The extent of the open forest of Charnwood immediately prior to enclosure is also shown (ref. 8); note that the north, west and south margins of the study area adjoined the forest.

Table 3.2. Woods on or near the Bradgate Estate in 1780. The reference numbers relate to the map of figure 3.13. The spellings and areas (in acres, roods and perches) are those of 1780. Principal sources are refs. 10, 11, 43, 44, 52, 53, 54, 57, 58, and old Ordnance Survey maps.

No.	Name	a:r:p	No.	Name	a:r:p
01	Swithland Wood (note 1),		18	John's Leys Wood	27:2:17
	incorporating:		19	Cropston Spinney	3:1:28
	Great Dunham Linns	46:1:34	20	Cover Cloud Wood	20:1:33
	Little Dunham Linns	6:0:29	21	Heyday Hey Wood	24:3:29
	Slate Pit Wood	30:2:04	22	Lawn Wood	73:3:33
	Slate Pit Wood	6:3:24	23	Old Wood	114:2:26
	Slate Pit Hay	26:3:07	24	Horse Close Rough	6:1:25
	(=Old Slate Pit Wood)		25	Carter's Rough	11:0:34
	Slate Pit Hill	5:0:00	26	Stewards Hay Spring Wood	73:2:08
02	Poultney's Wood (note 2)	14:2:34	27	Lady Hay Wood	17:3:02
03	Colbourne's Wood	24:2:07	28	Chaplins Rough	6:1:32
04	Stanywell Wood	35:2:38	29	Sheet Hedges Wood	104:0:29
05	Nowell Spring	?	30	Great Wood	?
06	Nether Rough	12:0:16	31	Whittington's Rough	?
07	Schittonmur Hill Wood	?	32	Bondman's Rough	?
08	Great Lee Wood	47:1:36	33	Choices Rough	2:0:28
09	Little Lee Wood	17:2:13	34	Lea's Wood	?
10	Bench Cliff Hay	15:1:22	35	Marten Shaw Wood	272:1:03
11	Foxley Hay	9:0:39	36	Ratby Burrough (note 5)	?
12	Blakehay (note 3)	53:0:08		(=Hunt's Burrough &	
13	New Hay Wood	8:1:24		Siddon's Burrough)	
14	Sandhills Wood (note 4)	14:1:22	37	Sumerfields Borough	23:2:10
15	Sandhills Spring (note 4)	18:1:10		(note 5)	
16	Browns Hay Wood Spring	11:3:32	38	Change Wood	6:3:36
17	Danvers Spring Wood	?			

Notes:

1. For an explanation of the woods comprising Swithland Wood refer to section 3.6.1.

2. No contemporary assessment is available but Poultney Wood appears not to have changed in area since 1796 (ref. 52). The area quoted is its modern area.

3. The 1773 map (ref. 53) gives the combined area of Blakehay and Foxely Hay as 62:1:07. The 1768 schedule (ref. 44) gives Foxley Hay as 9:0:39. The calculated difference is the area given in the table.

4. The names on two of the schedules (refs. 10 & 43) have been matched to the *areas* on the 1773 map (ref. 53). However, the *names* on the map are transposed, and have been presumed to be incorrect. It is unclear which was 'Sandhills (Wood)' and which 'Sandhills Rough'; the names used in the wood sale advertisements.

5. The various 'Burroughs' in Ratby seem to have been undergoing rapid change at this time. The schedules and maps do not easily relate to one another.

The coppicing records invariably refer to Swithland Wood by the names of the four compartments: Great Dunham Linns, Little Dunham Linns, Slate Pit Wood and Slate Pit Hay; as though they were separate woods. Curiously, the acquisition in 1819 of compartments 10 and 81 from Danvers had no discernible effect on the record; the same four compartments continued to be advertised and felled in just the same way. Either they were simply appended to adjacent compartments and felled with them, or else they were not coppiced but left to grow into timber.

Planting and felling of timber

A notable feature of the pre-1859 wood sales is that all timber was advertised as 'outwood'; that is from hedgerows, farmyards and gardens, rather than woods. With the exception of Foxley Hay previously noted, there is no clear evidence that standards were actually being taken out of the spring-woods, as was implied in the seventeenth century. One effect of the 1808 Charnwood Forest Enclosure Act was to allow trees to be re-established on the forest, particularly on the numerous rocky sites that were not susceptible to agricultural improvement. It seems that the Earl of Stamford could not wait for the Award of 1829, for he had already enclosed and planted up several places by 1821 (ref. 40). Figure 3.14 illustrates the range of species used in the new plantations. The broad-leaved species oak *Quercus* spp., ash *Fraxinus excelsior*, beech *Fagus sylvatica* and birch *Betula pendula* made up 52% of numbers but conifers were by now very much in fashion and three species made up another 40%. These were 'Scotch' or Scots pine *Pinus sylvestris*, 'Spruce fir' or Norway spruce *Picea abies* and European larch *Larix decidua*.

After 1858, the wood sales become irregular, the 21 year cycle having been abandoned. No longer are the advertisements entitled 'Spring Wood', but the word 'Timber' is generally prominent. Underwood and bark continued to be sold from the spring-woods into the twentieth century, but timber from both woods and plantations assumed ever increasing importance from 1859. Evidently, when new plantations were being made at the beginning of the century, timber trees were also being planted or promoted in the spring-woods, and some had now reached commercial maturity. Figure 3.15 shows the proportions of the various species being sold in around 1880. Oak was by far the most numerous with ash a poor second. The 'proper age for felling oak timber', according to Marshall (1790), was 100 to 200 years, depending on situation. If we assume these oaks were 150 years old, they must have been growing up among the underwood in the early 1700s. The three conifers only made up 7% of timber sales between them because they were generally felled at the 'pole' stage. The year 1859 thus marks a turning point for the woodlands of the Bradgate Estate. The ancient traditions of spring-wood management were giving way to the modern ideas of forestry.

3.6.3 The economic importance of woodlands

Local shortage of woodland

At the time of the Domesday survey, most Leicestershire settlements possessed no woodland (Darby & Terrett 1971, page 344; Rackham 1980, page 114). Yet, wood was both a vital fuel and the universal material for innumerable commodities; no community or industry could function without it. Certainly, hedgerows would have furnished timber and faggots, but regular supplies of straight, medium-diameter poles must have been brought in from areas such as Rockingham and Charnwood Forests, where plenty of spring-woods remained. The profit from this trade presumably exceeded the potential value of the woods as farmland.

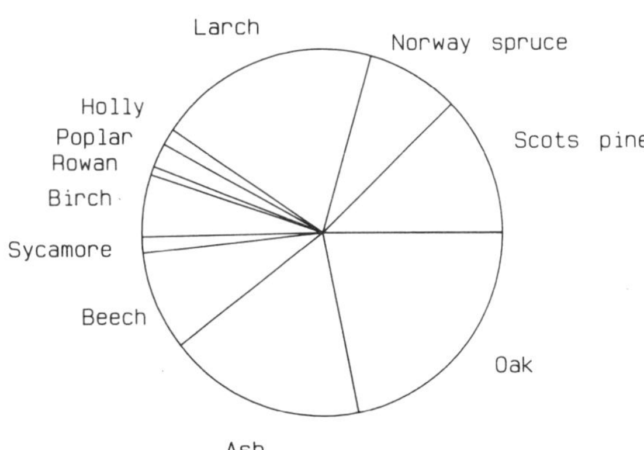

Figure 3.14. Tree species being planted in the new plantations on Charnwood Forest, 1820 & 1828. Based on records of 78,644 trees (ref. 40).

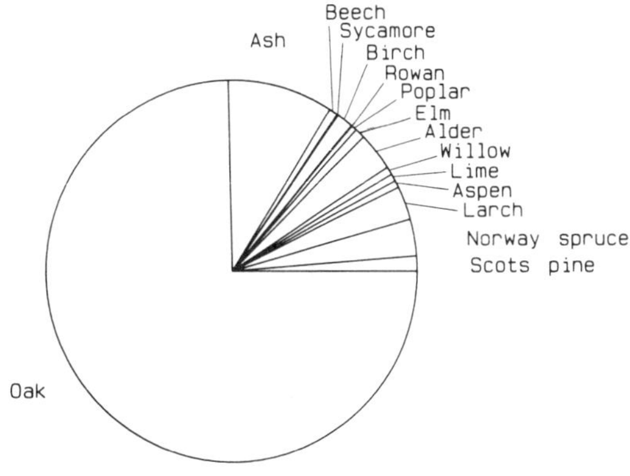

Figure 3.15. Relative importance of timber species on the Bradgate Estate, based on 12,726 trees advertised for sale in the *Leicester Journal* between 1874 and 1884. By this time, timber came mainly from woods and plantations. Due to the imprecise wording of the source material, the figures probably include a small quantity of hedgerow trees and poles.

Estate income and the contribution from woodlands 1512-1919

Early manorial valuations are difficult to interpret because the medieval economy was based as much on the exchange of services and privileges, as it was on cash. It is particularly unfortunate that the several woods known to exist at the time are neither individually nor collectively valued in the available documents. However, the estate was temporarily in the hands of the Crown in 1512 (ref. 2). Consequently, the accounts for that year have survived, and furnish the earliest intelligible details of manorial economics. The total income was £149, of which 66% was derived from the rents of tenant farmers and cottagers, 5% from agistment (rent for allowing cattle to graze) in the parks, 5% from court perquisites (fines, etc.) and a substantial 24% from timber and wood sales. The bulk of this income in that year came from just two woods, Sheet Hedges Wood and Great Lynds (part of Swithland Wood). Fellings in Ratby and a rent known as 'tack silver', for turning out pigs to feed on acorns in the woods (i.e. pannage), made up the remainder.

No further detailed accounts are available until the survey of 1677, previously referred to. Although the total income had risen sharply, this was largely due to high monetary inflation during the sixteenth century (Brown & Hopkins 1956) and in fact the contribution from trees and woods remained at 24% :

Timber (40 or more years old)	£ 160	11%
Underwood (less than 40 years old)	£ 120	8%
Topwood and bark	£ 60	4%
Rents	£1,095	76%
TOTAL	£1,435	100%

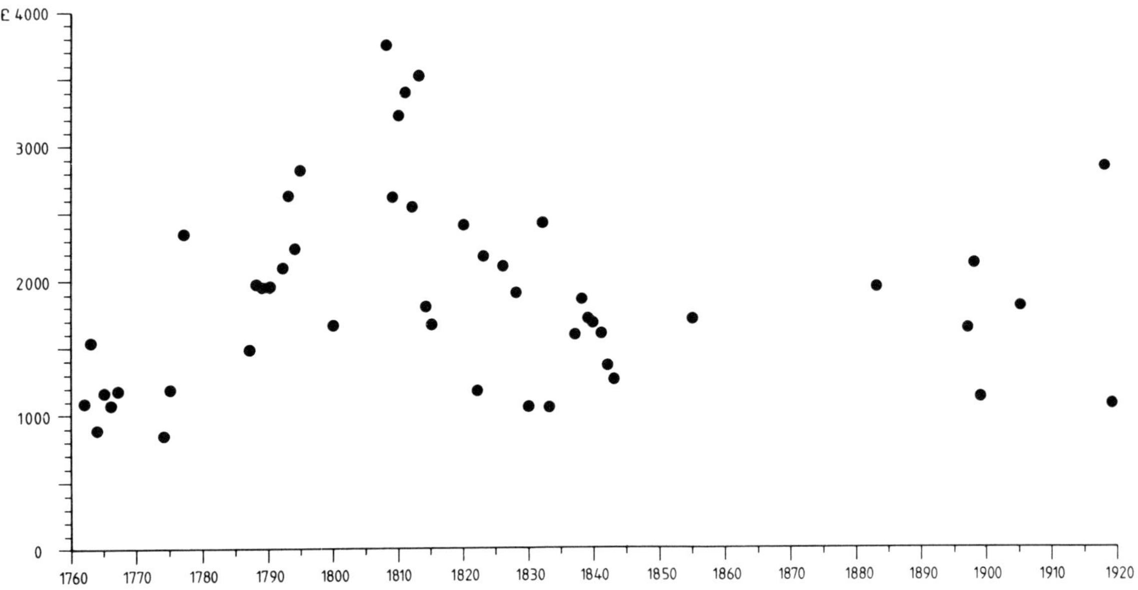

Figure 3.16. Income from the Bradgate Estate woods, 1762-1919. Includes wood, timber and bark. Compiled from numerous account books among the Stamford archives at Leicestershire Record Office and Enville Hall, Staffordshire.

Whether or not these figures are typical we have no means of knowing. From the mid eighteenth to the mid nineteenth centuries, a series of estate accounts (mainly ref. 45) reveal how the woodland income fluctuated considerably from year to year (figure 3.16). Of course, woods differed in species composition and in the quality of their underwood, but this is only part of the explanation. These accounts reveal that the predicted sale value of underwood often disagreed markedly with the sum actually raised, for example in 1820 wood valued at £1453 actually went for £1939. This may have been the consequence of selling by auction rather than fixing a price, the judgement of the bidders having perhaps been impaired by the traditional gathering at the hostelry beforehand! Hence, the relative value of woodland ought really to be averaged over a period of, say, five years. The fragmentary nature of the records rarely allows us to do this. Fortunately, the rental from about 1765 (ref. 41) provides a contemporary assessment of the average value. This was £1000 per annum, compared with £2656 for cottage and farm rents in that year. The proportion of total income derived from the woods had thus risen to 27%, even before the newly planted spring-woods had been felled.

Superimposed on the annual variation can be discerned a sharp general rise in income up to about 1808, when it peaked at £3752. Shortly afterwards, income fell rapidly again, settling around £1500 in the mid-nineteenth century. Again, this trend is largely a reflection of the general cost of living rather than the relative value of wood. Nonetheless, rentals for 1851 (ref. 48) show that £1500 represented only about 15% of estate income. Similarly, for seven of the years between 1883 and 1919 the average income from timber, underwood and bark was £1800, also about 15% of total estate income (refs. 17, 21, 25). Although the estate accounts do not break down the figures as far as one might wish, it is clear from other sources that, of all the woodland products, timber brought in the greatest revenue.

The economic affairs of the Greys themselves naturally influenced the running of the estate. Rackham (1980) has observed that timber was regarded as a reserve to be called upon in a financial emergency, and this would appear to explain the sudden preponderance of timber in the Bradgate wood sales from 1859. In that year, financial circumstances were such that the seventh earl was obliged to mortgage a substantial portion of the estate in order to raise capital (Woodward 1984, page 14).

Local woodland trades and markets

The business of working up raw material into saleable products was not one in which the estate was directly involved. Except for the requirements of estate builders, all timber and wood appears to have been sold, whether or not the purchasers operated within the estate. Since all these businesses were individually owned, the estate archives tell us virtually nothing about them. Judging from trade directories and a brief examination of probate records, local woodland trades included wheelwrights, framesmiths (makers of knitting frames), cabinet makers, scythe sneath and rake makers, charcoal burners, and various dealers in wood, bark and timber. Nichols' (1811) entry for Newtown Linford includes the following passage:

> 'several of the inhabitants live comfortably by dealing in timber at the Earl of Stamford's sales. The inhabitants indeed are principally employed in the woods ..., and the faggots which are sold from these woods are carried mostly to Leicester, and are of great use to the bakers for heating ovens. The timber also turns to good account.'

The very regular coppicing regime implies the existence of an unfailing market for 20 year old underwood. A local industry might create such a demand, but none has been demonstrated to be a major consumer, which might have influenced local woodland management. The coal mines in north-west Leicestershire would have required pit-props for which 20 year old coppice would have been suitable (Baker 1983, Jones 1961). In 1918 'pit-prop timber' was sold to Sir Tudor Walters (ref. 19), but this appears to be an isolated transaction, and in any case post-dates the lapse of regular coppicing. This size of material would also have been suitable for converting into charcoal, formerly an important industrial fuel. Again, the scarcity of documentary references to charcoal burning precludes any assessment of its importance. Within living memory, charcoal burners visited Martinshaw Wood, and the sites of hearths can still be traced (M. T. Ball, *pers. comm.*). In connection with local charcoal consumption, Nichols (1811) refers to iron forges at Whitwick in 1673. He also relates how, in the mid eighteenth century, huge oak trees growing around the Swithland slate pits (see page 54) were converted into charcoal and sent by pack-horse to furnaces at Melbourne, Derbyshire. Ancient pollards, as these seem to have been, were hardly ideal material for industrial charcoal and this must have been an exceptional sale.

The bark of coppiced oak was used for tanning leather (Clarkson 1974). Leicester is well known for its long-established leather industry (Allin 1981), which must have consumed large quantities of local bark before the introduction of synthetic tanning agents. Certainly, hundreds of tons were regularly sold, but in terms of value, bark was worth only a fraction the value of the wood. In the 1760s bark made up 13% of woodland revenue, increasing to 21% in the early 1800s.

Some of the later sale advertisements list the types of product for which the merchandise was claimed to be suitable. Presumably such claims were based on previous sales and therefore truly reflect actual markets. Frequent mention is made of bobbin-wood and crate-wood, the first used to supply local hosiery firms and the second for general packing purposes. Sallow, alder, birch and ash were the species generally offered for bobbin and crate-wood. In 1864 a sale of spruce and 'scotch' poles was addressed particularly to colliery proprietors, presumably for pit-props. In the same year builders of railway wagons were invited to a sale of 'well-grown' oak timber. Oak was also advertised for gate-posts, fence-posts, and for cleaving into spokes. Other applications mentioned in advertisements or accounts of actual sales include pea sticks, bean poles, set rods, hurdles, firewood and hammer shafts. A sale catalogue dated 1905 (ref. 23) states that the birch was very suitable for clog making.

3.6.4 Swithland Wood

Pollarding

As we noted in section 3.6.1, the earliest records show that parts of the wood were grazed and that trees were present as pollards. This is corroborated by an account, published by Nichols (1811, page 135), of an old man who was describing the area in about 1760:

> '... the old slate pits, near Hall gates, all in the Earl of Stamford's royalty, were covered with large oak-trees, the tops of many of them, cut off, yet shot-out large branches; most of them hollowed and decayed with age, and numbers whose circumferences were upwards of 20 feet.'

These were huge trees. Even allowing for some exaggeration, they must have been several centuries old. The allusion to 'large' branches implies that the practice of regular lopping had lapsed by that time.

Felling

Prior to 1859, Swithland Wood seems to have been treated just as any other wood on the estate, and no specific details can be added. Later, a general management plan for the estate woodlands is not apparent, but at least the available information on the individual sales is more detailed. The first of three sales in 1872 was held on 12 April, comprising a wide range of timber and underwood from Swithland Wood, Martinshaw, and others. The bark sale took place on 18 May, and included four lots, each of 10 tons, from Swithland Wood. The third sale, on 25 July, disposed of 500 oak timber trees and poles, 60 cords of firewood, 140 scores of kids (faggots) and 300 fence-posts, all from Swithland Wood.

Another sale took place on 5 March 1896. The advertisement (ref. 64) refers to '2202 oak, 101 ash, 118 lime, 88 birch and 107 alder standing blazed and numbered in Swithland Wood'. The following remarks are appended to the advertisement: 'the auctioneers beg to call special attention to the oak in Swithland Wood, the majority of the trees containing from 30 to 50 [cubic] feet with a fair number extending to 60 [cubic] feet and upwards. They are well-grown, long in the butt, and of very fine quality.' This was clearly a major felling, and the wood must have looked noticeably thinner afterwards.

The 1905 sale is well documented, for two copies of the printed catalogue survive, one marked up with the purchasers' names, the other with the volume, valuation, and the sum actually realised at auction (table 3.3). In 1907, a swathe was cut through the middle of the wood in preparation for a water main to be laid (see section 3.8). One hundred oaks, nine ash, two limes, one poplar and 107 'poles and small trees' were felled, together with hazel and other underwood. The last record of commercial management by the estate is from 1917, when £2 10s 10d were received from Cropston Allotment Society for bean poles and pea kids (ref. 19).

Planting

Records of planting in the estate woodlands are not as explicit as one might wish. The only unambiguous references to planting in Swithland Wood come from account books of 1909, which record payments to Mr Gretton and Mr Johnson for digging a total of 12,187 holes, planting saplings and erecting wire fencing (refs. 16 & 17). The species and location are not recorded. Other references to 'cleaning' (i.e. cutting back unwanted vegetation) in 1908, and fencing in 1901, imply that planting had been carried out previously in other parts of the wood.

Table 3.3. Details of the Swithland Wood part of the 1905 timber sale, taken from annotated sale catalogues (ref. 23). Oak, ash, lime and birch trees were valued at 1s 6d, 1s, 9d and 6d per cubic foot respectively.

Lot	Description	Cubic feet	Valuation £	Amount realised £
46	20 Oak	316	24	
47	32 Oak	429	32	
48	35 Oak	511	38	
49	49 Oak	652	50	
		1908	144	152
50	35 Lime poles	-	5	
51	18 Lime timber trees	233	10	
52	30 Lime timber trees	625	23	
53	36 Lime poles	-	5	
		858	43	40
54	13 Ash	95	5	10
55	41 Birch poles	174	5	8

3.7 The Slate Quarries

3.7.1 History

A detailed account of the slate industry in Leicestershire has been published by Ramsey (1986). There were two principal sources of good quality slate in the county; Groby and the Swithland area. Local slate found in Roman contexts, for example at the Jewry Wall in Leicester, may have come from either source. The earliest reference to slate quarrying at Swithland is in a document of 1343 (ref. 4). In 1377/8 Swithland Slate was used to repair Leicester Castle (Ball & Jones 1976). Once again, we cannot be sure that these quarries were the ones within our study area, since outcrops at The Brand, just to the north of the wood, may also have been worked at this time. The evidence we are seeking has, in fact, already been mentioned, when we noted that the part of the wood called Slate Pit Hay can be traced back to 1540 (ref. 14). How long slate was being taken from the wood prior to this is not known - it is even possible that the quarrying pre-dates the woodland.

Prior to the industrial revolution, slate quarrying would have been a matter of breaking slabs from the outcrops with hammers, wedges and crowbars, then splitting them into the required thicknesses. Gunpowder was unlikely to have been introduced much before 1700. Difficulties in transportation would originally have restricted the market for such a heavy product, and quarrying was probably no more than a part-time occupation for a few people. By the early nineteenth century, however, machinery had been introduced and slate quarrying had developed into a considerable local industry (figure 3.17).

Figure 3.17. Quarrying for Swithland slate in about 1875, showing a crane (with operator) and various sheds in the background. The precise location of this view is uncertain; it may be "Danver's Pit", SK538133, about 300 metres north of the study area. Photo originally published in *Spencer's Guide to Charnwood*, 1875.

Figure 3.18. Swithland slate wall and roof at Hallgates. (SK541114, July 1986.)

From 1688, we have documentary evidence regarding tenancies of the quarries. They were let rather than managed by their respective landowners. The Hind family were involved in slate at this time although they did not take up the lease of the 'Old Slate Pit' until 1811. This pit, in the centre of the wood, was latterly known as the 'Great Pit' (P15 in figure 2.3). The other large quarry (P25), at the time to the north of Swithland Wood but now enclosed within it, appears to have been opened up by Johnson in 1813. Upon his death in 1832, the lease was taken up by Bramley, but production ceased in 1838. It seems that trade was rather slack in the middle of the nineteenth century, doubtless due to the ease with which competing Welsh slate could now be brought into the midland counties via canals, river navigations and railways. Evidently, most builders did not share the view of Mott (1868), that 'every [Swithland slate] is worth three welshmen, both in respect of durability and picturesqueness, although an age of cheapness and bad taste prefers, of course, the flimsier article'. Hind's lease of the Old Slate Pit was allowed to lapse in 1849. It was taken up the following year by Thomas Rudkin, who was also working the quarries at Groby. In the 1860s, the leases again changed hands and the Ellis family were to retain the Old Slate Pit until its final closure in 1887. By this time, the depth of the pit had reached 55 m (180 feet).

After the closure of the pits, small quantities of slate continued to be sold on a commission basis by caretakers employed by the estate (ref. 12). In August 1911 Mr Harrison and others were paid for 'getting slate from spoil heaps for bacteria beds for the Leicester Corporation' (bacteria beds formed part of a sewage treatment works).

3.7.2 Uses

Slate cleaves relatively easily in one plane, but is otherwise difficult to shape without the use of a saw. This renders it suitable for applications which demand slabs or sheets rather than regular blocks. Thus, two of the most familiar uses are for roofs (figure 3.18) and for headstones. In view of the strength of roof timbers required to support them, roofing slates were made as thin as possible. It was worth the trouble of excavating deep quarries in order to obtain slate with superior cleavage properties, rather than work inferior slate at the surface. Although used since Roman times on buildings of high status; villas, castles, and the homes of the wealthy; slate roofs were not part of vernacular architecture until about 1750 (Ramsey 1986). Swithland roof slates are still much sought after by people restoring their cottages in the local architectural style. Welsh slates may be preferable from the builder's point of view (they are much thinner) but their purple sheen looks altogether out of character in Charnwood's villages.

Slate headstones rose in popularity at the end of the seventeenth century, and may be found in all local churchyards (Herbert 1946). Their surface was very amenable to engraving, and fine work has remained sharp for hundreds of years. Sawn slabs of slate were fashioned into various architectural and domestic items, including sundials, kerbstones, fireplaces, cheese presses, sinks and window-sills. A display of some of these may be found in the old chapel in Bradgate Park. The fabric of many old houses in Charnwood, and many tens of kilometres of dry stone walls, comprises irregular blocks of slate. It is difficult to estimate how much of this kind of material came from quarries - presumably vast amounts were picked up from the surface of ploughed fields.

3.8 Hallgates Filter Station

By the second half of the nineteenth century, Leicester's demand for water exceeded local supply. Under an Act of Parliament, the Derwent Valley Water Board was set up in 1899 with the aim of improving the supply to Sheffield, Nottingham, Derby and Leicester (Newton 1983). Water from Derbyshire was to be brought to a filter station at Hallgates, along a course which would take it through Swithland Wood. Leicester Corporation drew up plans in 1907 to lay two parallel water mains down the centre of the wood, from north to south (ref. 27). Trees were removed in that year (ref. 23), but it is believed that the first main (33 inch) was not laid until 1912 (Ainley *pers. comm.*). The second main (36 inch) was laid alongside in about 1930. The course of the mains has been kept clear of trees and now forms a broad ride. The mains are carried across low lying ground in compartment 4 by a substantial embankment.

Hallgates Filter Station was opened in 1921. Its purpose was to remove peat staining from the untreated water, and to correct its acidity prior to storage in service reservoirs. A by-product of these processes was sludge containing lime, aluminium sulphate, and other residues. The sludge had to be washed out of the filters from time to time. From 1921 until 1944, and again from 1957 to 1972, the filter backwash was discharged into the eastern end of a system of gulleys in Swithland Wood. The gulleys, presently about five metres wide and one metre deep (but originally larger), checked the flow and promoted settlement of the suspended material. The effluent emerged from the western end of the gulleys to feed the dammed stream. The original source of water for the stream had been diverted into a new straight channel, to flow directly north-eastwards into another stream. In more recent years, the sludge was taken away by tanker, and the redundant earthworks were cleaned out and partially levelled in the 1970s.

Figure 3.19. Excavations for a forty inch water main. (Compartment 9, SK53731175, March 1985.)

Further excavations were undertaken in 1985 for the connection of a 40 inch main into the system, but only a small area of the wood close to the filter station was disturbed (figure 3.19, ref. 68). Work recently completed at Cropston Reservoir has now rendered Hallgates Filter Station redundant.

3.9 Post-estate History

At the Bradgate Estate auction in July 1921, Swithland Wood was included in lot 25, together with Swithland Wood Farm and Hallgates Farm; 286 acres in all (ref. 15). It was purchased by William Gimson, a timber merchant, for £7300 (ref. 49). The newspapers reported a large attendance with keen competition (ref. 50).

3.9.1 Acquisition by Leicester Rotary Club

Gimson originally proposed to sell the timber through his own business (ref. 51). However, less than four years later he abandoned whatever commercial plans he may have had for Swithland Wood. No direct evidence of fellings has been found, but a letter commenting on the value of timber remaining in 1925 suggests that 'the valuable timber had been taken' (ref. 30). Gimson evidently sympathised with those who were concerned that recent extensive fellings in former estate woods were spoiling the beauty of Charnwood, and that some woodland ought to be preserved. He offered the wood at an advantageous price to Leicester Rotary Club, provided that the wood be dedicated to the use of the public. The price was £3000 (ref. 28). A Swithland Wood Committee was formed by the Rotary Club in January 1925, with the aim of raising this amount plus a further £2000 towards maintenance. Within a year, an appeal had brought in most of the purchase price from Rotarians, local businesses and the general public. Contracts were signed in March, and the transaction was completed on 1 August 1925. It appears that an offer from a 'speculative builder' of £500 above the asking price was received, but turned down (ref. 33).

Initially, the committee was uncertain as to the best way to look after the wood. It was proposed at one stage to plant up the wood with 'rhododendrons and flowering shrubs', and to construct a 'keeper's cottage with a canteen for refreshments' (ref. 28). In early 1926, the Forestry Commission was asked to put forward a management scheme. Some very brief notes on the Forestry Commission inspector's visit do survive (ref. 32). Areas of two to five acres were to be clear-felled and replanted with oak, along with larch as a nurse crop. The 'sycamore and hazel plantation near The Brand' (i.e. compartment 11) was described as 'useless', and birch timber was likewise deemed to be worthless. Other than this, little of ecological or historical interest is contained in these notes, and it is a pity that the full report of the inspector has not come to light.

At the committee meeting on 26 April 1926, it was decided that the Rotary Club should not, after all, become involved with forestry schemes. The spirit of the covenant with the vendor was to leave the wood more or less as it was. Nonetheless, there are references in the minutes to felling by outside contractors, and a woodman had been engaged by the Club in 1926. Perhaps it was he that introduced the rhododendrons which can be found in a few places.

3.9.2 Transfer to the Bradgate Park Trust

It was agreed that further funds should be raised as an endowment towards maintenance costs, so that Swithland Wood would be acceptable as a gift to the National Trust. In 1928, Bradgate Park became the property of the people of Leicestershire, through the generosity of Charles Bennion, a local businessman who had purchased the park from the Grey family (Forsyth 1974). The Bradgate Park Trust was set up in 1929 to look after this extensive tract of land. The new Trust was perceived to be a more appropriate body than the National Trust to assume responsibility for Swithland Wood, and was approached in 1930. The Bradgate Park Trustees accepted the offer from the Rotary Club, and Swithland Wood again changed hands in May 1931 (refs. 24 & 28).

So, Swithland Wood has not been commercially managed for about 65 years. Throughout most of the wood, there is little sign of recent planting, but in the late 1960s a portion of one of the Wood Meadows was enclosed and turned into a mixed plantation of mainly alien species. Car-parks were provided at both the north and south ends of the wood in about 1972. Shrubs and small trees were cleared, but the shapes of the parking areas were adapted to fit between the larger trees.

A management proposal for the wood, put forward in 1964 by the trustees, though never implemented, is worthy of note. For one thing it demonstrates public interest in the wood and how close it came to losing its most special features. An announcement was made in the *Leicester Mercury* on 11 November 1964, of a 'tree felling scheme - to preserve Swithland Woods' beauty'. The Forestry Commission had convinced the trustees of the need to fell the 'mature' timber, along with mis-shapen, dead and dying trees, and to replant. The writer has searched in vain for a copy of the proposals, and the survey upon which, presumably, they were based. *Mercury* readers, including relatives of those directly involved with securing the wood in the 1920s, wrote in to point out that economic forestry was an inappropriate management objective for what was intended to be a public amenity (ref. 63). Naturalists were horrified at the prospect of one of the county's best woods being spoiled for no good reason. The pressure from conservationists, individuals and *Mercury* correspondents (ref. 62) eventually persuaded the trustees to abandon their proposals.

Chapter 4

Ecological Survey

The ecological survey comprises several studies whose methods and results are the subject of the next three chapters. This chapter serves as a general introduction and is particularly intended for readers who are unfamiliar with the terms and concepts of ecological survey work. Hence, the chapter begins with a definition of *ecology* in its original scientific sense, and very briefly outlines the key ecological processes operating within woodlands. The aims of the ecological survey are then explained, and a discussion on the selection of appropriate methods follows. By setting these studies in their proper ecological context, and by drawing attention to the assumptions and limitations inherent in the various survey methods, it is hoped that the significance of the results will be clarified.

4.1 The Ecological Approach

In recent years, the proper meaning of the word *ecology* has been obscured by its misapplication to any 'green' issue (Moore 1987). Strictly, ecology is a science that seeks to explain the interactions which determine the distribution and abundance of organisms (Krebs 1978). Organisms may be studied at the level of individuals, *populations* of a particular species, or *communities* of many species (Begon, Harper & Townsend 1986). Interactions are of two kinds. Physical or *abiotic* interactions are those between the physical environment and the organisms within it, such as that between soil moisture and plant growth. In a wood, it is especially clear that abiotic interactions work in both directions: canopy trees restrict the light reaching the ground, which in turn affects the vegetation growing there, for example. *Biotic* interactions are those which take place between different organisms. Usually, one or more of the resources provided by the environment (for plants; primarily light, water, nutrients and space) is in limited supply, and plants find themselves in *competition* with one another. The organisms that are best fitted to exploit the resources of a particular *ecological niche* may eventually suppress some or all of their rivals, if the process of *competitive exclusion* is allowed to reach its conclusion. Wherever plants grow, there will be herbivorous animals intent on eating them - *herbivory* is another biotic interaction that influences abundance and distribution. Just as all animals depend ultimately on plant growth for sustenance, many plants are reliant on animals for pollination, seed dispersal, or as a pathway for the recovery of nutrients by way of their dung and dead bodies.

These interactions, among others, have been recognised as important ecological processes operating in woodlands (Neal 1958, Packham & Harding 1982). They play a crucial role in 'organising' woodland plant communities, both in terms of their species composition and physical structure. In lowland Britain, these natural processes would promote the development of temperate deciduous forest, given freedom from human interference and a sufficiently long time. Indeed, it is only by management as ploughland, grassland, heathland, and so on, that man holds back the *succession* to woodland that would otherwise ensue. If a ploughed field were abandoned, for example, arable weeds would rapidly move in, followed by rank grasses and perennial herbs, then scrub, and finally woodland. Following the last retreat of the glaciers, the process of natural succession resulted in the primeval forest that was encountered by the earliest pioneers. Some authors have described this as *climax* woodland, believing that the vegetation had attained an ultimate stability under the prevailing climate (Tansley 1939).

Woodland is thus the original home of most of our native wildlife. Long-established woods tend to be very rich in species. In view of such biological diversity, coupled with the variety of physical conditions which trees and shrubs provide, it will be appreciated that the network of ecological interactions must be imponderably complex. Consequently, few studies of woodland ecology have progressed much beyond the descriptive phase (Packham & Harding 1982, page 1). Even attempting simply to list the many thousands of animal and plant species that inhabit a typical wood is a task which even the most dedicated team of expert recorders might never complete (Peterken 1981, page 212). Studies that analyse interactions in any detail are invariably restricted to a handful of species, or else they lump together species into a manageable number of functional units, such as *primary producers* (plants), *herbivores*, *carnivores*, and so on.

The present project is no more than a small contribution to the descriptive phase; cataloguing what is present, where it is and in what quantity. It is restricted to the study of plants, and concentrates on the distribution and abundance of the flowering plants and ferns. These may represent substantially less than 10% of all the species of organism in the wood. From the ecological point of view, however, it can be argued that they are fundamentally important, being the primary producers in the food chain, forming the physical structure of the habitat, and constituting the bulk of the living matter or *biomass*. No attempt has been made to analyse ecological processes by experimental means, although inferences have been drawn from observation. It will be apparent from the references cited that much reliance has been placed on the work of other authors with regard to the ecology of particular species.

Finally, we must remember that Swithland Wood is by no means the work of nature alone. We have already discovered that its site was largely cleared of its original natural woodland, to be re-afforested some time later by secondary woodland. The latter has been actively managed for centuries, by felling and planting, and disturbed by quarrying. An attempt will be made in chapter 8 to draw together the significant ecological and historical influences which have brought Swithland Wood into its present condition, and to anticipate future changes.

4.2 Objectives

The professional or student ecologist would normally embark on a research project with a clearly defined set of objectives, and would expect to have to justify the choice of techniques. The writer falls into neither category, being a naturalist with a 'recreational' interest in ecological methods. Although the ecological studies are presented in a scientific manner, it is not claimed that the whole project is a coherent series of rigorous investigations, aimed at solving a particular problem. The objectives, although vague from a strictly scientific point of view, may be summarised in two statements. Firstly, it was desired to publish a general description of the flora and vegetation of the site, in a form that would be useful to (a) ecologists studying other woods, (b) future ecologists assessing changes in Swithland Wood and (c) present and future managers of the wood. Secondly, the project sought to detect botanical differences between the various compartments which, according to preliminary historical and archaeological research, were thought to possess individual origins and management histories.

4.2.1 Description of the flora

The *flora* of a site is, essentially, a list of the plants which occur there, usually with a subjective assessment of the abundance and distribution of each species. The Loughborough Naturalists' Club report *Swithland Wood: A Preliminary Survey* (1970) goes a long way towards providing this information, but was never produced as a generally available publication. One aim of the project was to build on the work of the LNC with a view to publishing a more complete and up-to-date list. Besides extra records discovered in the literature, it became clear during fieldwork that many species present in the wood had been omitted from the published lists. In order to improve the accuracy of distribution details, the fieldwork would aim to provide a species list for each compartment. Some assessment of the abundance of at least the more important species was desirable. The scope of the floristic survey would, of course, be restricted to those groups of plants that were familiar to the writer, i.e. flowering plants and ferns (the *vascular plants*), mosses and liverworts (the *bryophytes*). Although the author did not attempt to survey the lichen flora, an account of this group has been included, based on old records and some recent fieldwork by a professional lichenologist.

4.2.2 Description of the vegetation

The flora of a woodland site conveys little about its actual appearance. It tells us nothing about the growth-form and size of the trees and shrubs, nor their relative importance, nor anything about the patterns of variation in the communities of herbaceous species. These are all properties of the *vegetation*, as opposed to the flora. An aim of the survey was to describe the vegetation in terms of both stand structure and species composition. The description should embrace as much of the variety as possible. This type of description complements the floristic approach, which takes each species in turn and considers where it grows. A study of vegetation enables more meaningful comparisons to be made with other sites, or between various parts of the same site. It should also provide baseline data against which future surveys of Swithland Wood might be compared, in order to monitor the effects of management, for example.

4.3 Selection of Methods

The method for compiling species lists is self-evident: one simply searches each compartment thoroughly. Vegetation surveys, on the other hand, are by no means straightforward. There is no universal scheme for surveying or describing vegetation. Woodlands present particular problems due to their structural complexity. A suite of survey methods has been selected, collectively appropriate to the aims of the project and the resources available to the author. The combination of methods is doubtless unique to this project, although the methods are individually well documented in the ecological literature.

There are two approaches to vegetation ecology which may be called *classification* and *description*. Classification presumes that vegetation organises itself into more or less distinct *types*. Various attempts have been made to distinguish types of woodland vegetation: Tansley (1939), Peterken (1981), Bunce (1982 & 1989), and the National Vegetation Classification (forthcoming). It happens that G. F. Peterken includes, in the account of his *stand types* scheme, a vegetation map of Swithland Wood as a worked example. Reference to this will be made in chapter 7. Given that Swithland Wood has already been classified and mapped by Peterken, there seemed little point in repeating the exercise, even using one of the alternative schemes. Furthermore, to identify an area of woodland as a particular type, imparts very limited information about it; typically just the presence of certain characteristic species. We shall need more than this to achieve the project objectives. Therefore, the descriptive approach was selected as being more appropriate to this project.

A thorough review of the aims and methods of vegetation description is provided by Mueller-Dombois & Ellenberg (1974), who identify four decision-making stages:

(a) Recognition of entities

(b) Selection of samples

(c) Size and shape of samples

(d) What to record in the samples

The full details of each of the methods used in this project are given in the following chapters, but this will be a convenient point to discuss general considerations pertinent to the selection of methods.

4.3.1 Recognition of entities

The pattern of vegetation at the ultimate level of detail is determined by the exact location, size and form of each individual plant in the wood. Apart from the sheer impossibility of recording such detail, a survey to this degree of accuracy would generate an overwhelming mass of data. In simplifying the results to a comprehensible level, much of the detail so laboriously recorded would have to be discarded. For the sake of efficiency, it is important not to gather more field data than is actually needed. While planning the fieldwork for this survey, consideration was given to the following question, as a means of clarifying the requirements: what are smallest units of the study area whose internal patterns of variation are irrelevant to the objectives of the investigation? According to the methodology of Mueller-Dombois & Ellenberg, these units are known as *entities*. The survey should integrate or 'average out' any variation *within* them, but draw attention to differences *between* them. One of the objectives of the survey is to relate vegetation to management history, and it has been presumed that the compartments defined in chapter 2 were the basis of woodland management. Therefore, it is clear that compartments should form the basis of the entities. The simplest approach would be to define the whole of each compartment as an entity. In some cases this is satisfactory, but other compartments are large and obviously non-uniform - the requirement to provide a general description of the vegetation dictates that these compartments be further subdivided. For example, compartment 4 is mainly dry woodland with oak and birch, but contains a marshy area dominated by alders. An attempt to survey the whole compartment as one entity would yield absurd results, and steps were taken to avoid this. In general, however, variations within a compartment were perceived as subtle gradations, to be integrated by the method of survey. Furthermore, compartments form a practical subdivision of the site, in terms of their size and number.

4.3.2 Quantitative methods

It is easy enough to describe a woodland as having 'sparse shrubs', 'very large oaks', locally abundant bluebells', etc., but such subjective terms are of little use for comparative purposes. Quantitative methods have been devised to overcome these problems, and to place the description of vegetation on a sound scientific basis (Greig-Smith 1957). They require measurements, or at least estimates, to be made of particular properties of a stand of vegetation. As comparisons will need to be made, quantitative techniques are clearly appropriate to this project.

4.3.3 Selection of samples

Having considered the entities and adopted a quantitative approach, we must next consider how to obtain the required information from the compartments. As we have seen, it is neither practicable nor desirable to survey the whole of each compartment, and therefore the normal practice is to concentrate on *samples*, on the assumption that samples are representative of the entities. Where should the samples be placed and how many of them are needed to describe an entity adequately? A full discussion of these questions would take us into the realms of statistics, far beyond the bounds of this report. A few rather simplistic comments must suffice. To be truly objective and scientific, we would adopt a *random* sampling strategy, so that any place has an equal probability of being sampled. The price that must be paid for such objectivity is the relatively large number of samples required. This is necessary to accommodate the possibility that random samples, if there are few of them, might all happen to fall in atypical places. In addition, each sampling site must be accurately located using tables of random numbers and surveyor's tapes. A second strategy is to set out a *regular* series of samples; in a line or grid pattern. It is simpler to use in the field, but also requires a large number of samples, for the same reason. Furthermore, certain kinds of statistical test are invalid unless the data are from random samples. Thirdly, the samples can be *subjectively placed*, to avoid areas that appear to be atypical. This method is open to the criticism that the results of the survey will reflect the surveyor's personal bias (conscious or otherwise) as to what constitutes a typical sample. It is the least objective of the three strategies, but it is frequently used because of its speed; few samples are required and no measurements need to be made to locate the samples. Hybrid strategies are commonly used as a compromise, for example *stratified random* sampling involves dividing the entity into a number of regular or subjectively chosen units, then randomly sampling within each. The number of samples required depends on a number of factors, including the desired accuracy, the size of the samples and properties of the vegetation itself. The techniques actually used were each hybrids between regular and subjectively placed samples.

4.3.4 Size and shape of samples

Samples are most often small plots known as *quadrats;* traditionally (but not necessarily) square in shape. The size of the quadrat should be consistent with the scale of pattern in the vegetation. If the quadrat is too small then key species in the community would be missed altogether; too large a quadrat might merge several communities, incurs extra work, and renders quantitative techniques more difficult to apply. There is an optimum quadrat size appropriate to each different kind of vegetation; this will be discussed more fully in section 6.2.1. A quadrat of sufficient size in which the abundance of each species is assessed (see below), is sometimes called a *relevē.* Whereas smaller quadrats can only be regarded as samples within an entity, relevēs individually describe the vegetation in their immediate surroundings, and may be compared with one another. An alternative way of dealing with quadrat size is to decrease it to zero; in other words, to sample using points rather than plots. Naturally, *plotless* techniques gather less information per sample, so many more samples must be made. The methods that have been adopted in this survey include a relevē technique (chapter 6) and a plotless technique (chapter 7).

4.3.5 What to record in the samples

If large numbers of small quadrats are being used, then it is often sufficient to record the presence or absence of each species. The number of quadrats in which a species occurs is said to be its *frequency,* usually expressed as a percentage. Most ecological text books give an account of the significant effect of quadrat size on recorded frequency. If fewer quadrats are used, some assessment of *abundance* is desirable. The various measures of abundance (biomass, number of stems, cover, etc.) are explained in the respective chapters.

4.4 Stratification

British woodlands are traditionally described in terms of *ground, field, shrub,* and *canopy layers,* based on vegetation height (Packham & Harding 1982, page 5). The relative importance of the ground and field layers varies from one region to another. In western Britain, where the climate is most favourable for bryophytes, the ground layer is usually well developed, and could hardly be ignored during ecological survey. Further east, however, the ground layer declines in importance with respect to the field layer, and in Swithland Wood it is generally very sparse or absent. It makes only a minute contribution to the woodland vegetation as a whole, and it was therefore decided that the limited available fieldwork time would be better spent recording the field, shrub and canopy layers. Bryophytes will be rarely mentioned outside the flora chapter.

In this project, the field layer was taken to be all vegetation less than one metre in height, together with any herbaceous (i.e. non-woody) growth of greater height. In British woodlands, the field layer usually embraces the greatest number of species. These are not randomly distributed throughout the wood, but seem to form recurring communities. Sometimes, the communities appear to be well-defined, especially those that are dominated by a conspicuous plant such as greater woodrush *Luzula sylvatica.* Elsewhere, communities merge imperceptibly into one another, frustrating attempts to map vegetation types. In a wood such as Swithland with a *high forest* structure, where the canopy is formed by tall (typically more than 20 m), single-stemmed trees, it is generally easy to separate woody growth into shrub and a canopy layers. The shrub layer is generally understood to be woody growth less than about five metres in height. Typically, this layer is dominated by plants of shrubby growth-form, such as hazel *Corylus avellana,* but may include young regrowth from stumps and saplings of trees destined to reach the canopy.

The scope of each of the following three chapters may now be defined. Chapter 5 *Flora* lists all plant species (vascular plants, bryophytes and lichens) that have been recorded in the study area, irrespective of height. Chapter 6 *Vegetation - Field Layer* describes the range of communities of non-woody vascular plants, together with any woody plants that have not attained one metre in height. Chapter 7 *Vegetation - Shrub and Canopy Layers* describes the species composition and physical structure of the compartments. This study embraces all woody plants greater than one metre in height.

Chapter 5

Flora

The various groups of plants covered by this chapter have been dealt with in different ways, so each group has its own section. Flowering plants and ferns, known as the *vascular plants*, are covered in section 5.1. Section 5.2 deals with *bryophytes*:mosses and liverworts. *Lichens* are the subject of section 5.3. The species lists are located at the end of the chapter. Algae and fungi have not been studied for this project.

5.1 Vascular Plants

5.1.1 Fieldwork and other sources of records

All of the recording specifically for this project was carried out by the author, assisted on occasions by other amateur botanists. More than one hundred visits were made between 1982 and 1986, in all seasons. Following this period of intensive fieldwork, visits made for other purposes produced a few supplementary plant records, but no post-1988 records have been included. The topographical survey naturally required a full exploration of the whole site, during which plant species were noted. Additional botanical studies were made for the vegetation work, so it is believed that the flora of the study area has been fairly thoroughly covered; with the exceptions detailed below.

The parts which were not so exhaustively worked are the quarry enclosures, the plantation (cmpt 22), and the larger of the Wood Meadows (cmpt 21). The reasons are threefold. Firstly, the project was originally concerned solely with the woodland compartments. Only later, when publication was being contemplated, was it recognised that a report which neglected the quarries and meadows would present a seriously unbalanced account of the site as a whole. These habitats add a great deal to the biological diversity of Swithland Wood. Secondly, these areas are neither freely nor, in the case of the quarries, safely accessible. The author's dedication to the project did not extend to risking life and limb on the spoil heaps above the sheer quarry faces! With a few exceptions, most plants form a fringe of vegetation around the quarry enclosures where they can usually be identified (with binoculars when necessary) from the safety of the palings. Similarly, the plantation was only observed from the outside, but the gloom cast by the conifers appears to have suppressed all but a few species in the interior. Thirdly, compartment 21 and the quarry in compartment 5 had been thoroughly surveyed by P. H. Gamble a few years previously.

The problems associated with recording abundance have been discussed in chapter 4. The vegetation studies, to be presented in chapters 6 and 7, furnish quantitative assessments for the more widespread species. They are of little use, however, for those species which were either sufficiently rare or local as to be missed by the sampling techniques. For this majority there seems to be little alternative but to adopt the so-called 'ACFOR' frequency scale (Abundant, Common, Frequent, Occasional, Rare) despite the subjectivity and imprecision inevitably associated with it (Willis 1973).

The author's observations have been combined with other records, both published and unpublished. A list of these sources is given in table 5.1. Many of these are attributable to Gamble, whose 'habitat studies' for the recent *Flora of Leicestershire* (Primavesi & Evans 1988) have been especially valuable. The source of all first records and post-1970 records is included in the systematic list (table 5.9). Most old records are not localised to a compartment. It has been assumed that none of the species concerned was confined to the privately owned sections of the wood, and that all were present in the study area. One exception is the record in LNC (1970) for ramsons *Allium ursinum*, excluded here because it is known to occur only outside the study area. Old records which refer to 'Swithland Slate Pits' have been taken to mean the pits in the wood rather than the neighbouring pits in The Brand. It seems unlikely that these assumptions have claimed any species which do not genuinely occur in the study area.

Table 5.1. Sources of vascular plant records. The ref. numbers are those used in the References section, see page 226.

(a) Published sources searched for records:

Gamble 1965
Primavesi & Evans 1988
Loughborough Naturalists' Club 1962, 1963, 1970
Nature Conservancy Council 1975
Mott *et al.* 1886
Mott 1868
Horwood & Gainsborough 1933
Potter 1842

(b) Unpublished sources

Pulteney, R. 1747. Ms. Flora of Loughborough district. (ref. 65)
Timber sale catalogues 1905 & 1907, (ref. 23)
Leicester Rotary Club papers 1926, (refs. 28-35)
Mrs E. Hesselgreaves, Groby; personal communication
Mr P. H. Gamble, Quorn; personal communication

5.1.2 Plant identification

The author has been responsible for all determinations in the 1982-86 survey, unless otherwise noted. When necessary, I have sought advice informally from botanical friends. I cannot exclude the possibility of a few errors, but I have tried to indicate in the list where identification problems may have arisen. The principal guides to identification were Clapham, Tutin & Warburg (*CTW*) 1962 & 1981, Hubbard 1968, Keble Martin 1978, Hyde, Wade & Harrison 1978, Rose 1981, Mitchell 1974 and Jermy & Tutin 1968.

Some groups of plants are troublesome to novice and expert botanists alike. In surveys such as that for the *Flora of Leicestershire*, it is customary to collect 'voucher' specimens of such plants for verification by a specialist. I have not imposed such rigorous standards on the present survey. Instead, I have avoided the need to identify critical species by recording for the whole or part of such a group, rather than individual species. These groups are detailed below:

Rubus. I have recorded all brambles as *Rubus fruticosus* agg., although there are many records of segregates from other sources.

Hieracium. All hawkweeds were called *Hieracium* sp. These too have been recorded to species level by other workers.

Rosa. My knowledge of this group is weak and roses were deemed to be either *R. arvensis* or *R. canina* agg. Plants were often neither flowering nor fruiting.

Taraxacum. No attempt was made to identify individual dandelions, and all were referred to *Taraxacum* sp.

Ulmus. The only elms in the study area were non-suckering shrubs with large, very rough leaves. They have been called *Ulmus glabra*.

Callitriche. Very few specimens of star-wort were reliably identified, due to the scarcity of fruit, but those that were turned out to be *C. stagnalis*. It has been assumed that all similar-looking plants in the same habitat (i.e. muddy paths) were of the same species.

Aphanes and *Polypodium*. Entries for recent records of parsley piert *Aphanes arvensis* and polypody *Polypodium vulgare* each refer to the aggregate rather than the species in the strict sense, but information on previous accurate determinations is included with the notes.

I have not presumed to question the discretion of the editors responsible for the various publications from which I have abstracted records - their lists are assumed to be compiled from accurate determinations.

5.1.3 Results

Table 5.9 (pages 88-135) is a list of all vascular plant species that have been recorded for Swithland Wood, in the systematic order that is adopted in most floras. Both the *scientific names* and the sequence are mainly those of CTW (1981). Three groups were based on other works, as follows. For alien trees which are not listed in CTW, reference was made to Mitchell (1974). Species of bramble have been named and ordered according to Edees & Newton (1988). Species of *Hieracium* follow the scheme adopted in the *Flora of Leicestershire.*

Species not native to the British Isles are prefixed with an asterisk '*'. Species known, or strongly suspected, to have been originally introduced into the wood, even if they have subsequently spread by themselves, are prefixed by the symbol '>'.

Figure 5.1. *Carex pendula* is common along the streams and in marshy areas. This is one of the most striking British sedges, with its long, pendulous spikes of female flowers. It is an ancient woodland indicator - see page 80. (Compartment 7, SK537121, July 1981.)

Figure 5.2. The best show of *Anemone nemorosa* is to be found in compartment 9. Like most woodland herbs, it ensures an adequate supply of sunlight by appearing before the shrubs and trees come into leaf. (Photo: P. H. Gamble)

Species numbers, to the right of the scientific names, have been assigned to allow the list to be printed in systematic order. (N.B. these numbers do not conform to any other scheme, such as those used by the BRC.) For each species, further general information (i.e. not directly related to its occurrence in Swithland Wood) may be found in table 5.10, pages 136-143. The latter is sorted alphabetically and also serves as an index to the systematic list by way of of the species number.

English names are mainly from CTW, but grasses and some trees are named according to Hubbard and Mitchell respectively.

The *First record* entry refers to the list of sources given in table 5.1. Only these sources have been consulted. Most of them are publications containing records contributed by many botanists over many years.

Compartment records are shown by symbols below the compartment numbers *3 - 82*. A map of the compartments is given as figure 2.2. The symbol indicates the age of the latest record according to the scheme given in table 5.2. Symbols are listed in preferential order. If a record is not localised to a compartment then the *site* column contains the appropriate symbol. Where compartment records do exist, then the site column summarises them, again using the preference shown in table 5.2. In the case of a species which has been recorded since 1970 but not by the author (i.e. '+' in the *site* column) but whose first record pre-dates 1970, the source and date of the later record are given in the notes. Recorders' names are given in full except for those of the author (SFW) and P. H. Gamble (PHG). The symbols for 'not recorded' and 'old record' should not be assumed to mean 'absent' without first referring to *Rec code.* This code attempts to state how thoroughly the species concerned has been recorded in the author's survey. Refer to table 5.2 for the interpretation of these letters.

Comparts is the number of compartments (of 15) from which the species concerned has been recorded, counting records of any age. *Quadrats* is the percentage of vegetation samples (10 m square, 74 in all) which contained this species in the vegetation survey (see chapter 6 for details).

Brief notes on the abundance, location, habitat and status of the species appear at the bottom of each entry. These normally relate to the recent survey, but for species not re-found by the author the appropriate comment from the old record is given in 'quotes'. If there is more than one old record then the most recent is quoted in the notes, following the symbol '+'. With regard to status, the term *casual* is applied to species that are not true constituents of the plant communities in which they were found, but which survive, often in small numbers, for one or two generations only.

Table 5.10 is a list of the same species as above but in alphabetical order of the scientific name. In a few cases, where the plant does not appear under the same name in the *Flora of Leicestershire,* an explanation is given. In some figures and tables it has been necessary to abbreviate species names; *abbreviated names* are also given here. The next column gives the *species number* to allow cross-reference to table 5.9. The *Preferred habitats* column indicates the normal habitat preference(s) for the species in the county, according to the *Flora of Leicestershire.* Nine categories have been defined, but no more than two have been assigned to each species. The more usual habitat, if a preference can be discerned, is quoted first. Refer to table 5.2 for the habitat categories. Finally, the *Layer* column shows which of the woodland vegetation layers is occupied by a mature individual. Refer to table 5.2 for the layer categories. The purpose of the habitat assignments will become clear presently (page 78).

For the convenience of readers who do not know the scientific names, a cross-reference table of all species mentioned in the text is printed inside the back cover.

Table 5.2. Symbols and abbreviations used in the lists of vascular plants, tables 5.9 and 5.10. A brief list of the abbreviations also appears at the foot of the respective tables.

On Systematic list
(table 5.9)

Origin:
- * Alien
- > Introduced

Compartment and site records:
- / Recorded by SFW 1982-88 (mainly 82-86)
- \+ Recorded post-1970
- o Recorded pre-1970 but not since (o = old)
- . Not recorded

Recording code:
- A Adequately recorded - records truly reflect the status of this species.
- H Under-recorded - the typical habitat of this species was not fully searched.
- U Probably under-recorded - the species is either inconspicuous or else was not readily recognised.

On Alphabetical list
(table 5.10)

Preferred habitats:
- A Arable: cultivated ground
- G Grassland
- H Heathland
- F Forest: woodland
- W Water: aquatic habitats
- M Marsh or marshy meadow
- E Edge: marginal habitats
- R Ruderal
- S Saxicole

Layer:
- F Field layer
- S Shrub layer
- C Canopy layer

5.1.4 Discussion and conclusions

Species richness

The list of vascular plants contains 382 entries, two of which are aggregates (*Rubus fruticosus* agg. and *Hieracium* sp.) whose constituent species are also listed. Hence, the grand total of all plants recorded is 380 taxa (species, subspecies and hybrids). In terms of growth form, 34 are trees, 30 are shrubs and 316 occupy the field layer. For a study area of 59 hectares the total of 380 species is exceptionally high. In the *Flora of Leicestershire*, recording was carried out on the basis of grid squares, each with an area of 400 hectares. Only 4% of these squares contained more than 350 species. Too much should not be read into this comparison - it is certainly not intended to imply that richness ought to be proportional to area - but it does set the figure in a regional context. In fact, it represents 30% of the species found in the whole county (excluding Rutland).

There are few published studies of other local woods. I am grateful to M. B. Jeeves for allowing me to quote from his unpublished survey of Leicestershire woodlands. Beyond the county, particularly to the east, are a number of well-worked sites with which comparisons may be made. These are summarised in table 5.3. In terms of species richness, Swithland Wood ranks very high among these locally or nationally important woods. In seeking an explanation for species richness we must first recognise that Swithland Wood has been thoroughly searched. For at least 250 years it has attracted botanists, particularly since other formerly interesting local woods were spoiled. It must be presumed that the

Table 5.3. The number of vascular plant species and the areas of some other well-recorded woods.

Wood	Species	Area	Source
Swithland Wood (Leics.)	380 spp,	59 ha	(present work)
Owston Wood (Leics.)	246 spp,	146 ha	(Jeeves, unpublished)
Great Merrible (Leics.)	119 spp,	13 ha	(Jeeves, unpublished)
Prior's Coppice (Rutland)	230 spp,	29 ha	(Jeeves, unpublished)
Burley Wood (Rutland)	279 spp,	156 ha	(Evans 1989)
Hayley Wood (Cambs.)	302 spp,	49 ha	(Rackham 1975)
Bedford Purlieus (Cambs.)	462 spp,	212 ha	(Peterken & Welch 1975)
King's Wood (Northants.)	236 spp,	31 ha	(Best 1983)
Monk's Wood (Hunts.)	>370 spp,	157 ha	(Steele & Welch 1973)
Bradfield Woods (Suffolk)	370 spp,	65 ha	(Rackham 1980)
Northaw Wood (Herts.)	283 spp,	217 ha	(Sage 1966)

cumulative vigilance of the old botanists, members of Loughborough Naturalists' Club and the author has allowed very few species to evade detection. Exceptions are perhaps members of those 'difficult' groups (referred to above) which really require the attention of specialists. There are, nevertheless, good ecological reasons for the species richness of this site as the following analyses will show.

Origin

There is generally no way of discovering for certain how any particular species first arrived at a site, but its most likely origin can be judged from county and national studies of plant distribution (Primavesi & Evans 1988, Perring & Walters 1962). It is conventional to regard as *aliens* those species that arrived since Great Britain became an island (about 7000 years ago). So-called *native* species were already present at that time. For most aliens there are strong grounds for believing that they were brought here by man, either accidentally or on purpose (Webb 1985). The Swithland Wood species list includes 34 aliens (marked '*'). Of these it is considered that 20 have been deliberately introduced into Swithland Wood (also marked '>') either as plantation trees (e.g. giant fir *Abies grandis)* or casually by visitors (e.g. honesty *Lunaria annua*), and 14 have apparently established themselves naturally from other sites nearby (e.g. horse chestnut *Aesculus hippocastanum*). Seven species native to other parts of Britain, but not to Charnwood, occur in the wood. Bird droppings doubtless account for the yew seedlings *Taxus baccata,* mature specimens of which occur in The Brand; but the rest are casual introductions, sometimes by way of gardens, e.g. solomon's seal *Polygonatum multiflorum.* This leaves 339 species that are native to both Britain and Charnwood Forest.

Status

We should not expect the flora of a wood to remain fixed for all time, even if human disturbance could be eliminated. Fluctuations in plant populations are a consequence of normal ecological processes. Examples are the changes in shade caused by the development and ultimate death of canopy trees; the effects of extreme weather conditions; Dutch elm disease, and so on. All of these variables ensure that, at any point in time, some species are increasing in abundance at the expense of others. From time to time, new species arrive at the site, whereas others become locally extinct. Without a series of detailed surveys spanning many decades it is impossible to comment on how the populations of most

Figure 5.3. Common Spotted Orchid *Dactylorhiza fuchsii.* A plant of damp grassland, confined in Swithland Wood to the larger of the Wood Meadows, compartment 21.

species are changing. However, changes can be discerned in very small populations and for some of the rarer species in Swithland Wood a subjective assessment of status has been attempted.

Figure 5.5 suggests categories that may be used to describe status, in terms of how abundance is changing, and table 5.4 lists the species in each category. In the short term, populations of abundant species will appear to be stable (S). Many species are rare simply because of the limited extent of a specialised habitat. For example, the ferns *Asplenium* spp. and *Phyllitis scolopendrium,* and wall pennywort *Umbilicus rupestris* which grow in crevices around the quarry faces, must always have been rare and will continue to be so. Their populations seem to be stable at a low level (L).

Four categories of status can be distinguished for low populations which are evidently changing or have become extinct. Extinction can of course only be disproved, but these species (X) appear always to have been rare, have not been seen for many years, and are not likely to return of their own accord. It is possible that green-winged orchid *Orchis morio* survives as dormant seed, awaiting the right conditions for germination. This species re-appeared in Great Merrible Wood (Leicestershire) after an absence of several years (Jeeves, *pers. comm.*). On the other hand, the 24 species described as having

Figure 5.4. Broad buckler-fern *Dryopteris dilatata* is the most abundant fern in damper, shady areas. (Photo: E. Hesselgreaves)

'temporary' status (T) are of very low abundance (often a single plant) but are varieties which may easily return if the present populations die out. They are (a) weeds of disturbed ground, (b) plants that have found their way into unsuitable situations (intrusives), and (c) garden escapes.

Plants described as vulnerable (V) are those whose populations seem to be in decline and may soon become extinct. Many of them are also vulnerable in a wider geographical context, and might well justify appropriate conservation measures.

Two species, policeman's helmet *Impatiens glandulifera* and *Rhododendron ponticum*, are aliens which are clearly increasing. The former is an annual which first appeared towards the end of the survey on a stream bank. Its seeds have successfully dispersed and germinated but the plant is unlikely ever to occupy more than a small part of the bank in light shade. The familiar garden *Rhododendron* grows in a few places but where it does occur the large, dense bushes are surrounded by vigorous young plants. The spread of this alien should be regarded as a potentially serious threat to the native vegetation of the wood, going on experience elsewhere (Evans & Becker 1988).

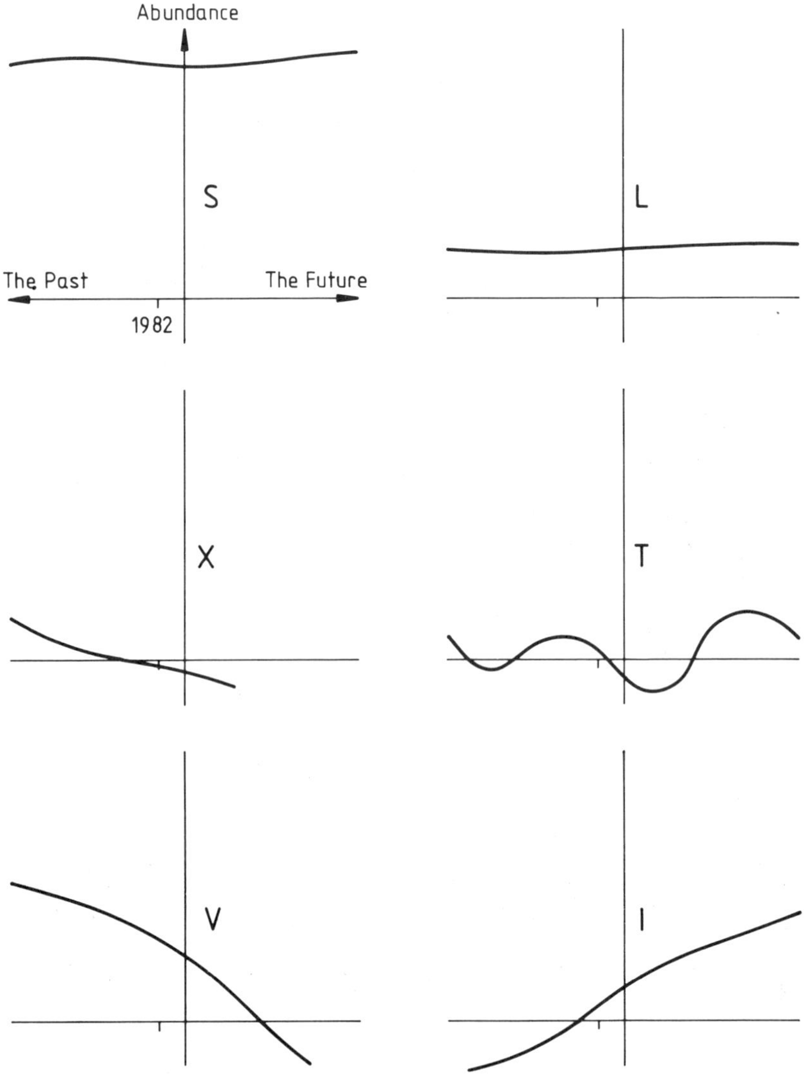

Figure 5.5. Six categories that may be used to describe the status of a plant population in terms of past and expected future changes in abundance. The time axis (horizontal) is referred to the end of the survey (1986). The abundance (vertical) scale is such that values above the time axis denote presence in the study area; values below the line indicate extinction within the study area but survival elsewhere. Species are allocated to these categories in table 5.4.

Compartments and habitats

Plants are more or less restricted to particular habitats, so it follows that a site which embraces various habitats will generally support more species than a uniform site of similar area (Begon, Harper & Townsend 1986, page 739). Habitat diversity is not an attribute that is easily quantified, but on a subjective assessment Swithland Wood ought to score highly. In addition to the woodland that covers most of the site there are ditches, streams and marshes, grassland, woodland edge and rides, slate outcrops and spoil heaps, trampled paths and other disturbed ground. These are all situations with their own characteristic species.

Table 5.4. List of species in each category of status, as defined in figure 5.5.

L Species that are stable at a low abundance:

Asplenium trichomanes
A. adiantum-nigrum
Phyllitis scolopendrium
Umbilicus rupestris
Acer campestre

T Casual species that persist for only a few generations and are likely to re-appear after temporary extinction:

(a) weeds of disturbed ground:
Geranium dissectum
Capsella bursa-pastoris
Potentilla reptans
Polygonum lapathifolium
Veronica hederifolia ssp. *hederifolia*
Tussilago farfara
Tripleurospermum inodorum
Matricaria matricarioides
Elymus repens
Geranium molle
Aethusa cynapium

(b) intrusives:
Ranunculus trichophyllus
Rorippa palustris
Myosoton aquaticum
Pastinaca sativa
Alopecurus aequalis

(c) garden escapes:
Lunaria annua
Aesculus hippocastanum
Prunus laurocerasus
Cotoneaster sp.
Muscari neglectum
Ornithogalum umbellatum
Convallaria majalis
Polygonatum multiflorum

V Species that are declining and/or vulnerable:

Ophioglossum vulgatum
Polystichum setiferum
Polystichum aculeatum
Ranunculus auricomus
Teesdalia nudicaulis
Viola canina
Lychnis flos-cuculi
Frangula alnus
Genista tinctoria
Trifolium medium
Lathyrus montanus
Chrysosplenium oppositifolium
Calluna vulgaris
Vaccinium myrtillus
Primula veris
Primula vulgaris
Melampyrum pratense
Lamiastrum galeobdolon
Solidago virgaurea
Serratula tinctoria
Iris pseudacorus
Listera ovata
Juncus kochii
Hypericum humifusum

I New colonisers or introductions that are increasing:

Impatiens glandulifera
Rhododendron ponticum

X Species that are extinct and are unlikely to return:

Anemone appenina
Corydalis lutea
Agrimonia procera
Galeopsis ladanum
Jasione montana
Orchis mascula
Carex pallescens

One way to investigate the contribution of the various habitats is to analyse the species list in terms of the known habitat preference of each species in the region. This has been done on the basis of the habitats allocated in table 5.10, derived from the *Flora of Leicestershire*. For the analysis, introduced species have been ignored, since they do not necessarily occupy habitats that they would choose for themselves. In order to see the effect of habitat diversity by compartment, segregates of those groups which are not adequately recorded by compartment (e.g. *Rubus fruticosus*) have also been excluded. This leaves 330 species.

The results are shown in figure 5.7, both for the whole site and individually for each compartment. The first point to note is that true *woodland* species contribute only 21% to the total. The non-woodland habitats, although comparitively small in area, evidently account for the majority of plant species on the site. Woodland plants are not even the largest group, being exceeded by *edge* species at 22.4%. Edge species are those that are found more often where one habitat grades into another rather than in the midst of either. Around the boundary of the wood and along rides, for example, can be found edge species that require the shelter of woody plants but which are intolerant of deep shade. These include typical 'hedgerow' plants such as hedge woundwort *Stachys sylvatica* and cow parsley *Anthriscus sylvestris*. The shape of the wood probably has some influence here. Taking into account the quarries and the Wood Meadows, the woodland is bounded by a convoluted outline which is long in relation to the area it encloses. This, together with the network of rides, gives plenty of scope for edge species.

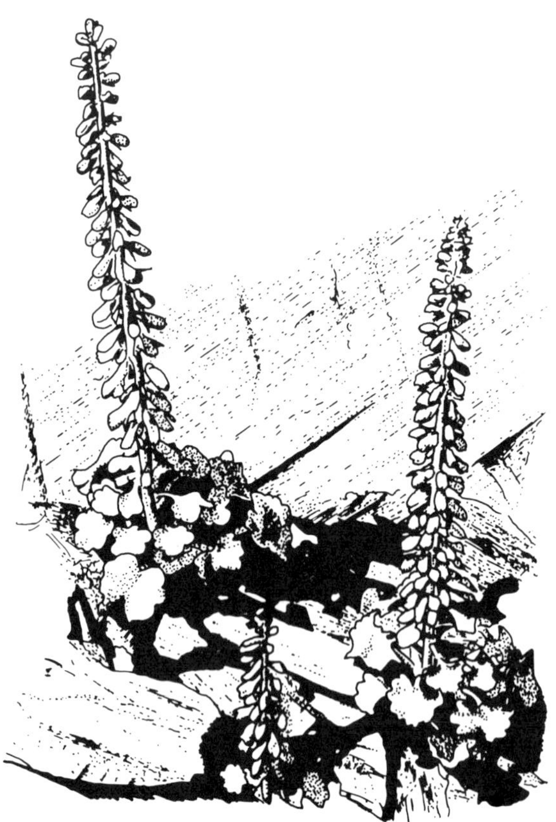

Figure 5.6. *Umbilicus rupestris*, one of Swithland Wood's specialities. It grows on the sheer rock faces in the disused quarries, in crevices and on narrow shelves. Pulteney first recorded this species here in 1747, and noted 'it is pretty plentiful and is fetched from there by the apothecaries for the *unguentum populneum*'.

In Swithland Wood, the areas we would loosely describe as *grassland*; the rides, meadows and various clearings; range in character from marshy to heathy. A true assessment of the floristic importance of these habitats is far greater than the 19.3% assigned to *grassland* species, and is probably nearer to the total for *grassland, heathland* and *marsh* species combined: i.e. 40%. No less than 48 kinds of grass have been recorded. It is not unusual to find that grassland species occur in greater variety within woodland glades and grassy rides than in the meadows, pastures and verges of the surrounding countryside (Peterken 1981, page 234). The reason is that grassland in general has been impoverished by agricultural 'improvement', whereas glades and rides within woods have generally escaped such treatment. In Swithland Wood, the grassland habitat (both heathy and marshy) is exceptionally well represented by compartments 21 and 23. The first of these (figure 5.8) is less than two hectares in extent, yet contains 156 species. This figure naturally includes many woodland and edge species, but there are 33 varieties that occur here exclusively. Indeed, many of them are grassland species that are restricted to rather few sites in the county; they include dyer's greenweed *Genista tinctoria*, saw-wort *Serratula tinctoria*, lousewort *Pedicularis sylvatica* and marsh valerian *Valeriana dioica*.

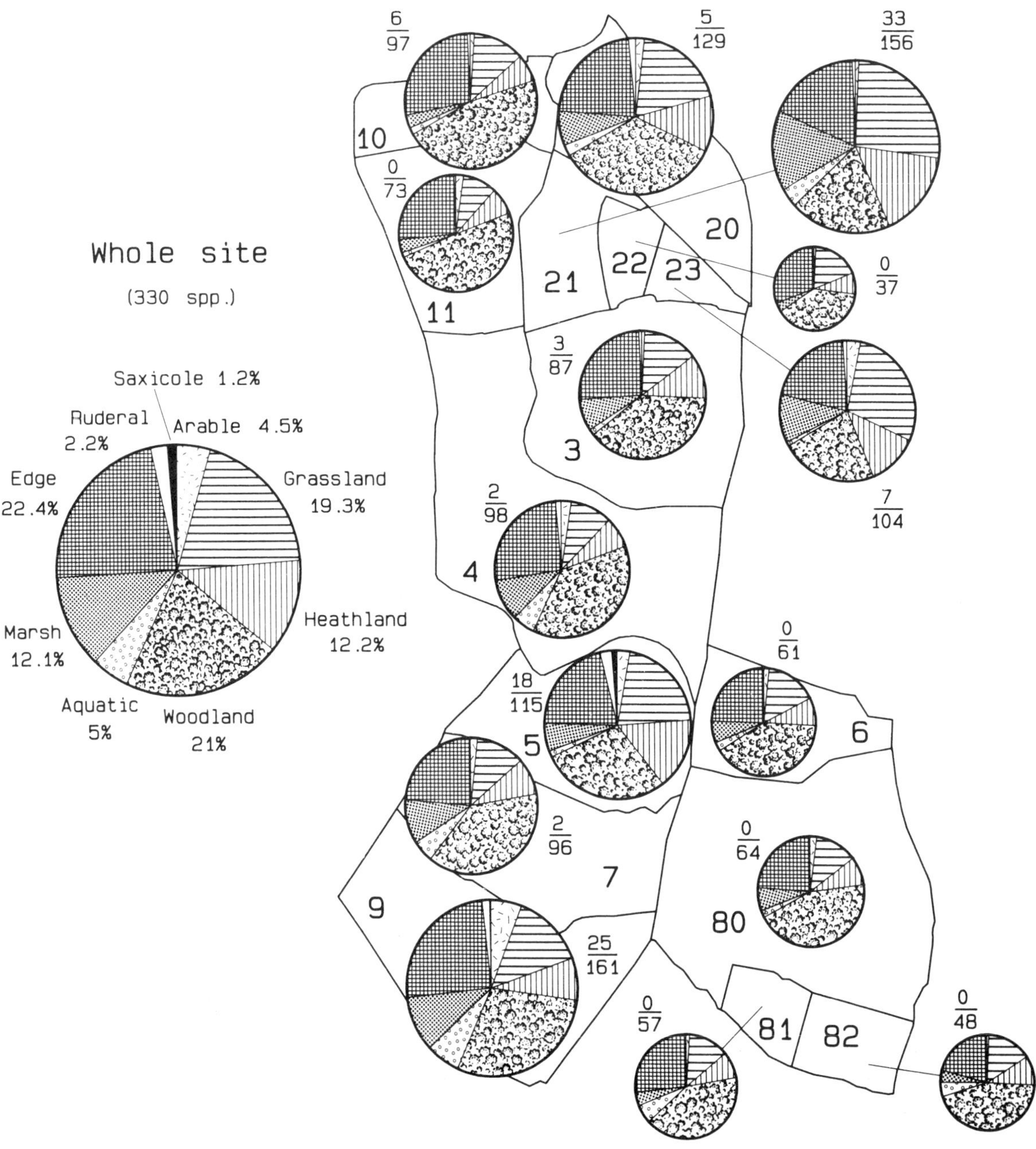

Figure 5.7. Analysis of site (left) and compartment (right) species lists by habitat preference. The pie areas are proportional to the number of species, which is given as the denominator (below the line) of the fraction shown alongside. The numerator is the number of species which occur in no other compartment. The slices of pie represent the number of species present which are normally associated with each of nine habitats. The habitat allocations for each species are given in table 5.10. When a species occurs in two habitats, it contributes two thirds to the score of the primary habitat and one third to that of the secondary habitat. The large numbers are the compartment reference numbers.

The *arable* category includes the 'weeds'; typically annual plants of temporary status (category T(a), above). For populations to persist from one year to the next, the seeds must fall on well-lit, disturbed soil on which to germinate. These conditions are common on cultivated land, but rare in woods. It is notable that the greatest number of these plants occurs in compartment 9, where a well-trampled car-park is situated, and where a major excavation was made during the survey. A few examples are cut-leaved cranesbill

Geranium dissectum, pale persicaria *Polygonum lapathifolium* and scentless mayweed *Tripleurospermum inodorum*. *Ruderals* are plants of waste or disturbed places. The quarries and their spoil heaps provide homes for a number of these, including *Umbilicus rupestris* (figure 5.6), shepherd's cress *Teesdalia nudicaulis* and American willow-herb *Epilobium ciliatum*. The proportion of *aquatic* species depends, not surprisingly, on whether or not a stream runs through the compartment, or whether it includes a pond or pit. Brooklime *Veronica beccabunga* and flote-grass *Glyceria fluitans* usually fringe the streams. Ponds often contain the latter species but with bittersweet *Solanum dulcamara*. Far down in the water-filled slate pits of compartments 5 and 20, one of the few plants that can be identified with confidence is amphibious bistort *Polygonum amphibium*. *Saxicoles* are plants that live on virtually bare rock, such as the *Aspleniums* previously mentioned.

Indicator species

Plant species vary in their tolerance of particular environmental conditions; some are indifferent whereas others are never found outside certain well-defined limits. With regard to soil reaction, for example, the beech tree *Fagus sylvatica* grows equally well on acid or alkaline sites (given good drainage), yet the wavy hair-grass *Deschampsia flexuosa* is strictly confined to acid soils. In this sense *Deschampsia* may be regarded as a faithful indicator of acid soils. Similarly, the stinging nettle *Urtica dioica* is an indicator of soils that are abnormally rich in nitrogen and phosphorus (Pigott & Taylor 1964). Properties of the soil and local climate can mostly be measured directly of course, but indicator species furnish a simple means of gauging local conditions without recourse to instruments.

Of more interest are those plants which indicate attributes of a site which are generally difficult or impossible to determine by direct means. The best known, and most relevant to this project, are those that relate to continuity of land-use. In central Lincolnshire and East Anglia, historical research has identified those sites which have been continuously wooded since 1600, the so-called ancient woods (Peterken 1974, Rackham 1980). By comparing their floras with woods of recent origin, lists of ancient woodland indicator species have been drawn up. Within these regions some species are rarely found outside ancient woods. The presence of such indicator species in a wood for which no historical records exist imply that it too is ancient in origin. Ancient woodland indicator species (figures 5.1 & 5.2) share two characteristics. Firstly, they cannot survive in the farmland that now surrounds and effectively isolates woods in eastern England, and secondly, their dispersal mechanisms are effective only over very short distances, a few metres at the most. Consequently, woods of recent origin will have acquired very few, if any, ancient woodland indicator species, unless they happen to abut an ancient wood.

The flora of Swithland Wood includes many plants that are indicators of ancient woods in central Lincolnshire (table 5.5), but we cannot assume that they all behave similarly in Leicestershire. Work in progress on woodland floras in Leicestershire by M. B. Jeeves provisionally confirms that at least four species are confined or nearly confined to ancient woods. Some others, on the other hand, show no such affinity. Indeed, bitter vetch *Lathyrus montanus* and pale sedge *Carex pallescens* are more commonly found in old grassland than woodland. With so little woodland in Leicestershire on which to base such a study, it is difficult to be sure whether or not these discrepancies are genuine reponses to environmental differences between the two counties. In the absence of clear evidence to the contrary, it seems reasonable to suppose that most of the plants on the Lincolnshire list behave similarly just 80 km to the south-west. If so, then the impressive list of indicator species can be put forward as supporting evidence for Swithland Wood's ancient status.

Clearly, indicator species only work for isolated woods. The various compartments of Swithland Wood have been in contact with one another for more than three centuries, plenty of time for even slow colonisers to diffuse from one to another. It would be injudicious to expect compartment lists to reveal the origin of individual parts of the wood, and

Table 5.5. Ancient woodland indicator species recorded from Swithland Wood. These species are completely or almost confined to primary woods in central Lincolnshire (Peterken 1974, groups 1, 2, 3 and 6). Provisional assessment for Leicestershire by Jeeves (unpublished) is shown.

Species	Leicestershire
Polystichum aculeatum	No
Anemone nemorosa	
Ranunculus auricomus	No
Viola reichenbachiana	No
Hypericum hirsutum	No
Tilia cordata	Yes
Oxalis acetosella	Not in Charnwood
Lathyrus montanus	No
Chrysosplenium oppositifolium	
Quercus petraea	Probably
Lysimachia nemorum	
Lamiastrum galeobdolon	
Scutellaria galericulata	No
Luzula pilosa	Yes
L. sylvatica	Yes
Carex laevigata	
C. pendula	Yes
C. pallescens	
C. remota	
Melica uniflora	Yes
Milium effusum	

this has not been attempted. Indeed, many other woods in Charnwood can hardly be regarded as truly isolated. The sensitivity of the indicator species technique in the Forest is correspondingly diminished. The *mapping* of key indicator species might be expected to reveal interesting patterns, but this is beyond the scope of the present chapter, being more closely related to *vegetation* studies, presented later.

Indicators of ecological continuity are not confined to woodland. For grasslands, many species such as hay-rattle *Rhinanthus minor*, betony *Stachys officinalis* and common spotted orchid *Dactylorhiza fuchsii* (figure 5.3) are said to be indicators of long-established meadows or pastures (Colebourn & Gibbons 1987). These are plants which are known to be slow to re-establish themselves following ploughing, and which are susceptible to modern agricultural chemicals. How well this relationship between certain plants and 'old grassland' holds true is difficult to ascertain objectively. Little has been published in the way of properly researched examples, presumably because continuity of grazing or mowing is difficult to demonstrate conclusively, and because the time-scales involved preclude an experimental approach. The state of knowledge on this topic is not sufficiently advanced for us to draw conclusions about the history of the Wood Meadows (figure 5.8) on the basis of their flora; except that they have been neither improved nor ploughed in recent decades.

Figure 5.8. The larger of the 'Wood Meadows'. With 156 recorded species, this small field must be one of the richest botanical sites in the county. (Compartment 21, SK53901283, May 1985.)

Figure 5.9. Guelder rose *Viburnum opulus* is a shrub that grows in the marshy parts of the wood. Whereas the conspicuous petals are borne on the outer flowers, styles and stamens are found only on the inner ones. (Photo: E. Hesselgreaves)

5.2 Bryophytes

5.2.1 Fieldwork and other sources of records

The survey of mosses and liverworts for this project was much less intensive than for vascular plants. It was conducted between 1984 and 1987 by the author and D. W. Ballard, both at that time novice bryologists. Consequently, there is a bias in these new records towards the common and conspicuous. Watson (1981) and Smith (1978) were the principal guides to identification. All but the most distinctive species have been confirmed by referees of the British Bryological Society. Published records, on the other hand, many by the late F. A. Sowter, appear to omit species which are now common. Sources of records are listed in table 5.6. The number of bryophyte observations does not justify their segregation into compartments.

The same limitations of access, as described in section 5.1.1, apply to the bryophyte survey. The consequences, however, are perhaps more significant. Firstly, very few bryophytes can be positively identified from the far side of a fence (many require microscopic examination); and secondly, many interesting species might be expected to inhabit precisely those areas of the quarries which are too dangerous to explore.

Table 5.6. Sources of bryophyte records

(a) Published sources searched for records

Bloxam 1831
Horwood 1909
Jackson 1905
Mott *et al.* 1886
Potter 1842
Sowter 1941, 1945, 1969, 1972
Sowter & Hawksworth 1970

(b) Unpublished sources

Mr D. W. Ballard, Groby; personal communication
Mrs E. Hesselgreaves, Groby; personal communication

5.2.2 Results

Table 5.11 (pages 144-150) lists liverworts and mosses, using the names of Corley & Hill (1981), whose species numbers are also given at the right. The recorder's name and year is given for the *first* and *latest record*, or combined as *only record*. Occasionally the 'latest record' is in fact a statement of its supposed extinction. Where the species name originally published is different, the old name is given in square brackets []. The notes normally apply to the recent survey, but when given in quotes they are extracts from old published records.

5.2.3 Discussion and conclusions

The bryophyte flora of Leicestershire is as yet poorly known. In the absence of up-to-date distribution data one cannot be sure how the wood's bryophytes compare with other sites or with the county as a whole. Including species which are believed to be extinct, the list stands at 23 liverworts and 75 mosses. There is plenty of scope for increasing these totals; certainly many species have been missed in the somewhat cursory survey for the present work. In the published records, localities are cited only for the rarer species, which means that specific site records for the more widespread varieties are few. Thus, the list for Swithland Wood probably lacks a number of common but inconspicuous species. Knowledge of the bryophyte flora lags far behind that of the higher plants. However, the author's impression is that Swithland Wood is unusually rich for Leicestershire. Again, as for higher plants, the range of long-established habitats would be expected to promote a rich flora. The substrates to be found within the wood encompass soil of various kinds, tree trunks and exposed roots, rotting wood, slate outcrops and spoil heaps, stone walls, brick and concrete structures. The biology of mosses and liverworts renders them very much more sensitive than higher plants to atmospheric conditions; particularly moisture and pollution. Charnwood Forest, being slightly elevated and towards the west of the county, has a measurably wetter than average climate. More significantly, perhaps, the rocky prominences and quarries within the wood provide sheltered slopes and dank crevices where these tiny plants can enjoy a more suitable 'microclimate'.

Some general remarks on the commoner plants and their habitats will perhaps offset the lack of proper distributional data. Under moderate shade, *Eurhynchium praelongum* and *Brachythecium rutabulum* are probably the most abundant mosses creeping across soil, litter and tree bases. In the damper places *Mnium hornum* forms conspicuous patches, particularly in early spring when the pale green of the new growth stands out against the darker old shoots. On the clayey soils derived from the marl, *Atrichum undulatum, Fissidens taxifolius* and *Plagiomnium undulatum* are to be found. Tree bases generally support a mixture of *Hypnum cupressiforme, Dicranoweisia cirrata* and a recent colonist from the southern hemisphere; *Orthodontium lineare.* Inspection of rotting wood nearly always produces the leafy liverwort *Lophocolea cuspidata,* the 'drumstick' moss *Aulacomnium androgynum* and occasionally *Tetraphis pellucida,* with what appear to be minute green 'flowers' (figure 5.10). The banks of wet ditches are the preferred habitat of the common thallose liverwort *Pellia epiphylla* and a moss with large, round leaves *Rhizomnium punctatum.* Some species are tolerant of exposure to full sunlight. These include the mosses *Dicranum scoparium, Polytrichum piliferum, P. juniperinum* and the leafy liverwort *Ptilidium ciliare* which occur on the slate spoil heaps, the first often in greater quantity than flowering plants. Others such as *Tortula muralis* and *Schistidium apocarpum* seem more at home on the tops of stone walls.

Sowter evidently searched the wood for some of the rarer species recorded in the nineteenth century, for he declared them to be extinct in his 1941 paper. More recently, Walpole (1971) came to the same conclusion. These are typically plants of western and northern distribution such as *Racomitrium canescens* and *Ulota crispa* which were near their geographical limits in Leicestershire. Species on the edge of their range are, of course, most susceptible to environmental change, and atmospheric pollution from Leicester and Loughborough seems to have been sufficient to tip the balance towards extinction.

< **Figure 5.10.** *Tetraphis pellucida,* a moss that is sometimes found on rotting stumps. The stems rarely exceed one centimetre in height. The expanded leaves at the end of mature stems form cups which contain vegetative propagules known as *gemmae.*

Pollution is not the only problem faced by bryophytes. *Leucobryum glaucum* is a distinctive moss which, in favourable situations, forms blue-green cushions of one metre diameter or more (Bates 1989). In Leicestershire, it is confined to Swithland Wood, and one or two other sites on Charnwood Forest. Only a few depauperate specimens have been found recently in compartment 20, after some searching. Since the opening of the car-park here, the area has been heavily trampled, which perhaps accounts for the precarious status of this handsome species. *Sphagnum capillifolium* has not been relocated in the recent survey. This bog-moss may have succumbed to increasing shade, since the marshy areas where it occurred are now overgrown with alders.

5.3 Lichens

5.3.1 Sources of records

The author has limited knowledge of this group and the following account has been prepared with the assistance of A. Fletcher of Leicestershire Museums. The species list is a compilation of old records, together with the results of recent surveys by Fletcher. All sources of records are listed in table 5.7.

Table 5.7. Sources of lichen records.

(a) Published sources searched for records

Hawksworth 1969
Hawksworth 1971
Horwood 1904
Horwood 1909
Horwood & Gainsborough 1933
Mott 1868
Mott *et al.* 1886
Potter 1842
Sowter 1972
Sowter & Hawksworth 1970

(b) Unpublished sources

S. R. Davey & N. Dove, 31 March 1972 (Leicestershire Museums)
A. Fletcher 1989 (Leicestershire Museums)
A. Fletcher 1990 (Leicestershire Museums)
D. L. Hawksworth 1966
D. L. Hawksworth 1967. A compilation of old records known to DLH, including the herbaria of F. A. Sowter and O. M. Dixon. This and the previous item are typescript lists, held on file at the museum.

Table 5.8. Sites for Fletcher's lichen records. 'B' sites were recorded on 1 October 1989 and 'C' sites on 18 September 1990.

Site	Grid Ref.	Compt	Description
B1	SK53751283	11	Oak, 15 inches dia. in shade among bracken. Fertile *Chaenotheca ferruginea* present.
B2	SK53751273	11	Oak beside ride with *Cladonia* at base.
B3	SK53831253	3	Large coppiced oak on outcrop, extensive exposed root system with a lot of *Ochrolechia androgyna*, *Parmelia*, etc.
B4	SK53981243	4	Oak beside stream, 4 feet. dia., with *Schismatomma decolorans*.
B5	SK54041258	3	Hazel coppice with oaks.
B6	SK54021251	3	Small-leaved lime in dense hazel coppice, shaded.
B7	SK54011248	3	Hazel and lime coppice.
B8	SK53981226	4	Decayed stump with dense *Cladonia*.
B9	SK54201215	6	Oak in open woodland.
B10	SK54201209	80	Oak by ride.
B11	SK54011191	80	Oak.
B12	SK54011204	80	Leaning oak in dense bramble and bracken.
B13	SK53911210	5	Slate spoil heap with slate outcrops.
C1	SK53881191	9	Hazel in shaded stream bed.
C2	SK53721196	7 & 9	Well shaded stream bed with exposed slate bedrock; abundant aquatic species and algae.
C3	SK53941209	5	Large fallen oak stump beside old quarry.

5.3.2 Results

All known records are given in table 5.12 (pages 151-153). The scientific names are in accordance with Cannon, Hawksworth & Sherwood-Pike (1985). The older records are not localised within the wood, but Fletcher's recording was carried out at the 16 sites identified in table 5.8.

5.3.3 Conclusions

The adjacent property known as The Brand, which also contains woodland and disused slate quarries, has proved to be one of Leicestershire's premier lichen sites, yet until very recently little work had been done in Swithland Wood. Fletcher's recent visits have refound most of the lichens recorded by Hawksworth in the 1960s, and added numerous new and interesting species. It is possible that further exploration would produce more species, although it does appear that some of the lichens recorded near the turn of the century (or earlier) are no longer present. The loss of several species in the twentieth century will be a familiar story to those who have studied lichen floras elsewhere in lowland Britain (Hawksworth, Coppins & Rose 1974, Seaward & Hitch 1982). Lichens are even more sensitive than bryophytes to atmospheric pollution, and the floras of midland and other industrialised regions have been severely depleted. In Swithland Wood the most widespread lichen is now *Lecanora conizaeoides*, which is one of the most pollution-tolerant. Foliose species with blue-green photobionts such as *Lobaria scrobiculata* are very sensitive, and its re-discovery in Swithland Wood now seems unlikely. However, within the past ten years or so, there have been clear signs of a recovery in the county, following clean air legislation (Fletcher, *pers. comm.*). Species such as *Evernia prunastri* and *Usnea subfloridana*, which had disappeared, are rapidly re-colonising suitable sites. Charnwood Forest is not particularly well sited to avoid polluted air, and the recovery is perhaps not as dramatic as elsewhere, but it will be very interesting to see how the lichen flora of Swithland Wood develops over the next few decades.

Whereas the retention of old trees is essential to slow-growing corticolous species, the long-term survival of such lichens depends on the presence of 'middle-aged' trees (150-200 years) onto which they may spread. Young trees will not sustain colonisation by these lichens, but they are, of course, the middle-aged trees of the future. Ideally, there would be a complete range of ages present. The analysis of the shrub and canopy layers in chapter 7 will show that this is not the case in Swithland Wood, due to a lack of regeneration over the last 60 years or so. On the positive side, opportunities for the more pollution-tolerant saxicolous species have surely increased, following the demise of the slate industry in the 1880s.

Apart from their value as indicators of atmospheric sulphur dioxide (Hawksworth & Rose 1970), lichens include many species that are good indicators of woodland continuity (Rose 1976). Unfortunately, the second property is of limited use in polluted areas unless old records are available. In this respect the nineteenth century record for *Lobaria scrobiculata* is noteworthy, for Rose has found this lichen to be 'faithful to old hardwood forests in Lowland Britain'. Surviving 'old forest indicators' in Swithland Wood include *Schismatomma decolorans* and *Lecanactis abietina*.

Areas of acid heath that remain around the slate quarries have a distinctive lichen flora, including *Coelocaulon aculeatum* and *Cladonia uncialis*. The streams which flow over fragments of slate provide a refuge for aquatic rock species such as *Verrucaria aethiobola* and *V. aquatilis* (at site C2 these are associated with the red alga *Hildenbrandia rivularis*). These two communities are more or less restricted to Charnwood Forest, where they are now becoming rare.

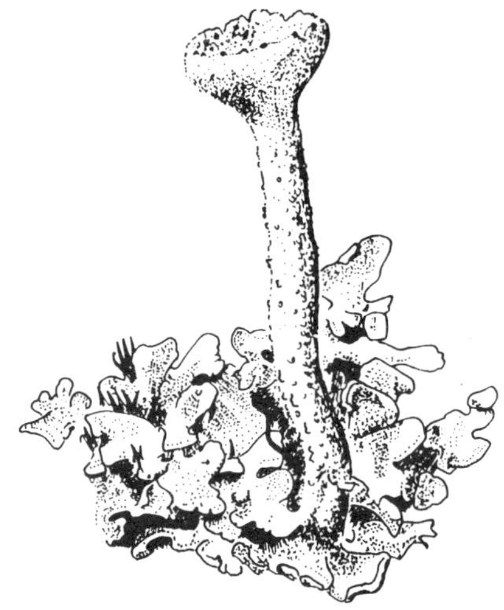

Figure 5.11. *Cladonia fimbriata*, one of many members of this genus of lichens which form cup-shaped *podetia*. This species is common on stumps.

Table 5.9. Systematic list of vascular plants. Table 5.10 may be used as an alphabetical index to this table. Refer to section 5.1.3 for a full explanation of the abbreviations and symbols.

Equisetum palustre L. — No: 10
Marsh Horsetail

Compartment	3	4	5	6	7	9	10	11	20	21	22	23	80	81	82	site
records:	.	.	.	.	.	.	.	.	.	+	.	.	.	.	.	+

Comparts: 1 — Quadrats: 0% — Rec code: A
First record: LNC 1970.
+PHG 1975 'locally frequent'.

Equisetum telmateia Ehrh. — No: 15
Great Horsetail

Compartment	3	4	5	6	7	9	10	11	20	21	22	23	80	81	82	site
records:	.	.	.	.	.	.	.	.	.	.	.	/	.	.	.	/

Comparts: 1 — Quadrats: 0% — Rec code: A
First record: Horwood & Gainsborough 1933.
The main colony is along the southern ditch of C1, but a few plants grow within study area.

Ophioglossum vulgatum L. — No: 20
Adder's Tongue

Compartment	3	4	5	6	7	9	10	11	20	21	22	23	80	81	82	site
records:	.	.	.	.	.	.	.	.	.	+	.	.	.	.	.	+

Comparts: 1 — Quadrats: 0% — Rec code: H
First record: Horwood & Gainsborough 1933.
+PHG 1975 'locally frequent, NW corner'. Not recorded since, but easily overlooked.

Pteridium aquilinum (L.) Kuhn — No: 30
Bracken

Compartment	3	4	5	6	7	9	10	11	20	21	22	23	80	81	82	site
records:	/	/	/	/	/	/	/	/	/	/	.	/	/	/	/	/

Comparts: 14 — Quadrats: 85% — Rec code: A
First record: Horwood & Gainsborough 1933.
Dominates field layer in some dry areas. Up to 2m tall in cmpt 80.

Asplenium adiantum-nigrum L. — No: 33
Black spleenwort

Compartment	3	4	5	6	7	9	10	11	20	21	22	23	80	81	82	site
records:	.	.	.	.	.	.	.	.	.	.	.	.	.	.	.	o

Comparts: 0 — Quadrats: 0% — Rec code: H
First record: Horwood & Gainsborough 1933.
May still be present in rock crevices.

Asplenium trichomanes L. — No: 35
Maidenhair Spleenwort

Compartment	3	4	5	6	7	9	10	11	20	21	22	23	80	81	82	site
records:	.	.	o	.	.	.	.	.	.	.	.	.	.	.	.	o

Comparts: 1 — Quadrats: 0% — Rec code: H
First record: Mott 1868.
Not found, but may occur only on inaccessible rock faces.

Phyllitis scolopendrium (L.) Newm. — No: 40
Hart's-tongue Fern

Compartment	3	4	5	6	7	9	10	11	20	21	22	23	80	81	82	site
records:	.	.	o	.	.	.	.	.	.	.	.	.	.	.	.	o

Comparts: 1 — Quadrats: 0% — Rec code: H
First record: P.H.Gamble 1965.
May well survive in crevices that could not be inspected.

Origin: * = alien, > = introduced. Records: / = SFW survey, + = post-1970, o = pre-1970. Rec code: Adequately recorded, Under-recorded, Habitat under-recorded.

Table 5.9. Systematic list of vascular plants (continued).

Athyrium filix-femina (L.) Roth — No: 50
Lady-fern
Compartment 3 4 5 6 7 9 10 11 20 21 22 23 80 81 82 site — Comparts: 9
records: / / . . / / / . / / . . / / . / — Quadrats: 15%
First record: P.H.Gamble 1965. — Rec code: A
Common beside ditches and in damp parts of wood.

Dryopteris affinis (Lowe) Fraser-Jenk — No: 60
Scaly Male Fern
Compartment 3 4 5 6 7 9 10 11 20 21 22 23 80 81 82 site — Comparts: 3
records: . / + . . / . . . . / — Quadrats: 0%
First record: LNC 1970. — Rec code: U
This species and the next could not always be distinguished from each other.

Dryopteris filix-mas (L.) Schott — No: 70
Male Fern
Compartment 3 4 5 6 7 9 10 11 20 21 22 23 80 81 82 site — Comparts: 14
records: / / / / / / / / / / / / / / . / — Quadrats: 34%
First record: P.H.Gamble 1965. — Rec code: A
Abundant and widespread.

Dryopteris dilatata (Hoffm.) A. Gray — No: 80
Broad Buckler-fern
Compartment 3 4 5 6 7 9 10 11 20 21 22 23 80 81 82 site — Comparts: 13
records: / / / / / / / / / . . / / / / / — Quadrats: 73%
First record: Horwood & Gainsborough 1933. — Rec code: A
Abundant and widespread.

Dryopteris carthusiana (Vill.) H.P.Fuchs — No: 90
Narrow Buckler-fern
Compartment 3 4 5 6 7 9 10 11 20 21 22 23 80 81 82 site — Comparts: 6
records: o / / . . / / / . . . . / — Quadrats: 12%
First record: P.H.Gamble 1965. — Rec code: U
Much less common than previous sp., but very similar and possibly under-recorded.

Polystichum setiferum (Forskal) Woynar — No: 94
Soft Shield-fern
Compartment 3 4 5 6 7 9 10 11 20 21 22 23 80 81 82 site — Comparts: 1
records: . . . . . / . . . . / — Quadrats: 0%
First record: P.H.Gamble 1975, unpublished. — Rec code: A
Only one plant known, in bottom of a shallow pit at SK53861185.

Polystichum aculeatum (L.) Roth — No: 96
Hard Shield-fern
Compartment 3 4 5 6 7 9 10 11 20 21 22 23 80 81 82 site — Comparts: 1
records: . . . . / . . . . . . / — Quadrats: 0%
First record: P.H.Gamble 1968, unpublished. — Rec code: A
Only one plant found, within quarry enclosure at SK53871302.

Polypodium interjectum Shivas — No: 100
Polypody
Compartment 3 4 5 6 7 9 10 11 20 21 22 23 80 81 82 site — Comparts: 3
records: . . + . . . / . / . . . . . . / — Quadrats: 0%
First record: P.H.Gamble 1965. — Rec code: A
Locally common on spoil in cmpt 20. Det. PHG. Included with P. vulgare group in old records.

Origin: * = alien, > = introduced. Records: / = SFW survey, + = post-1970, o = pre-1970. Rec code: Adequately recorded, Under-recorded, Habitat under-recorded.

Table 5.9. Systematic list of vascular plants (continued).

*>*Abies grandis* Lindl. No: 101
Giant Fir
Compartment 3 4 5 6 7 9 10 11 20 21 22 23 80 81 82 site Comparts: 1
records: . . . / . . . . / Quadrats: 0%
First record: SFW in present work 1982-86. Rec code: A
Two or three trees planted in c.1968; survivors of an abandoned underplanting scheme.

*>*Pseudotsuga taxifolia* Britton No: 102
Douglas-fir
Compartment 3 4 5 6 7 9 10 11 20 21 22 23 80 81 82 site Comparts: 1
records: . . . . o . . . . o Quadrats: 0%
First record: LNC 1970. Rec code: A
Introduced. A component of the forestry plantation.

**Picea abies* (L.) Karst. No: 103
Norway Spruce
Compartment 3 4 5 6 7 9 10 11 20 21 22 23 80 81 82 site Comparts: 2
records: . . . / . . . / . . . . / Quadrats: 0%
First record: LNC 1970. Rec code: A
A few apparently self-sown saplings.

*>*Larix decidua* Mill. No: 104
European Larch
Compartment 3 4 5 6 7 9 10 11 20 21 22 23 80 81 82 site Comparts: 2
records: . . . . / . / . . . . / Quadrats: 0%
First record: LNC 1970. Rec code: A
Introduced into plantation, one or two self-sown saplings elsewhere.

>*Pinus sylvestris* L. No: 105
Scots Pine
Compartment 3 4 5 6 7 9 10 11 20 21 22 23 80 81 82 site Comparts: 1
records: . . . . o . . . . o Quadrats: 0%
First record: LNC 1970. Rec code: A
Introduced. Important component of plantation. Many removed 1986.

*>*Pinus nigra* var. *maritima* (Ait.) Melville No: 106
Corsican pine
Compartment 3 4 5 6 7 9 10 11 20 21 22 23 80 81 82 site Comparts: 1
records: . . . . / . . . . / Quadrats: 0%
First record: LNC 1970. Rec code: A
Introduced. Five mature trees beside the main track through cmpt 11. Girths 1.3 to 1.85 m (1984).

Taxus baccata L. No: 107
Yew
Compartment 3 4 5 6 7 9 10 11 20 21 22 23 80 81 82 site Comparts: 4
records: . / + ... / / . . . . / Quadrats: 4%
First record: P.H.Gamble 1976 in P&E 1988. Rec code: A
Scatterd seedlings or small saplings, presumably bird-sown.

Caltha palustris L. No: 110
Marsh Marigold
Compartment 3 4 5 6 7 9 10 11 20 21 22 23 80 81 82 site Comparts: 3
records: . / . . / / . . . . / Quadrats: 0%
First record: Horwood & Gainsborough 1933. Rec code: A
Locally common in the marshes.

Origin: * = alien, > = introduced. Records: / = SFW survey, + = post-1970, o = pre-1970. Rec code: Adequately recorded, Under-recorded, Habitat under-recorded.

Table 5.9. Systematic list of vascular plants (continued).

Anemone nemorosa L. — No: 120
Wood Anemone

Compartment	3	4	5	6	7	9	10	11	20	21	22	23	80	81	82	site
records:	/	/	.	.	/	/	/	/	/	+	.	/	/	.	/	/

Comparts: 11
Quadrats: 32%
First record: Horwood & Gainsborough 1933. Rec code: A
Generally common, locally abundant.

*>*Anemone apennina* L. — No: 125
Blue Anemone

Compartment	3	4	5	6	7	9	10	11	20	21	22	23	80	81	82	site
records:	.	.	.	.	.	.	.	.	.	.	.	.	.	.	.	o

Comparts: 0
Quadrats: 0%
First record: Horwood & Gainsborough 1933. Rec code: A
Presumably a garden escape or introduction, no recent record, presumed extinct.

Ranunculus acris L. — No: 130
Meadow Buttercup

Compartment	3	4	5	6	7	9	10	11	20	21	22	23	80	81	82	site
records:	.	.	.	.	.	/	.	.	/	/	.	/	.	.	.	/

Comparts: 4
Quadrats: 0%
First record: LNC 1970. Rec code: A
In the pastures and beside paths.

Ranunculus repens L. — No: 140
Creeping Buttercup

Compartment	3	4	5	6	7	9	10	11	20	21	22	23	80	81	82	site
records:	/	/	/	/	/	/	/	/	/	/	.	/	/	/	/	/

Comparts: 14
Quadrats: 7%
First record: LNC 1970. Rec code: A
Abundant in grassland and in moist disturbed places.

Ranunculus bulbosus L. — No: 145
Bulbous buttercup

Compartment	3	4	5	6	7	9	10	11	20	21	22	23	80	81	82	site
records:	.	.	+	.	.	.	.	.	.	/	.	/	.	.	.	/

Comparts: 3
Quadrats: 0%
First record: P.H.Gamble 1976 in P&E 1988. Rec code: A
Occasional in pasture.

Ranunculus auricomus L. — No: 150
Goldilocks

Compartment	3	4	5	6	7	9	10	11	20	21	22	23	80	81	82	site
records:	.	o	.	.	.	.	.	.	/	.	.	.	.	.	.	/

Comparts: 2
Quadrats: 0%
First record: LNC 1970. Rec code: A
Only one or two plants found beside track in cmpt 20 opposite stone shed.

Ranunculus flammula L. — No: 160
Lesser Spearwort

Compartment	3	4	5	6	7	9	10	11	20	21	22	23	80	81	82	site
records:	.	.	.	.	/	.	.	.	.	.	.	.	.	.	.	/

Comparts: 1
Quadrats: 0%
First record: SFW in present work 1982-86. Rec code: A
Occasional in marsh.

Ranunculus sceleratus L. — No: 170
Celery-leaved Crowfoot

Compartment	3	4	5	6	7	9	10	11	20	21	22	23	80	81	82	site
records:	.	.	.	.	/	/	.	.	.	.	.	.	.	.	.	/

Comparts: 2
Quadrats: 0%
First record: SFW in present work 1982-86. Rec code: A
Occasional in marsh where line of water main intersects boundary between cmpts 7 & 9.

Origin: * = alien, > = introduced. Records: / = SFW survey, + = post-1970, o = pre-1970. Rec code: Adequately recorded, Under-recorded, Habitat under-recorded.

Table 5.9. Systematic list of vascular plants (continued).

Ranunculus trichophyllus Chaix No: 175
Short-leaved Water-Crowfoot
Compartment 3 4 5 6 7 9 10 11 20 21 22 23 80 81 82 site Comparts: 1
records: . . . . . / . . . . / Quadrats: 0%
First record: SFW in present work 1982-86. Rec code: A
One or two plants found 1986 on soil disturbed by machinery.
Unlikely to persist.

Ranunculus ficaria L. No: 180
Lesser Celandine
Compartment 3 4 5 6 7 9 10 11 20 21 22 23 80 81 82 site Comparts: 9
records: . . . . / / + / / / . / / . / / Quadrats: 0%
First record: Horwood & Gainsborough 1933. Rec code: A
Common in better-lit parts of wood.

**Corydalis lutea* (L.) DC No: 185
Yellow Fumitory
Compartment 3 4 5 6 7 9 10 11 20 21 22 23 80 81 82 site Comparts: 0
records: . . . . o Quadrats: 0%
First record: LNC 1970. Rec code: H
A garden escape or introduction. No recent record, presumed extinct.

Teesdalia nudicaulis (L.) R. Br. No: 190
Shepherd's Cress
Compartment 3 4 5 6 7 9 10 11 20 21 22 23 80 81 82 site Comparts: 1
records: . . / . . . . / Quadrats: 0%
First record: Pulteney 1747. Rec code: H
A small colony on slate spoil is the only known site in the county.

Capsella bursa-pastoris (L.) Medicus No: 192
Shepherd's Purse
Compartment 3 4 5 6 7 9 10 11 20 21 22 23 80 81 82 site Comparts: 1
records: . . . . . / . . . . / Quadrats: 0%
First record: SFW in present work 1982-86. Rec code: A
Casual; an arable weed recorded once only.

**Lunaria annua* L. No: 195
Honesty
Compartment 3 4 5 6 7 9 10 11 20 21 22 23 80 81 82 site Comparts: 1
records: . / . . . . / Quadrats: 0%
First record: SFW in present work 1982-86. Rec code: A
Casual; a garden escape.

Erophila verna (L.) Chevall. No: 197
Whitlow Grass
Compartment 3 4 5 6 7 9 10 11 20 21 22 23 80 81 82 site Comparts: 1
records: . . + ... + Quadrats: 0%
First record: P.H.Gamble 1976 in P&E 1988. Rec code: A
'Occasional.'

Cardamine pratensis L. No: 200
Lady's Smock
Compartment 3 4 5 6 7 9 10 11 20 21 22 23 80 81 82 site Comparts: 1
records: . . . . / . . . . . / Quadrats: 0%
First record: LNC 1970. Rec code: A
In the damp parts of the pasture.

Origin: * = alien, > = introduced. Records: / = SFW survey, + = post-1970, o = pre-1970. Rec code: Adequately recorded, Under-recorded, Habitat under-recorded.

Table 5.9. Systematic list of vascular plants (continued).

Cardamine amara L. No: 210
Large Bitter-cress
Compartment 3 4 5 6 7 9 10 11 20 21 22 23 80 81 82 site Comparts: 0
records: . . . . o Quadrats: 0%
First record: P.H.Gamble 1969, unpublished. Rec code: A

Cardamine flexuosa With. No: 220
Wood Bitter-cress
Compartment 3 4 5 6 7 9 10 11 20 21 22 23 80 81 82 site Comparts: 11
records: / / . / / / / / / / . / / . . / Quadrats: 9%
First record: Horwood & Gainsborough 1933. Rec code: A
Common in damp shady places.

Cardamine hirsuta L. No: 230
Hairy Bitter-cress
Compartment 3 4 5 6 7 9 10 11 20 21 22 23 80 81 82 site Comparts: 2
records: . . + . . / . . . . / Quadrats: 0%
First record: LNC 1970. Rec code: A
Occasional in dry places.

Nasturtium officinale R. Br. No: 240
Water-cress
Compartment 3 4 5 6 7 9 10 11 20 21 22 23 80 81 82 site Comparts: 0
records: . . . . o Quadrats: 0%
First record: LNC 1970. Rec code: A
'Marshy places.'

Rorippa palustris (L.) Besser No: 245
Marsh Yellow-cress
Compartment 3 4 5 6 7 9 10 11 20 21 22 23 80 81 82 site Comparts: 1
records: . . . . . / . . . . / Quadrats: 0%
First record: SFW in present work 1982-86. Rec code: A
Six plants appeared in 1985 following water main construction work at SK53751173. May not persist.

Alliaria petiolata (Bieb.)Cavara & Gr No: 250
Garlic Mustard
Compartment 3 4 5 6 7 9 10 11 20 21 22 23 80 81 82 site Comparts: 0
records: . . . . o Quadrats: 0%
First record: LNC 1970. Rec code: A
'Wood margins.'

Viola riviniana Rchb. No: 260
Common Violet
Compartment 3 4 5 6 7 9 10 11 20 21 22 23 80 81 82 site Comparts: 6
records: . . . . . / / / / + . / . . . / Quadrats: 5%
First record: Horwood & Gainsborough 1933. Rec code: A
Locally common, especially in cmpt 9.

Viola reichenbachiana Jord. ex Bor. No: 270
Pale Wood Violet
Compartment 3 4 5 6 7 9 10 11 20 21 22 23 80 81 82 site Comparts: 1
records: . . . . . . / . . . . / Quadrats: 0%
First record: P.H.Gamble 1972 in P&E 1988. Rec code: A
Occasional in cmpt 10 only.

Origin: * = alien, > = introduced. Records: / = SFW survey, + = post-1970, o = pre-1970. Rec code: Adequately recorded, Under-recorded, Habitat under-recorded.

Table 5.9. Systematic list of vascular plants (continued).

Viola canina L. — No: 280
Heath Violet

Compartment	3	4	5	6	7	9	10	11	20	21	22	23	80	81	82	site
records:	.	.	.	.	.	.	.	.	.	+	.	.	.	.	.	+

Comparts: 1 — Quadrats: 0% — Rec code: A
First record: P.H.Gamble 1975 in P&E 1988.
'Rare.'

Hypericum perforatum L. — No: 290
Common St. John's Wort

Compartment	3	4	5	6	7	9	10	11	20	21	22	23	80	81	82	site
records:	.	.	.	.	.	.	.	.	/	+	.	.	.	.	.	/

Comparts: 2 — Quadrats: 0% — Rec code: A
First record: LNC 1970.
In open areas.

Hypericum tetrapterum Fr. — No: 300
Square-stemmed St. John's Wort

Compartment	3	4	5	6	7	9	10	11	20	21	22	23	80	81	82	site
records:	o	o	.	.	/	o	.	.	o	.	.	.	.	.	.	/

Comparts: 5 — Quadrats: 0% — Rec code: A
First record: LNC 1970.
In moist places.

Hypericum humifusum L. — No: 310
Trailing St. John's Wort

Compartment	3	4	5	6	7	9	10	11	20	21	22	23	80	81	82	site
records:	.	.	.	.	.	/	+	.	.	.	.	.	.	.	.	/

Comparts: 2 — Quadrats: 1% — Rec code: A
First record: Pulteney 1747.
Single plant in a small glade at SK53581191.

Hypericum pulchrum L. — No: 320
Slender St. John's Wort

Compartment	3	4	5	6	7	9	10	11	20	21	22	23	80	81	82	site
records:	/	.	+	.	/	/	o	.	o	.	.	.	.	.	.	/

Comparts: 6 — Quadrats: 0% — Rec code: A
First record: P.H.Gamble 1965.
A few plants in well-lit places.

Hypericum hirsutum L. — No: 330
Hairy St. John's Wort

Compartment	3	4	5	6	7	9	10	11	20	21	22	23	80	81	82	site
records:	.	.	.	.	.	.	.	.	o	.	.	.	.	.	.	o

Comparts: 1 — Quadrats: 0% — Rec code: A
First record: LNC 1970.
'One locality only.'

Silene dioica (L.) Clairv. — No: 340
Red Campion

Compartment	3	4	5	6	7	9	10	11	20	21	22	23	80	81	82	site
records:	.	/	.	.	.	/	/	.	/	/	/	/	.	/	/	/

Comparts: 9 — Quadrats: 4% — Rec code: A
First record: Horwood & Gainsborough 1933.
Frequent and widespread.

Lychnis flos-cuculi L. — No: 350
Ragged Robin

Compartment	3	4	5	6	7	9	10	11	20	21	22	23	80	81	82	site
records:	.	.	.	.	.	o	.	.	.	.	.	.	.	.	.	o

Comparts: 1 — Quadrats: 0% — Rec code: A
First record: LNC 1970.
'Occasional in one marshy area'.

Origin: * = alien, > = introduced. Records: / = SFW survey, + = post-1970, o = pre-1970. Rec code: Adequately recorded, Under-recorded, Habitat under-recorded.

Table 5.9. Systematic list of vascular plants (continued).

Cerastium fontanum ssp. *glabrescens* Baumg. — No: 360
Common Mouse-ear Chickweed

Compartment	3	4	5	6	7	9	10	11	20	21	22	23	80	81	82	site
records:	.	.	/	.	/	/	.	.	/	/	.	.	.	.	.	/

Comparts: 5 — Quadrats: 0% — Rec code: A
First record: LNC 1970.
A weed of short grassland, on tracks etc.

Cerastium glomeratum Thuill. — No: 361
Sticky Mouse-ear Chickweed

Compartment	3	4	5	6	7	9	10	11	20	21	22	23	80	81	82	site
records:	.	.	+	.	.	.	.	.	/	.	.	/	.	.	.	/

Comparts: 3 — Quadrats: 0% — Rec code: A
First record: P.H.Gamble 1976 in P&E 1988.
Rare, trampled places.

Cerastium semidecandrum L. — No: 364
Little Mouse-ear Chickweed

Compartment	3	4	5	6	7	9	10	11	20	21	22	23	80	81	82	site
records:	.	.	+	.	.	.	.	.	.	.	.	.	.	.	.	+

Comparts: 1 — Quadrats: 0% — Rec code: A
First record: P.H.Gamble 1976 in P&E 1988.
'locally frequent.'

Myosoton aquaticum (L.) Moench — No: 367
Water Chickweed

Compartment	3	4	5	6	7	9	10	11	20	21	22	23	80	81	82	site
records:	.	.	.	.	.	/	.	.	.	.	.	.	.	.	.	/

Comparts: 1 — Quadrats: 0% — Rec code: A
First record: SFW in present work 1982-86.
On soil disturbed during mater main construction. Unlikely to persist.

Stellaria media (L.) Vill. — No: 370
Chickweed

Compartment	3	4	5	6	7	9	10	11	20	21	22	23	80	81	82	site
records:	/	/	/	/	/	/	/	/	/	+	.	/	.	.	.	/

Comparts: 11 — Quadrats: 0% — Rec code: A
First record: LNC 1970.
Very common on paths.

Stellaria holostea L. — No: 380
Greater Stitchwort

Compartment	3	4	5	6	7	9	10	11	20	21	22	23	80	81	82	site
records:	/	/	.	/	.	/	.	/	/	/	/	/	/	.	.	/

Comparts: 10 — Quadrats: 4% — Rec code: A
First record: Horwood & Gainsborough 1933.
Frequent throughout.

Stellaria graminea L. — No: 390
Lesser Stitchwort

Compartment	3	4	5	6	7	9	10	11	20	21	22	23	80	81	82	site
records:	/	.	.	.	/	.	.	.	.	+	/	/	.	.	.	/

Comparts: 5 — Quadrats: 0% — Rec code: A
First record: P.H.Gamble 1965.
Common in pastures, occasional in woodland glades.

Stellaria alsine Grimm — No: 400
Bog Stitchwort

Compartment	3	4	5	6	7	9	10	11	20	21	22	23	80	81	82	site
records:	.	/	.	.	/	.	.	.	/	+	.	/	.	.	.	/

Comparts: 5 — Quadrats: 1% — Rec code: A
First record: LNC 1970.
Locally frequent along banks of streams and muddy paths.

Origin: * = alien, > = introduced. Records: / = SFW survey, + = post-1970, o = pre-1970. Rec code: Adequately recorded, Under-recorded, Habitat under-recorded.

Table 5.9. Systematic list of vascular plants (continued).

Moenchia erecta (L.)Gaertn.Mey&Sch — No: 405
Upright Chickweed
Compartment 3 4 5 6 7 9 10 11 20 21 22 23 80 81 82 site — Comparts: 0
records: . . . . o — Quadrats: 0%
First record: Mott et al. 1886. — Rec code: U

Sagina apetala Ard. — No: 410
Common Pearlwort
Compartment 3 4 5 6 7 9 10 11 20 21 22 23 80 81 82 site — Comparts: 1
records: . . + ... + — Quadrats: 0%
First record: Mott et al. 1886. — Rec code: A
+PHG 1976 'occasional'.

Sagina procumbens L. — No: 420
Procumbent Pearlwort
Compartment 3 4 5 6 7 9 10 11 20 21 22 23 80 81 82 site — Comparts: 0
records: . . . . o — Quadrats: 0%
First record: LNC 1970. — Rec code: A

Moehringia trinervia (L.) Clairv. — No: 430
Three-nerved Sandwort
Compartment 3 4 5 6 7 9 10 11 20 21 22 23 80 81 82 site — Comparts: 4
records: . . . . . / / / / . . . . . . / — Quadrats: 8%
First record: LNC 1970. — Rec code: A
Occasional in shady places.

Tilia cordata Miller — No: 433
Small-leaved Lime
Compartment 3 4 5 6 7 9 10 11 20 21 22 23 80 81 82 site — Comparts: 12
records: / / / / o / / / / . . . / / / / — Quadrats: 8%
First record: Wood sale catalogue 1905 LRO. — Rec code: A
Presumed planted in cmpt 10 but native elsewhere. About 780 individuals in all.

>*Tilia* x *europaea* L. — No: 436
Common Lime
Compartment 3 4 5 6 7 9 10 11 20 21 22 23 80 81 82 site — Comparts: 1
records: . . . . / . . . . / — Quadrats: 0%
First record: SFW in present work 1982-86. — Rec code: A
A few trees in cmpts 10 & 11 appear to be this hybrid rather than pure T. cordata.

Geranium dissectum L. — No: 438
Cut-leaved Cranesbill
Compartment 3 4 5 6 7 9 10 11 20 21 22 23 80 81 82 site — Comparts: 1
records: . . . . . / . . . . / — Quadrats: 0%
First record: SFW in present work 1982-86. — Rec code: A
Casual, one plant only.

Geranium molle L. — No: 439
Dove's-foot Cranesbill
Compartment 3 4 5 6 7 9 10 11 20 21 22 23 80 81 82 site — Comparts: 1
records: . . / . . . . / — Quadrats: 0%
First record: SFW in present work 1987. — Rec code: A
Casual. A single plant on a gravelly track.

Origin: * = alien, > = introduced. Records: / = SFW survey, + = post-1970, o = pre-1970. Rec code: Adequately recorded, Under-recorded, Habitat under-recorded.

Table 5.9. Systematic list of vascular plants (continued).

Geranium robertianum L. No: 440
Herb Robert
Compartment 3 4 5 6 7 9 10 11 20 21 22 23 80 81 82 site Comparts: 11
records: . . / . / / / / / / / / / / . / Quadrats: 0%
First record: LNC 1970. Rec code: A
Frequent throughout.

*Impatiens glandulifera Royle No: 449
Policeman's Helmet
Compartment 3 4 5 6 7 9 10 11 20 21 22 23 80 81 82 site Comparts: 1
records: . . . . . / . . . . / Quadrats: 0%
First record: SFW in present work 1982-86. Rec code: A
A few plants appeared in 1986 beside stream at SK53761193.

Oxalis acetosella L. No: 450
Wood Sorrel
Compartment 3 4 5 6 7 9 10 11 20 21 22 23 80 81 82 site Comparts: 12
records: / / . . / / / / / / . / / / / / Quadrats: 28%
First record: P.H.Gamble 1965. Rec code: A
Common throughout.

*>Acer pseudoplatanus L. No: 451
Sycamore
Compartment 3 4 5 6 7 9 10 11 20 21 22 23 80 81 82 site Comparts: 12
records: / / / / / / / / / / / . / . . / Quadrats: 35%
First record: Rotary Club papers 1926 LRO. Rec code: A
Locally abundant (esp. cmpt 11 and parts of cmpt 10). An aggressive and unwelcome invader.

*Acer platanoides L. No: 452
Norway Maple
Compartment 3 4 5 6 7 9 10 11 20 21 22 23 80 81 82 site Comparts: 1
records: . . . . / . . . . . . / Quadrats: 0%
First record: SFW in present work 1982-86. Rec code: A
One or two young trees, possibly self-sown.

Acer campestre L. No: 453
Maple
Compartment 3 4 5 6 7 9 10 11 20 21 22 23 80 81 82 site Comparts: 4
records: . . . . . . / . / / o . . . . / Quadrats: 0%
First record: LNC 1970. Rec code: A
Less than 10 trees, none large, all in north of wood.

*Aesculus hippocastanum L. No: 454
Horse-chestnut
Compartment 3 4 5 6 7 9 10 11 20 21 22 23 80 81 82 site Comparts: 1
records: . . . . . / . . . . / Quadrats: 0%
First record: SFW in present work 1982-86. Rec code: A
One small sapling, self-sown.

Ilex aquifolium L. No: 456
Holly
Compartment 3 4 5 6 7 9 10 11 20 21 22 23 80 81 82 site Comparts: 13
records: / / / / / / / / / / . . / / / / Quadrats: 36%
First record: P.H.Gamble 1965. Rec code: A
Abundant, an important component of shrub layer, often forming impressive trees.

Origin: * = alien, > = introduced. Records: / = SFW survey, + = post-1970, o = pre-1970. Rec code: Adequately recorded, Under-recorded, Habitat under-recorded.

Table 5.9. Systematic list of vascular plants (continued).

Frangula alnus Mill. No: 458
Alder Buckthorn
Compartment 3 4 5 6 7 9 10 11 20 21 22 23 80 81 82 site Comparts: 2
records: . + . . / . . . . / Quadrats: 0%
First record: P.H.Gamble 1972 in P&E 1988. Rec code: A
One tree at SK53871195, girth 21 cm. The one in cmpt 4 now gone, but other specimens grow near to SW. [P.S. knocked down by storm, Dec 1990]

Genista tinctoria L. No: 460
Dyer's Greenweed
Compartment 3 4 5 6 7 9 10 11 20 21 22 23 80 81 82 site Comparts: 1
records: . . . . + ... + Quadrats: 0%
First record: PHG 1968 in P&E 1988. Rec code: H
+PHG 1975 'rare'.

Ulex europaeus L. No: 470
Gorse
Compartment 3 4 5 6 7 9 10 11 20 21 22 23 80 81 82 site Comparts: 2
records: . . + ... / . . . . . . / Quadrats: 0%
First record: LNC 1970. Rec code: A
Rare. A few plants on quarry spoil.

Ulex gallii Planchon No: 475
Western Gorse
Compartment 3 4 5 6 7 9 10 11 20 21 22 23 80 81 82 site Comparts: 1
records: . . . . + ... + Quadrats: 0%
First record: P.H.Gamble 1970, unpublished. Rec code: A
'Several bushes above quarry.'

Cytisus scoparius (L.) Link No: 480
Broom
Compartment 3 4 5 6 7 9 10 11 20 21 22 23 80 81 82 site Comparts: 1
records: . . / . . . . / Quadrats: 0%
First record: LNC 1970. Rec code: A
Rare. On quarry spoil.

Trifolium dubium Sibth. No: 490
Lesser Yellow Trefoil
Compartment 3 4 5 6 7 9 10 11 20 21 22 23 80 81 82 site Comparts: 1
records: . . / . . . . / Quadrats: 0%
First record: Mott et al. 1886. Rec code: A
Rare. In short grassland.

Trifolium repens L. No: 500
White Clover
Compartment 3 4 5 6 7 9 10 11 20 21 22 23 80 81 82 site Comparts: 6
records: . . / . / / . . / / . / . . . / Quadrats: 0%
First record: LNC 1970. Rec code: A
Frequent in pastures, occasional beside paths.

Trifolium medium L. No: 510
Zigzag Clover
Compartment 3 4 5 6 7 9 10 11 20 21 22 23 80 81 82 site Comparts: 1
records: . . . . + ... + Quadrats: 0%
First record: P.H.Gamble 1965. Rec code: H
+PHG 1975 'rare'.

Origin: * = alien, > = introduced. Records: / = SFW survey, + = post-1970, o = pre-1970. Rec code: Adequately recorded, Under-recorded, Habitat under-recorded.

Table 5.9. Systematic list of vascular plants (continued).

```
Trifolium pratense  L.                                          No: 520
Red Clover
Compartment 3 4 5 6 7 9 10 11 20 21 22 23 80 81 82 site   Comparts:  3
  records: / . . . . . .  .  .  /  .  /  .  .  .   /     Quadrats:  0%
First record: LNC 1970.                                   Rec code:  A
  Occasional.

Lotus corniculatus  L.                                          No: 530
Birdsfoot-trefoil
Compartment 3 4 5 6 7 9 10 11 20 21 22 23 80 81 82 site   Comparts:  3
  records: . . / . . . .  .  .  +  .  /  .  .  .   /     Quadrats:  0%
First record: P.H.Gamble 1965.                            Rec code:  A
  Rare.  In dry grassy areas.

Lotus uliginosus  Schkuhr                                       No: 540
Large Birdsfoot-trefoil
Compartment 3 4 5 6 7 9 10 11 20 21 22 23 80 81 82 site   Comparts:  5
  records: / . . . / /  .  .  .  +  .  /  .  .  .   /     Quadrats:  0%
First record: LNC 1970.                                   Rec code:  A
  Occasional in moist grassland and beside rides.

Vicia cracca  L.                                                No: 550
Tufted Vetch
Compartment 3 4 5 6 7 9 10 11 20 21 22 23 80 81 82 site   Comparts:  3
  records: . . . . . .  .  .  .  +  /  /  .  .  .   /     Quadrats:  0%
First record: P.H.Gamble 1965.                            Rec code:  A
  Occasional in grassland.

Vicia sepium  L.                                                No: 560
Bush Vetch
Compartment 3 4 5 6 7 9 10 11 20 21 22 23 80 81 82 site   Comparts:  4
  records: . . . . . .  .  .  /  +  /  /  .  .  .   /     Quadrats:  0%
First record: LNC 1970.                                   Rec code:  A
  Occasional in grassland.

Lathyrus pratensis  L.                                          No: 570
Meadow Vetchling
Compartment 3 4 5 6 7 9 10 11 20 21 22 23 80 81 82 site   Comparts:  3
  records: . . . . . .  .  .  /  +  .  /  .  .  .   /     Quadrats:  0%
First record: P.H.Gamble 1965.                            Rec code:  A
  Occasional in pasture and woodland edge.

Lathyrus montanus  Bernh.                                       No: 580
Bitter Vetch
Compartment 3 4 5 6 7 9 10 11 20 21 22 23 80 81 82 site   Comparts:  2
  records: . . . . . .  .  .  /  +  .  .  .  .  .   /     Quadrats:  0%
First record: LNC 1962.                                   Rec code:  A
  Rare.  Edge of woodland at SK53961278 and in pasture.

Filipendula ulmaria  (L.) Maxim.                                No: 590
Meadow-sweet
Compartment 3 4 5 6 7 9 10 11 20 21 22 23 80 81 82 site   Comparts:  3
  records: . . . . . /  .  .  .  /  .  /  .  .  .   /     Quadrats:  1%
First record: Horwood & Gainsborough 1933.                Rec code:  A
  In marshy places.
```

Origin: * = alien, > = introduced. Records: / = SFW survey, + = post-1970, o = pre-1970. Rec code: Adequately recorded, Under-recorded, Habitat under-recorded.

Table 5.9. Systematic list of vascular plants (continued).

Rubus idaeus L. — No: 600
Raspberry

Compartment	3	4	5	6	7	9	10	11	20	21	22	23	80	81	82	site
records:	.	/	/	.	.	/	/	/	.	.	.	.	/	.	.	/

First record: P.H.Gamble 1965.
Occasional.

Comparts: 6
Quadrats: 3%
Rec code: A

Rubus caesius L. — No: 650
Dewberry

Compartment	3	4	5	6	7	9	10	11	20	21	22	23	80	81	82	site
records:	.	.	.	.	.	.	.	.	.	.	.	.	.	.	.	o

First record: LNC 1970.
'A little in one area.'

Comparts: 0
Quadrats: 0%
Rec code: U

Rubus fruticosus agg. — No: 700
Bramble

Compartment	3	4	5	6	7	9	10	11	20	21	22	23	80	81	82	site
records:	/	/	/	/	/	/	/	/	/	/	/	/	/	/	/	/

First record: P.H.Gamble 1965.
Very abundant, locally dominates field layer.

Comparts: 15
Quadrats: 96%
Rec code: A

Rubus lindleianus Lees — No: 717
Bramble

Compartment	3	4	5	6	7	9	10	11	20	21	22	23	80	81	82	site
records:	.	+	.	.	.	.	.	.	.	.	.	.	.	.	.	+

First record: E.Hesselgreaves 1984, unpublished.
Det. A. Newton.

Comparts: 1
Quadrats: 0%
Rec code: U

Rubus platyacanthus Mueller & Lef. — No: 719
Bramble

Compartment	3	4	5	6	7	9	10	11	20	21	22	23	80	81	82	site
records:	.	.	.	.	.	.	+	.	.	.	.	.	.	.	.	o

First record: E.S.Edees 1969 in P&E 1988.

Comparts: 1
Quadrats: 0%
Rec code: U

Rubus pyramidalis Kaltenb. — No: 721
Bramble

Compartment	3	4	5	6	7	9	10	11	20	21	22	23	80	81	82	site
records:	.	.	.	.	.	.	.	.	.	.	.	.	.	.	.	+

First record: A.Newton 1977 in P&E 1988.

Comparts: 0
Quadrats: 0%
Rec code: U

Rubus cardiophyllus Lef. & Mueller — No: 725
Bramble

Compartment	3	4	5	6	7	9	10	11	20	21	22	23	80	81	82	site
records:	.	.	.	.	.	.	.	.	.	.	.	.	.	.	.	o

First record: E.S.Edees 1969 in P&E 1988.

Comparts: 0
Quadrats: 0%
Rec code: U

Rubus lindebergii Mueller — No: 728
Bramble

Compartment	3	4	5	6	7	9	10	11	20	21	22	23	80	81	82	site
records:	.	.	.	.	.	.	.	.	.	.	.	.	.	.	.	+

First record: E.S.Edees 1969 in P&E 1988.
+E. Hesselgreaves 1984 (det. A. Newton).

Comparts: 0
Quadrats: 0%
Rec code: U

Rubus polyanthemus Lindeb. — No: 730
Bramble

Compartment	3	4	5	6	7	9	10	11	20	21	22	23	80	81	82	site
records:	.	.	.	.	.	.	.	.	.	.	.	.	.	.	.	+

First record: A.Newton 1977 in P&E 1988.

Comparts: 0
Quadrats: 0%
Rec code: U

Origin: * = alien, > = introduced. Records: / = SFW survey, + = post-1970, o = pre-1970. Rec code: Adequately recorded, Under-recorded, Habitat under-recorded.

Table 5.9. Systematic list of vascular plants (continued).

Rubus diversus W. Wats. No: 746
Bramble
Compartment 3 4 5 6 7 9 10 11 20 21 22 23 80 81 82 site Comparts: 0
records: . . . . + Quadrats: 0%
First record: E.S.Edees 1969 in P&E 1988. Rec code: U
+E. Hesselgreaves 1982 (det. A. Newton).

Rubus bloxamianus Coleman ex Purchas No: 757
Bramble
Compartment 3 4 5 6 7 9 10 11 20 21 22 23 80 81 82 site Comparts: 0
records: . . . . + Quadrats: 0%
First record: E.S.Edees 1969 in P&E 1988. Rec code: U
+E. Hesselgreaves 1982 (det. A. Newton)

Rubus echinatus Lindley No: 759
Bramble
Compartment 3 4 5 6 7 9 10 11 20 21 22 23 80 81 82 site Comparts: 0
records: . . . . + Quadrats: 0%
First record: J.R.I.Wood 1974 in P&E 1988. Rec code: U

Rubus flexuosus Mueller & Lef. No: 760
Bramble
Compartment 3 4 5 6 7 9 10 11 20 21 22 23 80 81 82 site Comparts: 0
records: . . . . + Quadrats: 0%
First record: A.Newton 1977 in P&E 1988. Rec code: U

Rubus pallidus Weihe No: 762
Bramble
Compartment 3 4 5 6 7 9 10 11 20 21 22 23 80 81 82 site Comparts: 1
records: . . . . . . + ... o Quadrats: 0%
First record: E.S.Edees 1969 in P&E 1988. Rec code: U

Rubus rudis Weihe No: 764
Bramble
Compartment 3 4 5 6 7 9 10 11 20 21 22 23 80 81 82 site Comparts: 0
records: . . . . + Quadrats: 0%
First record: A.Newton 1977 in P&E 1988. Rec code: U

Rubus rufescens Lef. & Mueller No: 766
Bramble
Compartment 3 4 5 6 7 9 10 11 20 21 22 23 80 81 82 site Comparts: 1
records: + ... + Quadrats: 0%
First record: J.R.I.Wood 1974 in P&E 1988. Rec code: U

Rubus dasyphyllus (Rogers) Marshall No: 768
Bramble
Compartment 3 4 5 6 7 9 10 11 20 21 22 23 80 81 82 site Comparts: 1
records: . . . . + ... + Quadrats: 0%
First record: E.Hesselgreaves 1984, unpublished. Rec code: U
Det. A. Newton.

Rubus hylocharis W.C.R. Wats. No: 769
Bramble
Compartment 3 4 5 6 7 9 10 11 20 21 22 23 80 81 82 site Comparts: 1
records: . + ... + Quadrats: 0%
First record: J.R.I.Wood 1974 in P&E 1988. Rec code: U

Origin: * = alien, > = introduced. Records: / = SFW survey, + = post-1970, o = pre-1970. Rec code: Adequately recorded, Under-recorded, Habitat under-recorded.

Table 5.9. Systematic list of vascular plants (continued).

Rubus watsonii W.H.Mills — No: 773
Bramble

Compartment	3	4	5	6	7	9	10	11	20	21	22	23	80	81	82	site
records:	.	.	.	.	.	.	.	.	.	.	.	.	.	.	.	o

Comparts: 0 · Quadrats: 0% · Rec code: U
First record: E.S.Edees 1969 in P&E 1988.

Rubus eboracensis W.C.R.Watson — No: 778
Bramble

Compartment	3	4	5	6	7	9	10	11	20	21	22	23	80	81	82	site
records:	.	.	.	.	.	.	.	.	.	.	.	.	.	.	.	o

Comparts: 0 · Quadrats: 0% · Rec code: U
First record: E.S.Edees 1969 in P&E 1988.

Rubus hystrix Weihe — No: 790
Bramble

Compartment	3	4	5	6	7	9	10	11	20	21	22	23	80	81	82	site
records:	.	.	.	.	.	.	.	.	.	.	.	.	.	.	.	o

Comparts: 0 · Quadrats: 0% · Rec code: U
First record: Mott et al. 1886.

Potentilla sterilis (L.) Garcke — No: 800
Barren Strawberry

Compartment	3	4	5	6	7	9	10	11	20	21	22	23	80	81	82	site
records:	.	.	/	.	.	/	/	/	/	+	.	.	.	.	.	/

Comparts: 6 · Quadrats: 0% · Rec code: A
First record: Horwood & Gainsborough 1933.
In dry places; quarry spoil etc.

Potentilla anserina L. — No: 810
Silverweed

Compartment	3	4	5	6	7	9	10	11	20	21	22	23	80	81	82	site
records:	.	.	.	.	.	.	.	.	.	.	.	/	.	.	.	/

Comparts: 1 · Quadrats: 0% · Rec code: A
First record: LNC 1970.
On trampled ground.

Potentilla erecta (L.) Rausch. — No: 820
Common Tormentil

Compartment	3	4	5	6	7	9	10	11	20	21	22	23	80	81	82	site
records:	.	.	/	.	.	/	.	.	.	+	.	/	.	.	.	/

Comparts: 4 · Quadrats: 0% · Rec code: A
First record: LNC 1970.
Occasional in short grassland beside rides.

Potentilla reptans L. — No: 825
Creeping Cinquefoil

Compartment	3	4	5	6	7	9	10	11	20	21	22	23	80	81	82	site
records:	.	.	.	.	.	.	.	.	.	.	.	/	.	.	.	/

Comparts: 1 · Quadrats: 0% · Rec code: A
First record: SFW in present work 1982-86.
Casual, a single plant.

Fragaria vesca L. — No: 830
Wild Strawberry

Compartment	3	4	5	6	7	9	10	11	20	21	22	23	80	81	82	site
records:	.	.	/	.	.	/	/	.	/	.	.	.	.	.	.	/

Comparts: 4 · Quadrats: 8% · Rec code: A
First record: LNC 1970.
Occasional.

Origin: * = alien, > = introduced. Records: / = SFW survey, + = post-1970, o = pre-1970. Rec code: Adequately recorded, Under-recorded, Habitat under-recorded.

Table 5.9. Systematic list of vascular plants (continued).

Geum urbanum L. — No: 840
Wood Avens
Compartment 3 4 5 6 7 9 10 11 20 21 22 23 80 81 82 site — Comparts: 10
records: / / / . / / / / / / . / . . . / — Quadrats: 8%
First record: Horwood & Gainsborough 1933. — Rec code: A
Common in shady places.

Agrimonia eupatoria L. — No: 850
Common Agrimony
Compartment 3 4 5 6 7 9 10 11 20 21 22 23 80 81 82 site — Comparts: 2
records: . . / . . . . . . / . . . . . . / — Quadrats: 0%
First record: P.H.Gamble 1965. — Rec code: A
Beside open rides and in pasture.

Agrimonia procera Wallr. — No: 860
Fragrant Agrimony
Compartment 3 4 5 6 7 9 10 11 20 21 22 23 80 81 82 site — Comparts: 0
records: . . . . o — Quadrats: 0%
First record: P.H.Gamble 1965. — Rec code: H
'Not seen recently.' Probably extinct, only one other site in the county.

Alchemilla filicaulis ssp. *vestita* Buser — No: 870
Lady's Mantle
Compartment 3 4 5 6 7 9 10 11 20 21 22 23 80 81 82 site — Comparts: 3
records: . . . . . / . . . . + . / . . . . / — Quadrats: 0%
First record: P.H.Gamble 1975 in P&E 1988. — Rec code: A
On footpaths.

Alchemilla xanthochlora Rothm. — No: 880
Lady's Mantle
Compartment 3 4 5 6 7 9 10 11 20 21 22 23 80 81 82 site — Comparts: 0
records: . . . . o — Quadrats: 0%
First record: P.H.Gamble 1965. — Rec code: A
'Field and by paths.'

Aphanes arvensis agg. — No: 890
Parsley Piert
Compartment 3 4 5 6 7 9 10 11 20 21 22 23 80 81 82 site — Comparts: 3
records: . . + ... / + ... / — Quadrats: 0%
First record: LNC 1970. — Rec code: A
Small patches. PHG (1976) identified those in cmpt 5 as A. microcarpa (Boiss. & Reut.) Rothm.

Sanguisorba officinalis L. — No: 900
Great Burnet
Compartment 3 4 5 6 7 9 10 11 20 21 22 23 80 81 82 site — Comparts: 2
records: . . . . + . / . . . . / — Quadrats: 0%
First record: LNC 1970. — Rec code: A
Frequent in pasture.

Rosa arvensis Huds. — No: 902
Field Rose
Compartment 3 4 5 6 7 9 10 11 20 21 22 23 80 81 82 site — Comparts: 11
records: / . / / . + o / / + . / / / . / — Quadrats: 3%
First record: P.H.Gamble 1965. — Rec code: A
Frequent throughout.

Origin: * = alien, > = introduced. Records: / = SFW survey, + = post-1970, o = pre-1970. Rec code: Adequately recorded, Under-recorded, Habitat under-recorded.

Table 5.9. Systematic list of vascular plants (continued).

Rosa canina agg. No: 904
Dog Rose
Compartment 3 4 5 6 7 9 10 11 20 21 22 23 80 81 82 site Comparts: 8
records: / / / . . / . / / / . / . . . / Quadrats: 1%
First record: P.H.Gamble 1965. Rec code: A
Frequent throughout.

Rosa tomentosa Sm. No: 920
Downy Rose
Compartment 3 4 5 6 7 9 10 11 20 21 22 23 80 81 82 site Comparts: 0
records: . . . . o Quadrats: 0%
First record: Mott et al. 1886. Rec code: U

Prunus spinosa L. No: 935
Blackthorn
Compartment 3 4 5 6 7 9 10 11 20 21 22 23 80 81 82 site Comparts: 9
records: / . . . / / . . / / . / / / / / Quadrats: 0%
First record: P.H.Gamble 1965. Rec code: A
Forming occasional patches by suckering.

**Prunus domestica* ssp. *insititia* (L.) C.K. Schneid. No: 937
Bullace
Compartment 3 4 5 6 7 9 10 11 20 21 22 23 80 81 82 site Comparts: 0
records: . . . . / Quadrats: 0%
First record: Horwood & Gainsborough 1933. Rec code: U
Rare, location not recorded.

Prunus avium (L.) L. No: 940
Wild Cherry
Compartment 3 4 5 6 7 9 10 11 20 21 22 23 80 81 82 site Comparts: 6
records: . . / . / . / / / . / . . . . / Quadrats: 1%
First record: LNC 1970. Rec code: A
Occasional small trees.

*>*Prunus laurocerasus* L. No: 945
Cherry-Laurel
Compartment 3 4 5 6 7 9 10 11 20 21 22 23 80 81 82 site Comparts: 1
records: . . . . . / . . . . / Quadrats: 0%
First record: LNC 1970. Rec code: A
One large bush by southern car-park. Planted.

**Cotoneaster* sp. Medic. No: 950
Cotoneaster
Compartment 3 4 5 6 7 9 10 11 20 21 22 23 80 81 82 site Comparts: 1
records: . . / . . . . / Quadrats: 0%
First record: SFW in present work 1982-86. Rec code: A
One plant near Swithland Camp, garden escape.

Crataegus monogyna x *laevigata* No: 956
Hawthorn hybrids
Compartment 3 4 5 6 7 9 10 11 20 21 22 23 80 81 82 site Comparts: 1
records: . . . . / . . . . / Quadrats: 0%
First record: SFW in present work 1982-86. Rec code: A
Growing on a bank beside course of water main.

Origin: * = alien, > = introduced. Records: / = SFW survey, + = post-1970, o = pre-1970. Rec code: Adequately recorded, Under-recorded, Habitat under-recorded.

Table 5.9. Systematic list of vascular plants (continued).

Crataegus monogyna Jacq. No: 960
Hawthorn

Compartment	3	4	5	6	7	9	10	11	20	21	22	23	80	81	82	site
records:	/	/	/	/	/	/	/	/	/	/	/	/	/	/	/	/

Comparts: 15
Quadrats: 16%
First record: P.H.Gamble 1965. Rec code: A
Very common as a shrub or small tree.

Sorbus aucuparia L. No: 970
Rowan

Compartment	3	4	5	6	7	9	10	11	20	21	22	23	80	81	82	site
records:	/	/	+	/	/	/	/	/	/	/	.	/	/	.	.	/

Comparts: 12
Quadrats: 15%
First record: P.H.Gamble 1965. Rec code: A
Common throughout.

*>*Sorbus intermedia* (Ehrh.) Pers. No: 976
Swedish Whitebeam

Compartment	3	4	5	6	7	9	10	11	20	21	22	23	80	81	82	site
records:	.	.	.	.	.	.	.	.	.	.	/	.	.	.	.	/

Comparts: 1
Quadrats: 0%
First record: SFW in present work 1982-86. Rec code: A
Planted. A small sapling found in cmpt 10 was possibly this species.

Malus sylvestris Mill. No: 980
Crab Apple

Compartment	3	4	5	6	7	9	10	11	20	21	22	23	80	81	82	site
records:	.	/	.	/	.	/	.	.	.	.	.	.	.	.	.	/

Comparts: 3
Quadrats: 0%
First record: P.H.Gamble 1965. Rec code: A
Rare.

Umbilicus rupestris (Salisb.) Dandy No: 983
Navelwort

Compartment	3	4	5	6	7	9	10	11	20	21	22	23	80	81	82	site
records:	.	.	/	.	.	.	.	.	/	.	.	.	.	.	.	/

Comparts: 2
Quadrats: 0%
First record: Pulteney 1747. Rec code: A
Confined in Leics. to quarry faces here and at the Brand. In 1740s was gathered by apothecaries.

Chrysosplenium oppositifolium L. No: 987
Golden Saxifrage

Compartment	3	4	5	6	7	9	10	11	20	21	22	23	80	81	82	site
records:	.	o	.	.	o	.	.	.	.	.	.	.	.	.	.	o

Comparts: 2
Quadrats: 0%
First record: P.H.Gamble 1965. Rec code: A
Not found despite many suitable sites having been examined.

Ribes rubrum L. No: 989
Red Currant

Compartment	3	4	5	6	7	9	10	11	20	21	22	23	80	81	82	site
records:	.	/	.	.	/	/	.	.	.	.	.	.	.	/	.	/

Comparts: 4
Quadrats: 3%
First record: LNC 1970. Rec code: A
Occasional.

Ribes nigrum L. No: 990
Black Currant

Compartment	3	4	5	6	7	9	10	11	20	21	22	23	80	81	82	site
records:	.	.	.	.	.	/	.	.	.	.	.	.	.	.	.	/

Comparts: 1
Quadrats: 0%
First record: SFW in present work 1982-86. Rec code: A
Rare.

Origin: * = alien, > = introduced. Records: / = SFW survey, + = post-1970, o = pre-1970. Rec code: Adequately recorded, Under-recorded, Habitat under-recorded.

Table 5.9. Systematic list of vascular plants (continued).

Ribes uva-crispa L. No: 991
Gooseberry

Compartment	3	4	5	6	7	9	10	11	20	21	22	23	80	81	82	site
records:	.	.	.	.	.	.	+	.	.	.	.	.	.	.	.	+

Comparts: 1
Quadrats: 0%
Rec code: A
First record: P.H.Gamble 1972 in P&E 1988.
'Rare.'

Epilobium hirsutum L. No: 992
Great Hairy Willow-herb

Compartment	3	4	5	6	7	9	10	11	20	21	22	23	80	81	82	site
records:	.	/	.	.	/	/	.	.	/	.	.	.	.	.	/	/

Comparts: 5
Quadrats: 1%
Rec code: A
First record: LNC 1970.
Locally common on marshy ground.

Epilobium montanum L. No: 996
Broad-leaved Willow-herb

Compartment	3	4	5	6	7	9	10	11	20	21	22	23	80	81	82	site
records:	.	.	+	.	.	/	+	.	/	.	.	.	.	.	.	/

Comparts: 4
Quadrats: 1%
Rec code: U
First record: LNC 1970.
Occasional.

Epilobium roseum Schreb. No:1000
Small-flowered Willow-herb

Compartment	3	4	5	6	7	9	10	11	20	21	22	23	80	81	82	site
records:	.	.	.	.	.	.	.	.	.	.	.	.	.	.	.	o

Comparts: 0
Quadrats: 0%
Rec code: U
First record: LNC 1970.
'Occasional on damp rides'.

**Epilobium ciliatum* Rafin. No:1010
American Willow-herb

Compartment	3	4	5	6	7	9	10	11	20	21	22	23	80	81	82	site
records:	.	/	.	.	.	/	+	.	/	+	.	.	.	.	.	/

Comparts: 5
Quadrats: 0%
Rec code: U
First record: P.H.Gamble 1975 in P&E 1988.
Occasional. Introduced to Britain 100 years ago, spreading rapidly.

Epilobium obscurum Schreb. No:1020
Dull-leaved Willow-herb

Compartment	3	4	5	6	7	9	10	11	20	21	22	23	80	81	82	site
records:	.	.	.	.	.	/	.	.	.	.	.	.	.	.	.	/

Comparts: 1
Quadrats: 0%
Rec code: U
First record: LNC 1970.
Inconspicuous and probably under-recorded.

Epilobium palustre L. No:1030
Marsh Willow-herb

Compartment	3	4	5	6	7	9	10	11	20	21	22	23	80	81	82	site
records:	.	.	.	.	.	.	.	.	.	+	.	.	.	.	.	+

Comparts: 1
Quadrats: 0%
Rec code: U
First record: P.H.Gamble 1975 in P&E 1988.
'occasional'.

Chamerion angustifolium (L.) J. Holub No:1040
Rose-bay Willow-herb

Compartment	3	4	5	6	7	9	10	11	20	21	22	23	80	81	82	site
records:	/	/	/	/	/	/	/	.	/	+	.	/	/	.	.	/

Comparts: 11
Quadrats: 12%
Rec code: A
First record: LNC 1970.
Common on dry, disturbed sites especially slate spoil.

Origin: * = alien, > = introduced. Records: / = SFW survey, + = post-1970, o = pre-1970. Rec code: Adequately recorded, Under-recorded, Habitat under-recorded.

Table 5.9. Systematic list of vascular plants (continued).

Circaea lutetiana L. No:1050
Enchanter's Nightshade
Compartment 3 4 5 6 7 9 10 11 20 21 22 23 80 81 82 site Comparts: 12
records: / / . / / / / / / / / . . / / / Quadrats: 26%
First record: Horwood & Gainsborough 1933. Rec code: A
Common in shady places.

Callitriche stagnalis Scop. No:1060
Star-wort
Compartment 3 4 5 6 7 9 10 11 20 21 22 23 80 81 82 site Comparts: 6
records: / / . / / / . . / . . . . . . / Quadrats: 3%
First record: LNC 1970. Rec code: A
Common on muddy footpaths.

Hedera helix L. No:1065
Ivy
Compartment 3 4 5 6 7 9 10 11 20 21 22 23 80 81 82 site Comparts: 15
records: / / / / / / / / / / / / / / / / Quadrats: 34%
First record: LNC 1970. Rec code: A
Abundant.

Sanicula europaea L. No:1070
Sanicle
Compartment 3 4 5 6 7 9 10 11 20 21 22 23 80 81 82 site Comparts: 4
records: . . / . . / / / . . . . / Quadrats: 3%
First record: Horwood & Gainsborough 1933. Rec code: A
Locally common in moist shady places.

Anthriscus sylvestris (L.) Hoffm. No:1080
Cow Parsley
Compartment 3 4 5 6 7 9 10 11 20 21 22 23 80 81 82 site Comparts: 4
records: . . + ... / / / . . . . / Quadrats: 3%
First record: LNC 1970. Rec code: A
Occasional in open places.

Conopodium majus (Gouan) Loret No:1090
Pignut
Compartment 3 4 5 6 7 9 10 11 20 21 22 23 80 81 82 site Comparts: 5
records: . . . . . / . . / + / / . . . / Quadrats: 0%
First record: Horwood & Gainsborough 1933. Rec code: A
Locally frequent in grassland, rare elsewhere.

Pimpinella major (L.) Huds. No:1100
Greater Burnet Saxifrage
Compartment 3 4 5 6 7 9 10 11 20 21 22 23 80 81 82 site Comparts: 1
records: . . . . + ... + Quadrats: 0%
First record: P.H.Gamble 1975 in P&E 1988. Rec code: H
'Locally frequent.'

Aegopodium podagraria L. No:1110
Ground Elder
Compartment 3 4 5 6 7 9 10 11 20 21 22 23 80 81 82 site Comparts: 0
records: . . . . o Quadrats: 0%
First record: LNC 1970. Rec code: H
'Wood margin in one area.'

Origin: * = alien, > = introduced. Records: / = SFW survey, + = post-1970, o = pre-1970. Rec code: Adequately recorded, Under-recorded, Habitat under-recorded.

Table 5.9. Systematic list of vascular plants (continued).

Aethusa cynapium L. — No:1115

Fool's Parsley

Compartment	3	4	5	6	7	9	10	11	20	21	22	23	80	81	82	site
records:	.	.	/	.	.	.	.	.	.	.	.	.	.	.	.	/

Comparts: 1 · Quadrats: 0% · Rec code: A

First record: SFW in present work 1988.

Casual. Several plants brought in with gravel in 1988, edge of track.

Apium nodiflorum (L.) Lag. — No:1120

Fool's Watercress

Compartment	3	4	5	6	7	9	10	11	20	21	22	23	80	81	82	site
records:	.	.	.	.	.	.	.	.	.	.	.	.	.	.	.	o

Comparts: 0 · Quadrats: 0% · Rec code: A

First record: LNC 1970.

'Occasional in one marshy area.'

Angelica sylvestris L. — No:1130

Wild Angelica

Compartment	3	4	5	6	7	9	10	11	20	21	22	23	80	81	82	site
records:	/	.	.	.	/	/	.	.	.	+	/	/	/	/	/	/

Comparts: 9 · Quadrats: 0% · Rec code: A

First record: Horwood & Gainsborough 1933.

Occasional beside wet ditches.

Pastinaca sativa L. — No:1135

Wild Parsnip

Compartment	3	4	5	6	7	9	10	11	20	21	22	23	80	81	82	site
records:	.	.	.	.	.	.	/	.	.	.	.	.	.	.	.	/

Comparts: 1 · Quadrats: 0% · Rec code: A

First record: SFW in present work 1982-86.

A single plant seen in one season only at SK53661296.

Heracleum sphondylium L. — No:1140

Hogweed

Compartment	3	4	5	6	7	9	10	11	20	21	22	23	80	81	82	site
records:	/	.	.	.	.	.	.	.	/	/	/	/	.	.	.	/

Comparts: 5 · Quadrats: 0% · Rec code: A

First record: LNC 1970.

Occasional.

Torilis japonica (Houtt.) DC — No:1150

Upright Hedge-parsley

Compartment	3	4	5	6	7	9	10	11	20	21	22	23	80	81	82	site
records:	.	/	.	.	.	/	.	.	/	+	.	/	.	.	.	/

Comparts: 5 · Quadrats: 0% · Rec code: A

First record: P.H.Gamble 1975 in P&E 1988.

Pastures and wood-edge.

Mercurialis perennis L. — No:1160

Dog's Mercury

Compartment	3	4	5	6	7	9	10	11	20	21	22	23	80	81	82	site
records:	/	/	/	.	.	.	/	/	/	.	.	/	.	.	/	/

Comparts: 8 · Quadrats: 3% · Rec code: A

First record: Horwood & Gainsborough 1933.

Occasional small patches, especially where moist.

Polygonum aviculare agg. — No:1170

Knotgrass

Compartment	3	4	5	6	7	9	10	11	20	21	22	23	80	81	82	site
records:	.	/	.	.	.	/	.	.	/	.	.	/	.	.	.	/

Comparts: 4 · Quadrats: 0% · Rec code: A

First record: LNC 1970.

A weed of footpaths and trampled places.

Origin: * = alien, > = introduced. Records: / = SFW survey, + = post-1970, o = pre-1970. Rec code: Adequately recorded, Underrecorded, Habitat under-recorded.

Table 5.9. Systematic list of vascular plants (continued).

Polygonum amphibium L. No:1175
Amphibious Bistort
Compartment 3 4 5 6 7 9 10 11 20 21 22 23 80 81 82 site Comparts: 2
records: . . + ... + ... + Quadrats: 0%
First record: P.H.Gamble 1976 in P&E 1988. Rec code: H
'Locally abundant.'

Polygonum persicaria L. No:1180
Red Shank
Compartment 3 4 5 6 7 9 10 11 20 21 22 23 80 81 82 site Comparts: 1
records: . . . . . / . . . . / Quadrats: 0%
First record: LNC 1970. Rec code: A
Casual, an arable weed.

Polygonum lapathifolium L. No:1190
Pale Persicaria
Compartment 3 4 5 6 7 9 10 11 20 21 22 23 80 81 82 site Comparts: 1
records: . . . . . / . . . . / Quadrats: 0%
First record: LNC 1970. Rec code: A
A few plants beside the drive to the southern car-park.

Polygonum hydropiper L. No:1200
Water-pepper
Compartment 3 4 5 6 7 9 10 11 20 21 22 23 80 81 82 site Comparts: 8
records: / / / / / / . . . / . . / . . / Quadrats: 1%
First record: LNC 1970. Rec code: A
Frequent on muddy rides.

Rumex acetosella agg. No:1210
Sheep's Sorrel
Compartment 3 4 5 6 7 9 10 11 20 21 22 23 80 81 82 site Comparts: 2
records: . . / . . . . . / . . . . . . / Quadrats: 1%
First record: LNC 1970. Rec code: A
Locally common on quarry spoil among very short vegetation.

Rumex acetosa L. No:1220
Sorrel
Compartment 3 4 5 6 7 9 10 11 20 21 22 23 80 81 82 site Comparts: 5
records: / . . . . . / . . / / / . . . / Quadrats: 0%
First record: LNC 1970. Rec code: A
Disturbed, open places.

Rumex crispus L. No:1230
Curled Dock
Compartment 3 4 5 6 7 9 10 11 20 21 22 23 80 81 82 site Comparts: 0
records: . . . . o Quadrats: 0%
First record: LNC 1970. Rec code: U
'Wood margins.'

Rumex obtusifolius L. No:1240
Broad-leaved Dock
Compartment 3 4 5 6 7 9 10 11 20 21 22 23 80 81 82 site Comparts: 5
records: . / . . . / + . . / . / . . . / Quadrats: 0%
First record: LNC 1970. Rec code: U
Disturbed places.

Origin: * = alien, > = introduced. Records: / = SFW survey, + = post-1970, o = pre-1970. Rec code: Adequately recorded, Under-recorded, Habitat under-recorded.

Table 5.9. Systematic list of vascular plants (continued).

Rumex sanguineus L. — No:1250
Red-veined Dock

Compartment	3	4	5	6	7	9	10	11	20	21	22	23	80	81	82	site
records:	/	/	.	/	/	/	+	/	/	+	.	/	/	/	.	/

Comparts: 12 · Quadrats: 3% · Rec code: A
First record: P.H.Gamble 1975 in P&E 1988.
Common throughout.

Rumex conglomeratus Murr. — No:1260
Sharp Dock

Compartment	3	4	5	6	7	9	10	11	20	21	22	23	80	81	82	site
records:	.	.	.	.	.	+	.	.	.	+	.	.	.	.	.	+

Comparts: 2 · Quadrats: 0% · Rec code: U
First record: LNC 1970.
Probably under-recorded due to problems identifying non-flowering plants. +PHG 1976 'occasional'.

Urtica dioica L. — No:1270
Stinging Nettle

Compartment	3	4	5	6	7	9	10	11	20	21	22	23	80	81	82	site
records:	/	/	/	/	/	/	/	/	/	/	/	/	/	/	/	/

Comparts: 15 · Quadrats: 8% · Rec code: A
First record: LNC 1970.
Very common.

Ulmus glabra Huds. — No:1275
Wych Elm

Compartment	3	4	5	6	7	9	10	11	20	21	22	23	80	81	82	site
records:	.	/	.	/	/	/	/	/	.	.	.	.	.	.	.	/

Comparts: 6 · Quadrats: 0% · Rec code: A
First record: LNC 1970.
Occasional in moist places, usually in the form of a shrub.

Betula pendula Roth — No:1279
Silver Birch

Compartment	3	4	5	6	7	9	10	11	20	21	22	23	80	81	82	site
records:	/	/	/	/	/	/	/	/	/	/	/	/	/	/	/	/

Comparts: 15 · Quadrats: 8% · Rec code: A
First record: Wood sale catalogue 1905 LRO.
Abundant everywhere.

Betula pubescens Ehrh. — No:1280
Hairy Birch

Compartment	3	4	5	6	7	9	10	11	20	21	22	23	80	81	82	site
records:	.	/	+	/	/	/	.	/	.	.	.	.	.	.	.	/

Comparts: 6 · Quadrats: 3% · Rec code: A
First record: P.H.Gamble 1976 in P&E 1988.
Occasional.

Alnus glutinosa (L.) Gaertn. — No:1282
Alder

Compartment	3	4	5	6	7	9	10	11	20	21	22	23	80	81	82	site
records:	/	/	/	.	/	/	+	.	.	.	.	.	.	/	.	/

Comparts: 7 · Quadrats: 3% · Rec code: A
First record: P.H.Gamble 1965.
Locally abundant in the marshes and along former course of stream in cmpt 9.

>*Carpinus betulus* L. — No:1284
Hornbeam

Compartment	3	4	5	6	7	9	10	11	20	21	22	23	80	81	82	site
records:	.	.	.	/	.	.	/	.	.	.	.	.	.	.	.	/

Comparts: 2 · Quadrats: 0% · Rec code: A
First record: P.H.Gamble 1965.
A few scattered small trees. Not native to Charnwood.

Origin: * = alien, > = introduced. Records: / = SFW survey, + = post-1970, o = pre-1970. Rec code: Adequately recorded, Under-recorded, Habitat under-recorded.

Table 5.9. Systematic list of vascular plants (continued).

Corylus avellana L. — No:1286
Hazel

Compartment	3	4	5	6	7	9	10	11	20	21	22	23	80	81	82	site
records:	/	/	/	/	/	/	/	/	/	/	/	/	/	/	/	/

Comparts: 15 — Quadrats: 16%
First record: Wood sale catalogue 1907 LRO. — Rec code: A
Abundant, the most important shrub species.

>*Fagus sylvatica* L. — No:1288
Beech

Compartment	3	4	5	6	7	9	10	11	20	21	22	23	80	81	82	site
records:	/	/	.	/	.	/	/	/	/	.	o	.	/	.	/	/

Comparts: 10 — Quadrats: 1%
First record: LNC 1970. — Rec code: A
Common as saplings, few large trees. Planted or self-sown but not native to Charnwood.

*>*Castanea sativa* Mill. — No:1290
Sweet Chestnut

Compartment	3	4	5	6	7	9	10	11	20	21	22	23	80	81	82	site
records:	.	.	.	/	.	.	.	/	/	.	.	.	.	.	/	/

Comparts: 4 — Quadrats: 0%
First record: LNC 1970. — Rec code: A
Two large trees in cmpt 11, girth 1.7 m, a few smaller ones elsewhere.

*>*Quercus cerris* L. — No:1291
Turkey Oak

Compartment	3	4	5	6	7	9	10	11	20	21	22	23	80	81	82	site
records:	.	/	.	/	.	.	.	/	.	.	.	.	.	.	.	/

Comparts: 3 — Quadrats: 3%
First record: SFW in present work 1982-86. — Rec code: A
Occasional small trees. Probably a mixture of planted and self-sown trees.

Quercus robur L. — No:1292
Common Oak

Compartment	3	4	5	6	7	9	10	11	20	21	22	23	80	81	82	site
records:	/	/	/	/	.	/	o	/	/	/	o	/	/	.	.	/

Comparts: 12 — Quadrats: 0%
First record: Horwood & Gainsborough 1933. — Rec code: A
Common but far less abundant than Q. petraea or hybrids.

Quercus petraea x *robur* — No:1293
Oak hybrid

Compartment	3	4	5	6	7	9	10	11	20	21	22	23	80	81	82	site
records:	/	/	/	/	/	.	/	/	/	/	.	.	/	/	.	/

Comparts: 11 — Quadrats: 0%
First record: SFW in present work 1982-86. — Rec code: A
Abundant everywhere. Trees with intermediate leaf characters were recorded as this hybrid.

Quercus petraea (Mattuschka) Liebl — No:1294
Durmast Oak

Compartment	3	4	5	6	7	9	10	11	20	21	22	23	80	81	82	site
records:	/	/	+	/	/	/	/	/	/	.	.	.	/	/	/	/

Comparts: 12 — Quadrats: 0%
First record: LNC 1970. — Rec code: A
By far the most abundant tree in terms of cover.

*>*Quercus maxima* (Marsh.) Ashe — No:1295
Red Oak

Compartment	3	4	5	6	7	9	10	11	20	21	22	23	80	81	82	site
records:	.	.	.	.	.	.	.	.	.	.	o	.	.	.	.	o

Comparts: 1 — Quadrats: 0%
First record: LNC 1970. — Rec code: A
Introduced into plantation.

Origin: * = alien, > = introduced. Records: / = SFW survey, + = post-1970, o = pre-1970. Rec code: Adequately recorded, Under-recorded, Habitat under-recorded.

Table 5.9. Systematic list of vascular plants (continued).

```
*>Quercus coccinea  Muenchh.                                   No:1296
Scarlet Oak
Compartment 3 4 5 6 7 9 10 11 20 21 22 23 80 81 82 site   Comparts:  1
  records:  . . . . . .  .  .  .  .  /  .  .  .  .   /    Quadrats:  0%
First record: SFW in present work 1982-86.                Rec code:  A
  Planted.  The previous record should perhaps refer to this species.

*>Populus alba  L.                                             No:1298
White Poplar
Compartment 3 4 5 6 7 9 10 11 20 21 22 23 80 81 82 site   Comparts:  0
  records:  . . . . . .  .  .  .  .  .  .  .  .  .   o    Quadrats:  0%
First record: LNC 1970.                                   Rec code:  A

Populus canescens  (Ait.) Sm.                                  No:1299
Grey Poplar
Compartment 3 4 5 6 7 9 10 11 20 21 22 23 80 81 82 site   Comparts:  1
  records:  . . . . . .  +  .  .  .  .  .  .  .  .   o    Quadrats:  0%
First record: LNC 1970.                                   Rec code:  A

Populus tremula  L.                                            No:1300
Aspen
Compartment 3 4 5 6 7 9 10 11 20 21 22 23 80 81 82 site   Comparts: 10
  records:  / / . / / .  /  /  /  /  /  .  .  /  .   /    Quadrats:  1%
First record: P.H.Gamble 1965.                            Rec code:  A
  Occasional extensive clonal patches of many slender stems.  Damp
  places.

*>Populus x canadensis  Moench                                 No:1305
Hybrid Black Poplar
Compartment 3 4 5 6 7 9 10 11 20 21 22 23 80 81 82 site   Comparts:  1
  records:  . . . . . .  .  .  .  .  /  .  .  .  .   /    Quadrats:  0%
First record: SFW in present work 1982-86.                Rec code:  A
  Planted.

Salix caprea  L.                                               No:1312
Goat Willow
Compartment 3 4 5 6 7 9 10 11 20 21 22 23 80 81 82 site   Comparts:  7
  records:  / / / . / /  .  .  /  .  .  /  .  .  .   /    Quadrats:  3%
First record: Horwood & Gainsborough 1933.                Rec code:  A
  Occasional in damp parts of wood.

Salix cinerea ssp. oleifolia  Macreight                        No:1315
Common Sallow
Compartment 3 4 5 6 7 9 10 11 20 21 22 23 80 81 82 site   Comparts:  1
  records:  . . . . . .  +  .  .  .  .  .  .  .  .   o    Quadrats:  0%
First record: P.H.Gamble 1965.                            Rec code:  U

Salix aurita  L.                                               No:1319
Eared Sallow
Compartment 3 4 5 6 7 9 10 11 20 21 22 23 80 81 82 site   Comparts:  0
  records:  . . . . . .  .  .  .  .  .  .  .  .  .   o    Quadrats:  0%
First record: LNC 1970.                                   Rec code:  U
```

Origin: * = alien, > = introduced. Records: / = SFW survey, + = post-1970, o = pre-1970. Rec code: Adequately recorded, Under-recorded, Habitat under-recorded.

Table 5.9. Systematic list of vascular plants (continued).

```
Salix aurita x cinerea                                        No:1322
Sallow
Compartment 3 4 5 6 7 9 10 11 20 21 22 23 80 81 82 site   Comparts:  0
  records:  . . . . . . .  .  .  .  .  .  .  .  .   +     Quadrats:  0%
First record: E.Hesselgreaves 1984, unpublished.          Rec code:  U
  Location not recorded; det. E.Hesselgreaves.

*>Rhododendron ponticum  L.                                   No:1327
Rhododendron
Compartment 3 4 5 6 7 9 10 11 20 21 22 23 80 81 82 site   Comparts:  5
  records:  . / / . / .  .  .  .  .  .  .  /  .  /   /     Quadrats:  4%
First record: LNC 1970.                                   Rec code:  A
  Locally abundant, a few large bushes and many saplings.  Threatens to
  smother native species.

Calluna vulgaris  (L.) Hull                                   No:1330
Heather, Ling
Compartment 3 4 5 6 7 9 10 11 20 21 22 23 80 81 82 site   Comparts:  1
  records:  . . / . . .  .  .  .  .  .  .  .  .  .   /     Quadrats:  0%
First record: LNC 1963.                                   Rec code:  A
  Rare.  On quarry spoil.

Vaccinium myrtillus  L.                                       No:1332
Bilberry
Compartment 3 4 5 6 7 9 10 11 20 21 22 23 80 81 82 site   Comparts:  2
  records:  . . . . . /  .  .  .  +  .  .  .  .  .   /     Quadrats:  0%
First record: LNC 1970.                                   Rec code:  A
  Rare.  Seen only on woodbank near SK53611183.

Primula veris  L.                                             No:1336
Cowslip
Compartment 3 4 5 6 7 9 10 11 20 21 22 23 80 81 82 site   Comparts:  1
  records:  . . . . . .  .  .  /  .  .  .  .  .  .   /     Quadrats:  0%
First record: Horwood & Gainsborough 1933.                Rec code:  A
  Occasional in pasture.

Primula vulgaris  Huds.                                       No:1338
Primrose
Compartment 3 4 5 6 7 9 10 11 20 21 22 23 80 81 82 site   Comparts:  2
  records:  . / . . . /  .  .  .  .  .  .  .  .  .   /     Quadrats:  0%
First record: Horwood & Gainsborough 1933.                Rec code:  A
  Less than 5 plants seen, most in very wet alder carr where protected
  from public.

Lysimachia nemorum  L.                                        No:1340
Yellow Pimpernel
Compartment 3 4 5 6 7 9 10 11 20 21 22 23 80 81 82 site   Comparts: 12
  records:  / / / / / /  /  /  /  +  .  .  /  .  /   /     Quadrats: 31%
First record: Horwood & Gainsborough 1933.                Rec code:  A
  Very common.

*>Lysimachia punctata  L.                                     No:1342
Yellow Loosestrife
Compartment 3 4 5 6 7 9 10 11 20 21 22 23 80 81 82 site   Comparts:  1
  records:  . . . . . /  .  .  .  .  .  .  .  .  .   /     Quadrats:  0%
First record: SFW in present work 1982-86.                Rec code:  A
  A plant introduced near car-park.
```

Origin: * = alien, > = introduced. Records: / = SFW survey, + = post-1970, o = pre-1970. Rec code: Adequately recorded, Under-recorded, Habitat under-recorded.

Table 5.9. Systematic list of vascular plants (continued).

Fraxinus excelsior L. — No:1345
Ash

Compartment	3	4	5	6	7	9	10	11	20	21	22	23	80	81	82	site
records:	/	/	/	.	/	/	/	/	/	/	/	.	/	/	/	/

Comparts: 13 Quadrats: 53%
First record: Wood sale catalogue 1905 LRO. Rec code: A
Locally abundant. Saplings thick S of quarry in cmpt 20, and in moist places.

Myosotis laxa ssp. *caespitosa* (C.F.Schultz)Hylan — No:1360
Water Forget-me-not

Compartment	3	4	5	6	7	9	10	11	20	21	22	23	80	81	82	site
records:	.	.	.	.	.	.	.	.	.	+	.	.	.	.	.	+

Comparts: 1 Quadrats: 0%
First record: Horwood & Gainsborough 1933. Rec code: U
+PHG 1975 'occasional'.

Myosotis arvensis (L.) Hill — No:1370
Common Forget-me-not

Compartment	3	4	5	6	7	9	10	11	20	21	22	23	80	81	82	site
records:	.	.	.	.	.	/	.	.	.	+	.	.	.	.	.	/

Comparts: 2 Quadrats: 0%
First record: LNC 1970. Rec code: A
Rare.

Convolvulus arvensis L. — No:1380
Bindweed

Compartment	3	4	5	6	7	9	10	11	20	21	22	23	80	81	82	site
records:	.	.	.	.	.	.	.	.	.	.	.	.	.	.	.	o

Comparts: 0 Quadrats: 0%
First record: LNC 1970. Rec code: A
'Paths in one area.'

**Calystegia sepium* (L.) R.Br. — No:1385
Bellbine

Compartment	3	4	5	6	7	9	10	11	20	21	22	23	80	81	82	site
records:	.	.	.	.	.	/	.	.	.	.	.	.	.	.	.	/

Comparts: 1 Quadrats: 0%
First record: SFW in present work 1982-86. Rec code: A
One plant only, edge of water main ride.

Solanum dulcamara L. — No:1390
Bittersweet

Compartment	3	4	5	6	7	9	10	11	20	21	22	23	80	81	82	site
records:	.	/	.	.	/	/	/	.	/	/	.	/	.	/	.	/

Comparts: 8 Quadrats: 11%
First record: LNC 1970. Rec code: A
Common in bottom of small quarries and other damp places.

Scrophularia nodosa L. — No:1400
Figwort

Compartment	3	4	5	6	7	9	10	11	20	21	22	23	80	81	82	site
records:	/	.	+	.	.	/	/	/	/	/	.	.	/	.	.	/

Comparts: 8 Quadrats: 4%
First record: LNC 1970. Rec code: A
Occasional beside ditches.

Scrophularia auriculata L. — No:1410
Water Betony

Compartment	3	4	5	6	7	9	10	11	20	21	22	23	80	81	82	site
records:	.	.	+	.	.	.	.	.	.	.	.	.	.	.	.	+

Comparts: 1 Quadrats: 0%
First record: LNC 1970. Rec code: A
+PHG 1976 'occasional'.

Origin: * = alien, > = introduced. Records: / = SFW survey, + = post-1970, o = pre-1970. Rec code: Adequately recorded, Under-recorded, Habitat under-recorded.

Table 5.9. Systematic list of vascular plants (continued).

```
Digitalis purpurea  L.                                            No:1420
Foxglove
Compartment 3 4 5 6 7 9 10 11 20 21 22 23 80 81 82 site   Comparts:  5
  records: / / / . . .  /  .  .  /  .  .  .  .  .  /      Quadrats:  0%
First record: LNC 1970.                                    Rec code:  A
  Locally frequent on quarry spoil and other dry areas.

Veronica beccabunga  L.                                           No:1430
Brooklime
Compartment 3 4 5 6 7 9 10 11 20 21 22 23 80 81 82 site   Comparts:  5
  records: . . . / / .  .  .  .  +  .  .  .  /  /  /      Quadrats:  1%
First record: Horwood & Gainsborough 1933.                 Rec code:  A
  In streams and wet ditches.

Veronica officinalis  L.                                          No:1440
Common Speedwell
Compartment 3 4 5 6 7 9 10 11 20 21 22 23 80 81 82 site   Comparts:  1
  records: . . . . . .  +  .  .  .  .  .  .  .  .  +      Quadrats:  0%
First record: P.H.Gamble 1965.                             Rec code:  U
  +PHG 1972 in P&E (1988) 'occasional'.

Veronica montana  L.                                              No:1450
Wood Speedwell
Compartment 3 4 5 6 7 9 10 11 20 21 22 23 80 81 82 site   Comparts:  3
  records: o . / . . .  /  .  .  .  .  .  .  .  .  /      Quadrats:  0%
First record: P.H.Gamble 1965.                             Rec code:  A
  Occasional small patches.

Veronica chamaedrys  L.                                           No:1460
Germander Speedwell
Compartment 3 4 5 6 7 9 10 11 20 21 22 23 80 81 82 site   Comparts:  6
  records: . . . . . /  /  .  /  +  .  /  .  /  .  /      Quadrats:  0%
First record: Horwood & Gainsborough 1933.                 Rec code:  A
  Occasional beside rides.

Veronica serpyllifolia  L.                                        No:1470
Thyme-leaved Speedwell
Compartment 3 4 5 6 7 9 10 11 20 21 22 23 80 81 82 site   Comparts:  3
  records: . . . . / .  .  .  /  .  .  /  .  .  .  /      Quadrats:  0%
First record: LNC 1970.                                    Rec code:  A
  Occasional.

Veronica arvensis  L.                                             No:1480
Wall Speedwell
Compartment 3 4 5 6 7 9 10 11 20 21 22 23 80 81 82 site   Comparts:  1
  records: . . + . . .  .  .  .  .  .  .  .  .  .  +      Quadrats:  0%
First record: LNC 1970.                                    Rec code:  U
  +PHG 1976 'locally frequent'.

Veronica hederifolia ssp. hederifolia  L.                         No:1485
Ivy-leaved Speedwell
Compartment 3 4 5 6 7 9 10 11 20 21 22 23 80 81 82 site   Comparts:  2
  records: . . . . . /  .  /  .  .  .  .  .  .  .  /      Quadrats:  0%
First record: SFW in present work 1982-86.                 Rec code:  A
  Casual, one or two plants found in disturbed places.
```

Origin: * = alien, > = introduced. Records: / = SFW survey, + = post-1970, o = pre-1970. Rec code: Adequately recorded, Under-recorded, Habitat under-recorded.

Table 5.9. Systematic list of vascular plants (continued).

Pedicularis sylvatica L. — No:1490
Lousewort

Compartment	3	4	5	6	7	9	10	11	20	21	22	23	80	81	82	site
records:	.	.	.	.	.	.	.	.	.	+	.	.	.	.	.	+

Comparts: 1
Quadrats: 0%
Rec code: H
First record: LNC 1970.
+PHG 1975 'frequent'.

Rhinanthus minor L. — No:1500
Yellow-Rattle

Compartment	3	4	5	6	7	9	10	11	20	21	22	23	80	81	82	site
records:	.	.	.	.	.	.	.	.	.	+	.	.	.	.	.	+

Comparts: 1
Quadrats: 0%
Rec code: H
First record: LNC 1970.
+PHG 1975 'occasional'.

Melampyrum pratense L. — No:1510
Common Cow-wheat

Compartment	3	4	5	6	7	9	10	11	20	21	22	23	80	81	82	site
records:	.	.	.	/	.	.	.	.	/	.	.	.	/	.	.	/

Comparts: 3
Quadrats: 0%
Rec code: A
First record: PHG 1968 in P&E 1988.
Rare. Near stone shed in cmpt 20, edge of cmpt 80 at SK53981184.

Euphrasia officinalis agg. — No:1520
Eyebright

Compartment	3	4	5	6	7	9	10	11	20	21	22	23	80	81	82	site
records:	.	.	.	.	.	.	.	.	.	.	.	.	.	.	.	o

Comparts: 0
Quadrats: 0%
Rec code: H
First record: P.H.Gamble 1965.
'In field.'

Mentha aquatica L. — No:1530
Water Mint

Compartment	3	4	5	6	7	9	10	11	20	21	22	23	80	81	82	site
records:	.	+	.	.	.	/	.	.	.	+	.	.	.	.	.	/

Comparts: 3
Quadrats: 0%
Rec code: A
First record: P.H.Gamble 1965.
Locally frequent in moist places.

Prunella vulgaris L. — No:1540
Self-heal

Compartment	3	4	5	6	7	9	10	11	20	21	22	23	80	81	82	site
records:	/	.	.	.	/	/	.	.	/	+	.	/	.	.	.	/

Comparts: 6
Quadrats: 0%
Rec code: A
First record: LNC 1970.
A weed of footpaths.

Stachys sylvatica L. — No:1550
Hedge Woundwort

Compartment	3	4	5	6	7	9	10	11	20	21	22	23	80	81	82	site
records:	/	/	.	.	/	/	/	/	.	/	.	/	.	/	.	/

Comparts: 9
Quadrats: 1%
Rec code: A
First record: LNC 1970.
Occasional, woodland edge.

Stachys officinalis (L.) Trevisan — No:1560
Betony

Compartment	3	4	5	6	7	9	10	11	20	21	22	23	80	81	82	site
records:	.	.	.	.	.	.	.	.	.	/	.	/	.	.	.	/

Comparts: 2
Quadrats: 0%
Rec code: A
First record: P.H.Gamble 1965.
Occasional in pastures.

Origin: * = alien, > = introduced. Records: / = SFW survey, + = post-1970, o = pre-1970. Rec code: Adequately recorded, Under-recorded, Habitat under-recorded.

Table 5.9. Systematic list of vascular plants (continued).

Lamiastrum galeobdolon (L.) Ehrend. & Pol — No:1570
Yellow Archangel

Compartment	3	4	5	6	7	9	10	11	20	21	22	23	80	81	82	site
records:	/	.	.	.	.	.	.	.	o	.	.	.	.	.	.	/

Comparts: 2 — Quadrats: 1% — Rec code: A
First record: Horwood & Gainsborough 1933.
Confined to a few plants at NE of cmpt 3.

Lamium album L. — No:1580
White Dead-nettle

Compartment	3	4	5	6	7	9	10	11	20	21	22	23	80	81	82	site
records:	.	.	.	.	/	/	/	.	.	.	.	.	.	.	.	/

Comparts: 3 — Quadrats: 0% — Rec code: A
First record: SFW in present work 1982-86.
Casual weed of disturbed places.

**Galeopsis ladanum* L. — No:1585
Red Hemp-nettle

Compartment	3	4	5	6	7	9	10	11	20	21	22	23	80	81	82	site
records:	.	.	.	.	.	.	.	.	.	.	.	.	.	.	.	o

Comparts: 0 — Quadrats: 0% — Rec code: H
First record: Potter 1842.
No recent record, presumed extinct.

Galeopsis tetrahit agg. — No:1590
Common Hemp-nettle

Compartment	3	4	5	6	7	9	10	11	20	21	22	23	80	81	82	site
records:	.	/	/	.	/	/	.	.	/	.	.	/	/	.	.	/

Comparts: 7 — Quadrats: 0% — Rec code: A
First record: SFW in present work 1982-86.
Common along ride between cmpts 7 & 80, occasional elsewhere.

Glechoma hederacea L. — No:1600
Ground Ivy

Compartment	3	4	5	6	7	9	10	11	20	21	22	23	80	81	82	site
records:	.	.	/	.	.	/	/	.	.	+	.	/	.	.	.	/

Comparts: 5 — Quadrats: 4% — Rec code: A
First record: LNC 1970.
Locally common beside paths.

Scutellaria galericulata L. — No:1610
Skull-cap

Compartment	3	4	5	6	7	9	10	11	20	21	22	23	80	81	82	site
records:	.	/	.	.	.	/	.	/	.	/	.	.	.	/	.	/

Comparts: 5 — Quadrats: 3% — Rec code: A
First record: P.H.Gamble 1965.
In moist places, usually below taller herbs.

Teucrium scorodonia L. — No:1620
Wood Sage

Compartment	3	4	5	6	7	9	10	11	20	21	22	23	80	81	82	site
records:	/	/	/	/	/	/	.	/	/	/	.	.	/	/	/	/

Comparts: 12 — Quadrats: 19% — Rec code: A
First record: LNC 1970.
Common on dry, acid soils especially on slate spoil.

Ajuga reptans L. — No:1630
Bugle

Compartment	3	4	5	6	7	9	10	11	20	21	22	23	80	81	82	site
records:	/	/	.	.	/	/	/	/	.	/	.	/	/	.	.	/

Comparts: 9 — Quadrats: 14% — Rec code: A
First record: Horwood & Gainsborough 1933.
Common in marshes and muddy rides.

Origin: * = alien, > = introduced. Records: / = SFW survey, + = post-1970, o = pre-1970. Rec code: Adequately recorded, Under-recorded, Habitat under-recorded.

Table 5.9. Systematic list of vascular plants (continued).

Plantago major L. No:1640
Great Plantain

Compartment	3	4	5	6	7	9	10	11	20	21	22	23	80	81	82	site
records:	/	/	/	/	/	/	/	/	/	.	.	/	.	.	.	/

Comparts: 10 Quadrats: 0% Rec code: A
First record: LNC 1970.
Common weed of trampled places.

Plantago lanceolata L. No:1650
Ribwort

Compartment	3	4	5	6	7	9	10	11	20	21	22	23	80	81	82	site
records:	.	.	/	.	.	.	.	/	/	/	.	/	.	.	.	/

Comparts: 5 Quadrats: 0% Rec code: A
First record: LNC 1970.
Occasional weed of trampled places.

Jasione montana L. No:1655
Sheep's-bit

Compartment	3	4	5	6	7	9	10	11	20	21	22	23	80	81	82	site
records:	.	.	.	.	.	.	.	.	.	.	.	.	.	.	.	o

Comparts: 0 Quadrats: 0% Rec code: H
First record: Horwood & Gainsborough 1933.
Extinct from both site and county.

Galium mollugo L. No:1660
Hedge Bedstraw

Compartment	3	4	5	6	7	9	10	11	20	21	22	23	80	81	82	site
records:	.	.	.	.	.	.	.	.	.	+	.	.	.	.	.	+

Comparts: 1 Quadrats: 0% Rec code: H
First record: LNC 1970.
+PHG 1975 'rare'.

Galium verum L. No:1670
Lady's Bedstraw

Compartment	3	4	5	6	7	9	10	11	20	21	22	23	80	81	82	site
records:	.	.	.	.	.	.	.	.	.	+	/	/	.	.	.	/

Comparts: 3 Quadrats: 0% Rec code: A
First record: P.H.Gamble 1965.
Occasional, confined to pastures.

Galium saxtile L. No:1680
Heath Bedstraw

Compartment	3	4	5	6	7	9	10	11	20	21	22	23	80	81	82	site
records:	/	.	/	.	/	.	/	.	/	.	.	.	.	.	.	/

Comparts: 5 Quadrats: 4% Rec code: A
First record: LNC 1970.
Occasional on thin soil around outcrops.

Galium palustre agg. No:1690
Marsh Bedstraw

Compartment	3	4	5	6	7	9	10	11	20	21	22	23	80	81	82	site
records:	.	/	.	.	.	/	.	.	.	+	.	.	/	.	.	/

Comparts: 4 Quadrats: 1% Rec code: A
First record: LNC 1970.
Common in marshes.

Galium uliginosum L. No:1700
Fen Bedstraw

Compartment	3	4	5	6	7	9	10	11	20	21	22	23	80	81	82	site
records:	.	.	.	.	.	.	.	.	.	+	.	.	.	.	.	+

Comparts: 1 Quadrats: 0% Rec code: U
First record: LNC 1970.
+PHG 1975 'occasional'.

Origin: * = alien, > = introduced. Records: / = SFW survey, + = post-1970, o = pre-1970. Rec code: Adequately recorded, Under-recorded, Habitat under-recorded.

Table 5.9. Systematic list of vascular plants (continued).

Galium aparine L. — No:1710
Cleavers

Compartment	3	4	5	6	7	9	10	11	20	21	22	23	80	81	82	site
records:	.	/	/	/	/	/	/	/	/	/	/	/	.	/	/	/

First record: SFW in present work 1982-86.
Common.

Comparts: 13
Quadrats: 15%
Rec code: A

Sambucus nigra L. — No:1715
Elder

Compartment	3	4	5	6	7	9	10	11	20	21	22	23	80	81	82	site
records:	.	/	.	.	.	/	/	/	/	.	/	/	.	/	/	/

First record: Horwood & Gainsborough 1933.
Occasional bushes in damper parts.

Comparts: 9
Quadrats: 5%
Rec code: A

Viburnum opulus L. — No:1717
Guelder Rose

Compartment	3	4	5	6	7	9	10	11	20	21	22	23	80	81	82	site
records:	.	/	.	.	/	/	/	/	/	.	.	/	/	/	/	/

First record: Horwood & Gainsborough 1933.
Common in marshes and damp hollows.

Comparts: 10
Quadrats: 8%
Rec code: A

Lonicera periclymenum L. — No:1720
Honeysuckle

Compartment	3	4	5	6	7	9	10	11	20	21	22	23	80	81	82	site
records:	/	/	/	/	/	/	/	/	/	/	/	.	/	/	/	/

First record: P.H.Gamble 1965.
Abundant as ground cover; less frequent as a climber.

Comparts: 14
Quadrats: 80%
Rec code: A

Valeriana officinalis L. — No:1730
Valerian

Compartment	3	4	5	6	7	9	10	11	20	21	22	23	80	81	82	site
records:	.	/	.	.	/	/	.	.	.	+	.	.	.	.	.	/

First record: Horwood & Gainsborough 1933.
Occasional in ditches and marshes.

Comparts: 4
Quadrats: 3%
Rec code: A

Valeriana dioica L. — No:1740
Marsh Valerian

Compartment	3	4	5	6	7	9	10	11	20	21	22	23	80	81	82	site
records:	.	/	.	.	/	/	.	.	.	+	.	.	.	.	.	/

First record: Horwood & Gainsborough 1933.
Confined to marshes.

Comparts: 4
Quadrats: 1%
Rec code: A

Succisa pratensis Moench — No:1750
Devil's-bit Scabious

Compartment	3	4	5	6	7	9	10	11	20	21	22	23	80	81	82	site
records:	.	.	.	.	.	.	.	.	.	+	.	.	.	.	.	+

First record: LNC 1970.
+PHG 1975 'frequent'.

Comparts: 1
Quadrats: 0%
Rec code: H

Senecio jacobaea L. — No:1760
Ragwort

Compartment	3	4	5	6	7	9	10	11	20	21	22	23	80	81	82	site
records:	.	.	/	.	.	/	.	.	/	+	.	.	.	.	.	/

First record: LNC 1970.
A plant of dry, disturbed conditions.

Comparts: 4
Quadrats: 0%
Rec code: A

Origin: * = alien, > = introduced. Records: / = SFW survey, + = post-1970, o = pre-1970. Rec code: Adequately recorded, Under-recorded, Habitat under-recorded.

Table 5.9. Systematic list of vascular plants (continued).

Senecio aquaticus Hill — No:1770
Marsh Ragwort

Compartment	3	4	5	6	7	9	10	11	20	21	22	23	80	81	82	site
records:	.	.	.	.	.	.	.	.	.	.	.	.	.	.	.	o

Comparts: 0 — Quadrats: 0% — Rec code: A
First record: LNC 1970.
'Occasional in one wet area.'

Senecio sylvaticus L. — No:1780
Wood Groundsel

Compartment	3	4	5	6	7	9	10	11	20	21	22	23	80	81	82	site
records:	.	.	+	.	.	.	.	.	.	.	.	.	.	.	.	+

Comparts: 1 — Quadrats: 0% — Rec code: H
First record: LNC 1970.
+PHG 1976 'locally frequent'.

Senecio vulgaris L. — No:1790
Groundsel

Compartment	3	4	5	6	7	9	10	11	20	21	22	23	80	81	82	site
records:	.	.	+	.	.	/	.	.	.	.	.	/	.	.	.	/

Comparts: 3 — Quadrats: 0% — Rec code: A
First record: LNC 1970.
Rare. A weed of disturbed sites.

Tussilago farfara L. — No:1800
Coltsfoot

Compartment	3	4	5	6	7	9	10	11	20	21	22	23	80	81	82	site
records:	/	.	+	.	.	/	.	.	/	+	.	.	.	.	.	/

Comparts: 5 — Quadrats: 0% — Rec code: A
First record: LNC 1970.
Rare, casual.

Pulicaria dysenterica (L.) Bernh. — No:1810
Fleabane

Compartment	3	4	5	6	7	9	10	11	20	21	22	23	80	81	82	site
records:	.	.	.	.	.	.	.	.	.	+	.	.	.	.	.	+

Comparts: 1 — Quadrats: 0% — Rec code: H
First record: P.H.Gamble 1975 in P&E 1988.
'Locally frequent.'

Gnaphalium uliginosum L. — No:1820
Marsh Cudweed

Compartment	3	4	5	6	7	9	10	11	20	21	22	23	80	81	82	site
records:	.	.	.	.	.	/	.	.	.	.	.	.	.	.	.	/

Comparts: 1 — Quadrats: 0% — Rec code: A
First record: SFW in present work 1982-86.
A few plants on water main ride.

Solidago virgaurea L. — No:1825
Golden-rod

Compartment	3	4	5	6	7	9	10	11	20	21	22	23	80	81	82	site
records:	/	.	.	.	.	.	.	.	.	.	.	.	.	.	.	/

Comparts: 1 — Quadrats: 0% — Rec code: A
First record: SFW in present work 1982-86.
One plant at woodland edge SK53961269. A county rarity.

Bellis perennis L. — No:1830
Daisy

Compartment	3	4	5	6	7	9	10	11	20	21	22	23	80	81	82	site
records:	.	.	.	.	.	/	.	.	.	+	.	.	.	.	.	/

Comparts: 2 — Quadrats: 0% — Rec code: A
First record: LNC 1970.
Trampled areas within grassland.

Origin: * = alien, > = introduced. Records: / = SFW survey, + = post-1970, o = pre-1970. Rec code: Adequately recorded, Under-recorded, Habitat under-recorded.

Table 5.9. Systematic list of vascular plants (continued).

Achillea millefolium L. No:1840
Yarrow
Compartment 3 4 5 6 7 9 10 11 20 21 22 23 80 81 82 site Comparts: 3
records: . . . . . / . . . . / . / . . . . / Quadrats: 0%
First record: LNC 1970. Rec code: A
Occasional in grassland.

Achillea ptarmica L. No:1850
Sneezewort
Compartment 3 4 5 6 7 9 10 11 20 21 22 23 80 81 82 site Comparts: 3
records: . . . . . o . . . . + . / . . . . / Quadrats: 0%
First record: P.H.Gamble 1965. Rec code: A
Rare, in pasture only. One or two flowering shoots seen in most years.

Tripleurospermum inodorum Schultz Bip. No:1855
Scentless Mayweed
Compartment 3 4 5 6 7 9 10 11 20 21 22 23 80 81 82 site Comparts: 1
records: . . . . . / . . . . / Quadrats: 0%
First record: SFW in present work 1982-86. Rec code: A
Rare. An arable weed.

**Matricaria matricarioides* (Less.) Porter No:1860
Pineapple Weed
Compartment 3 4 5 6 7 9 10 11 20 21 22 23 80 81 82 site Comparts: 2
records: . . . . . / . . . . . . / . . . . / Quadrats: 0%
First record: LNC 1970. Rec code: A
Rare. An arable weed.

Leucanthemum vulgare Lam. No:1870
Ox-eye Daisy
Compartment 3 4 5 6 7 9 10 11 20 21 22 23 80 81 82 site Comparts: 1
records: . . . . + ... + Quadrats: 0%
First record: LNC 1970. Rec code: A
+PHG 1975 'locally frequent'.

Arctium minus agg. No:1880
Lesser Burdock
Compartment 3 4 5 6 7 9 10 11 20 21 22 23 80 81 82 site Comparts: 5
records: . . . . . / / / / + ... / Quadrats: 8%
First record: LNC 1970. Rec code: A
Occasional in woodland.

Cirsium vulgare (Savi) Ten. No:1890
Spear Thistle
Compartment 3 4 5 6 7 9 10 11 20 21 22 23 80 81 82 site Comparts: 2
records: . . . . . / . . . . / . . . . . . / Quadrats: 1%
First record: LNC 1970. Rec code: A
In disturbed places.

Cirsium palustre (L.) Scop. No:1900
Marsh Thistle
Compartment 3 4 5 6 7 9 10 11 20 21 22 23 80 81 82 site Comparts: 2
records: . . . . / . / . . . . / Quadrats: 0%
First record: Horwood & Gainsborough 1933. Rec code: A
In wetter parts of pasture and in ditches.

Origin: * = alien, > = introduced. Records: / = SFW survey, + = post-1970, o = pre-1970. Rec code: Adequately recorded, Under-recorded, Habitat under-recorded.

Table 5.9. Systematic list of vascular plants (continued).

Cirsium arvense (L.) Scop. No:1910
Creeping Thistle
Compartment 3 4 5 6 7 9 10 11 20 21 22 23 80 81 82 site Comparts: 5
records: / . . . . / . . / / . / . . . / Quadrats: 4%
First record: LNC 1970. Rec code: A
A weed of paths and pastures.

Centaurea nigra L. No:1920
Hardheads
Compartment 3 4 5 6 7 9 10 11 20 21 22 23 80 81 82 site Comparts: 2
records: . . . . / . / . . . / Quadrats: 0%
First record: LNC 1970. Rec code: A
Occasional in pasture.

Serratula tinctoria L. No:1930
Saw-wort
Compartment 3 4 5 6 7 9 10 11 20 21 22 23 80 81 82 site Comparts: 1
records: . . . . + ... + Quadrats: 0%
First record: P.H.Gamble 1965. Rec code: H
+PHG 1975 'occasional'.

Lapsana communis L. No:1940
Nipplewort
Compartment 3 4 5 6 7 9 10 11 20 21 22 23 80 81 82 site Comparts: 6
records: / . . . . / . . / . / . / / . / Quadrats: 0%
First record: LNC 1970. Rec code: A
Occasional in woodland.

Hypochaeris radicata L. No:1950
Cat's Ear
Compartment 3 4 5 6 7 9 10 11 20 21 22 23 80 81 82 site Comparts: 2
records: . . + ... + ... + Quadrats: 0%
First record: LNC 1970. Rec code: U
+PHG 1975 'frequent'.

Leontodon autumnalis L. No:1960
Autumnal Hawkbit
Compartment 3 4 5 6 7 9 10 11 20 21 22 23 80 81 82 site Comparts: 1
records: . . . . + ... + Quadrats: 0%
First record: LNC 1970. Rec code: H
+PHG 1975 'locally frequent'.

Mycelis muralis (L.) Dumort No:1965
Wall Lettuce
Compartment 3 4 5 6 7 9 10 11 20 21 22 23 80 81 82 site Comparts: 0
records: . . . . o Quadrats: 0%
First record: Mott et al. 1886. Rec code: A

Sonchus arvensis L. No:1970
Field Milk-Thistle
Compartment 3 4 5 6 7 9 10 11 20 21 22 23 80 81 82 site Comparts: 0
records: . . . . o Quadrats: 0%
First record: LNC 1970. Rec code: A
'Occasional by paths and quarries.'

Origin: * = alien, > = introduced. Records: / = SFW survey, + = post-1970, o = pre-1970. Rec code: Adequately recorded, Under-recorded, Habitat under-recorded.

Table 5.9. Systematic list of vascular plants (continued).

Sonchus oleraceus L. — No:1980
Sow-Thistle

Compartment	3	4	5	6	7	9	10	11	20	21	22	23	80	81	82	site
records:	.	.	.	.	.	.	.	.	.	.	.	/	.	.	.	/

First record: LNC 1970.
Rare.

Comparts: 1
Quadrats: 0%
Rec code: A

Sonchus asper (L.) Hill — No:1990
Spiny Sow-Thistle

Compartment	3	4	5	6	7	9	10	11	20	21	22	23	80	81	82	site
records:	.	.	.	.	.	/	.	.	.	.	.	.	.	.	.	/

First record: LNC 1970.
Rare.

Comparts: 1
Quadrats: 0%
Rec code: A

Hieracium sp. — No:1999
Hawkweed

Compartment	3	4	5	6	7	9	10	11	20	21	22	23	80	81	82	site
records:	/	.	/	.	/	/	+	.	.	+	.	.	.	.	.	/

First record: SFW in present work 1982-86.

Comparts: 6
Quadrats: 1%
Rec code: A

**Hieracium maculatum* Sm. — No:2000
Spotted Hawkweed

Compartment	3	4	5	6	7	9	10	11	20	21	22	23	80	81	82	site
records:	.	.	.	.	.	.	.	.	.	.	.	.	.	.	.	o

First record: Mott et al. 1886.
'Slate pits.'

Comparts: 0
Quadrats: 0%
Rec code: U

Hieracium diaphanum Fries — No:2001
Hawkweed

Compartment	3	4	5	6	7	9	10	11	20	21	22	23	80	81	82	site
records:	.	.	+	.	.	.	.	.	.	.	.	.	.	.	.	+

First record: P.H.Gamble 1976 in P&E 1988.
'Locally frequent.'

Comparts: 1
Quadrats: 0%
Rec code: U

Hieracium salticola (Sudre)Sell & West — No:2002
Hawkweed

Compartment	3	4	5	6	7	9	10	11	20	21	22	23	80	81	82	site
records:	.	.	+	.	.	.	.	.	.	.	.	.	.	.	.	+

First record: P.H.Gamble 1976 in P&E 1988.
'Locally frequent.'

Comparts: 1
Quadrats: 0%
Rec code: U

Hieracium vulgatum Fries — No:2003
Hawkweed

Compartment	3	4	5	6	7	9	10	11	20	21	22	23	80	81	82	site
records:	.	.	+	.	.	.	.	.	.	.	.	.	.	.	.	+

First record: P.H.Gamble 1976 in P&E 1988.
'Locally frequent.'

Comparts: 1
Quadrats: 0%
Rec code: U

Hieracium vagum Jordan — No:2004
Hawkweed

Compartment	3	4	5	6	7	9	10	11	20	21	22	23	80	81	82	site
records:	.	.	.	.	.	.	+	.	.	.	.	.	.	.	.	+

First record: P.H.Gamble 1971, unpublished.

Comparts: 1
Quadrats: 0%
Rec code: U

Origin: * = alien, > = introduced. Records: / = SFW survey, + = post-1970, o = pre-1970. Rec code: Adequately recorded, Under-recorded, Habitat under-recorded.

Table 5.9. Systematic list of vascular plants (continued).

Hieracium strumosum (W.R.Linton)A.Ley — No:2010
Hawkweed

Compartment	3	4	5	6	7	9	10	11	20	21	22	23	80	81	82	site
records:	.	.	.	.	.	.	o	.	.	.	.	.	.	.	.	o

Comparts: 1 Quadrats: 0% Rec code: U
First record: LNC 1970.

Hieracium perpropinquum (Zahn) Druce — No:2030
Hawkweed

Compartment	3	4	5	6	7	9	10	11	20	21	22	23	80	81	82	site
records:	.	.	.	.	.	.	.	.	.	.	.	.	.	.	.	o

Comparts: 0 Quadrats: 0% Rec code: U
First record: E.Hesselgreaves 1967 in P&E 1988.
'Wood margin near stream.'

Hieracium rigens Jord. — No:2035
Hawkweed

Compartment	3	4	5	6	7	9	10	11	20	21	22	23	80	81	82	site
records:	.	.	.	.	.	.	.	.	.	.	.	.	.	.	.	o

Comparts: 0 Quadrats: 0% Rec code: U
First record: T.G.Tutin 1959 in P&E 1988.

Pilosella officinarum C.H. & F.W.Schultz — No:2040
Mouse-ear Hawkweed

Compartment	3	4	5	6	7	9	10	11	20	21	22	23	80	81	82	site
records:	.	.	/	.	.	.	.	.	.	+	.	.	.	.	.	/

Comparts: 2 Quadrats: 0% Rec code: A
First record: LNC 1970.
Locally common on quarry spoil.

Crepis capillaris (L.) Wallr. — No:2050
Smooth Hawk's-beard

Compartment	3	4	5	6	7	9	10	11	20	21	22	23	80	81	82	site
records:	.	.	.	.	.	.	.	.	.	.	.	.	.	.	.	o

Comparts: 0 Quadrats: 0% Rec code: H
First record: LNC 1970.
'Occasional in quarry areas'.

Taraxacum section Vulgaria Dahlst. — No:2060
Common Dandelion

Compartment	3	4	5	6	7	9	10	11	20	21	22	23	80	81	82	site
records:	.	.	/	/	/	/	/	.	/	+	/	/	/	.	/	/

Comparts: 11 Quadrats: 1% Rec code: A
First record: LNC 1970.
Common in grassland fringing paths. Listed as T. officinale Weber

Taraxacum section Erythrosperma (H. Lindb) Dahlst. — No:2070
Lesser Dandelion

Compartment	3	4	5	6	7	9	10	11	20	21	22	23	80	81	82	site
records:	.	.	+	.	.	.	.	.	.	.	.	.	.	.	.	+

Comparts: 1 Quadrats: 0% Rec code: U
First record: LNC 1970.
+PHG 1976 'frequent'. Listed as T. laevigatum (Willd.) DC.

>*Convallaria majalis* L. — No:2080
Lily-of-the-Valley

Compartment	3	4	5	6	7	9	10	11	20	21	22	23	80	81	82	site
records:	.	.	.	.	.	/	.	.	.	.	.	.	.	.	.	/

Comparts: 1 Quadrats: 0% Rec code: A
First record: SFW in present work 1982-86.
Introduced. Two or three plants at SK53531195, presumably thrown over wall.

Origin: * = alien, > = introduced. Records: / = SFW survey, + = post-1970, o = pre-1970. Rec code: Adequately recorded, Under-recorded, Habitat under-recorded.

Table 5.9. Systematic list of vascular plants (continued).

>*Polygonatum multiflorum* (L.) All. No:2085
Solomon's Seal
Compartment 3 4 5 6 7 9 10 11 20 21 22 23 80 81 82 site Comparts: 1
records: . . . . . / . . . . / Quadrats: 0%
First record: SFW in present work 1982-86. Rec code: A
Introduced. One plant near southern car-park at SK53721180.

*>*Ornithogalum umbellatum* L. No:2090
Star-of-Bethlehem
Compartment 3 4 5 6 7 9 10 11 20 21 22 23 80 81 82 site Comparts: 1
records: . . . . . / . . . . / Quadrats: 0%
First record: SFW in present work 1982-86. Rec code: A
A small group of plants. Introduced. Persisted for a couple of years only.

Hyacinthoides non-scripta (L.)Chouard ex Rot No:2100
Bluebell
Compartment 3 4 5 6 7 9 10 11 20 21 22 23 80 81 82 site Comparts: 14
records: / / / / / / / / / / . / / / / / Quadrats: 42%
First record: Horwood & Gainsborough 1933. Rec code: A
Generally common and locally abundant. Said to be decreasing but difficult to demonstrate.

*>*Muscari neglectum* Guss. ex Ten. No:2105
Grape-Hyacinth
Compartment 3 4 5 6 7 9 10 11 20 21 22 23 80 81 82 site Comparts: 1
records: . . . . . . / . . . . / Quadrats: 0%
First record: SFW in present work 1982-86. Rec code: A
A few plants introduced from gardens.

Juncus bufonius L. No:2120
Toad Rush
Compartment 3 4 5 6 7 9 10 11 20 21 22 23 80 81 82 site Comparts: 8
records: / / . / / / . . / . . / / . . / Quadrats: 0%
First record: LNC 1970. Rec code: A
Common on muddy paths.

Juncus kochii Schultz No:2121
Bulbous Rush
Compartment 3 4 5 6 7 9 10 11 20 21 22 23 80 81 82 site Comparts: 1
records: . / . . . . / Quadrats: 0%
First record: SFW in present work 1987. Rec code: U
Single plant. Often regarded as a form of J. bulbosus, but normal form of the latter not seen.

Juncus inflexus L. No:2125
Hard Rush
Compartment 3 4 5 6 7 9 10 11 20 21 22 23 80 81 82 site Comparts: 1
records: / . . . . / Quadrats: 0%
First record: SFW in present work 1982-86. Rec code: A
One plant found on water main ride.

Juncus effusus L. No:2130
Soft Rush
Compartment 3 4 5 6 7 9 10 11 20 21 22 23 80 81 82 site Comparts: 13
records: / / / / / / / / / / . . / / / / Quadrats: 8%
First record: LNC 1970. Rec code: A
Common throughout in ditches and wet hollows.

Origin: * = alien, > = introduced. Records: / = SFW survey, + = post-1970, o = pre-1970. Rec code: Adequately recorded, Under-recorded, Habitat under-recorded.

Table 5.9. Systematic list of vascular plants (continued).

Juncus conglomeratus L. — No:2140
Conglomerate Rush

Compartment	3	4	5	6	7	9	10	11	20	21	22	23	80	81	82	site
records:	.	.	/	.	/	.	.	.	.	+	.	/	.	.	.	/

First record: LNC 1970.
Occasional in rides.
Comparts: 4 — Quadrats: 0% — Rec code: U

Juncus acutiflorus Ehrh. ex Hoffm — No:2150
Sharp-flowered Rush

Compartment	3	4	5	6	7	9	10	11	20	21	22	23	80	81	82	site
records:	.	.	.	.	.	.	.	.	.	+	.	.	.	.	.	+

First record: LNC 1970.
+PHG 1975 'locally frequent'.
Comparts: 1 — Quadrats: 0% — Rec code: H

Juncus articulatus L. — No:2160
Jointed Rush

Compartment	3	4	5	6	7	9	10	11	20	21	22	23	80	81	82	site
records:	.	.	.	.	.	.	.	.	.	+	.	.	.	.	.	+

First record: Horwood & Gainsborough 1933.
+PHG 1975 'locally frequent'.
Comparts: 1 — Quadrats: 0% — Rec code: H

Luzula pilosa (L.) Willd. — No:2170
Hairy Woodrush

Compartment	3	4	5	6	7	9	10	11	20	21	22	23	80	81	82	site
records:	/	.	.	.	/	/	/	/	/	.	.	.	.	.	.	/

First record: P.H.Gamble 1965.
Locally frequent.
Comparts: 6 — Quadrats: 8% — Rec code: A

Luzula sylvatica (Huds.) Gaud. — No:2180
Greater Woodrush

Compartment	3	4	5	6	7	9	10	11	20	21	22	23	80	81	82	site
records:	/	/	/	/	/	/	/	/	/	.	.	.	/	/	/	/

First record: Horwood & Gainsborough 1933.
Locally abundant. Forms dense swards though which little else can grow.
Comparts: 12 — Quadrats: 46% — Rec code: A

Luzula campestris (L.) DC — No:2190
Sweep's Brush

Compartment	3	4	5	6	7	9	10	11	20	21	22	23	80	81	82	site
records:	.	/	+	.	.	.	.	.	/	/	.	/	.	.	.	/

First record: LNC 1970.
Locally common in pastures and rides.
Comparts: 5 — Quadrats: 0% — Rec code: A

Luzula multiflora (Retz.) Lej. — No:2200
Many-headed Woodrush

Compartment	3	4	5	6	7	9	10	11	20	21	22	23	80	81	82	site
records:	o	.	/	.	/	/	.	.	/	+	.	.	/	.	.	/

First record: LNC 1970.
Occasional in more open areas.
Comparts: 7 — Quadrats: 1% — Rec code: A

*>*Narcissus* sp. L. — No:2205
Daffodil (cultivated)

Compartment	3	4	5	6	7	9	10	11	20	21	22	23	80	81	82	site
records:	.	.	.	.	.	/	.	/	.	.	.	.	/	.	.	/

First record: SFW in present work 1982-86.
A few plants of the garden variety introduced here and there.
Comparts: 3 — Quadrats: 0% — Rec code: A

Origin: * = alien, > = introduced. Records: / = SFW survey, + = post-1970, o = pre-1970. Rec code: Adequately recorded, Under-recorded, Habitat under-recorded.

Table 5.9. Systematic list of vascular plants (continued).

Iris pseudacorus L. No:2210
Yellow Flag
Compartment 3 4 5 6 7 9 10 11 20 21 22 23 80 81 82 site Comparts: 1
records: . . . . . / . . . . / Quadrats: 0%
First record: SFW in present work 1982-86. Rec code: A
One or two plants in the marsh at the E of cmpt 9.

*>*Tritonia* x *crocosmiflora* (Lemoine)Nicholson No:2220
Montbretia
Compartment 3 4 5 6 7 9 10 11 20 21 22 23 80 81 82 site Comparts: 2
records: . . . . . / / . . . . / Quadrats: 0%
First record: SFW in present work 1982-86. Rec code: A
Two or three isolated plants, garden escapes or perhaps introduced.

Tamus communis L. No:2230
Black Bryony
Compartment 3 4 5 6 7 9 10 11 20 21 22 23 80 81 82 site Comparts: 1
records: . . . . . / . . . . / Quadrats: 1%
First record: LNC 1970. Rec code: A
Rare.

Epipactis helleborine (L.) Crantz No:2240
Broad Helleborine
Compartment 3 4 5 6 7 9 10 11 20 21 22 23 80 81 82 site Comparts: 6
records: . . + . / / / . / / . . . . . / Quadrats: 1%
First record: LNC 1970. Rec code: A
Several spikes near culvert in cmpt 7, occasional S of car-park in cmpt 10, rare elsewhere.

Listera ovata (L.) R.Br. No:2250
Twayblade
Compartment 3 4 5 6 7 9 10 11 20 21 22 23 80 81 82 site Comparts: 2
records: . . . . . + . . . + ... + Quadrats: 0%
First record: Horwood & Gainsborough 1933. Rec code: H
Not found in cmpt 9, may survive in cmpt 21. +PHG 1975 'locally frequent in cmpt 21'.

Orchis mascula (L.) L. No:2260
Early Purple Orchid
Compartment 3 4 5 6 7 9 10 11 20 21 22 23 80 81 82 site Comparts: 0
records: . . . . o Quadrats: 0%
First record: Horwood & Gainsborough 1933. Rec code: H
'Very rare'. No recent record.

Dactylorhiza fuchsii (Druce) Soo No:2270
Common Spotted Orchid
Compartment 3 4 5 6 7 9 10 11 20 21 22 23 80 81 82 site Comparts: 1
records: . . . . / . . . . . / Quadrats: 0%
First record: LNC 1970. Rec code: H
Occasional in pasture.

Dactylorhiza maculata ssp. *ericetorum* (Linton) P.F. Hunt No:2280
Heath Spotted Orchid
Compartment 3 4 5 6 7 9 10 11 20 21 22 23 80 81 82 site Comparts: 1
records: . . . . + ... + Quadrats: 0%
First record: LNC 1970. Rec code: H
+PHG 1975 'locally frequent'.

Origin: * = alien, > = introduced. Records: / = SFW survey, + = post-1970, o = pre-1970. Rec code: Adequately recorded, Under-recorded, Habitat under-recorded.

Table 5.9. Systematic list of vascular plants (continued).

Arum maculatum L. No:2290
Lords-and-Ladies
Compartment 3 4 5 6 7 9 10 11 20 21 22 23 80 81 82 site Comparts: 6
records: . . . . / / / . / / . . . . / / Quadrats: 0%
First record: Horwood & Gainsborough 1933. Rec code: A
Occasional plants, usually in deep shade.

Eleocharis palustris (L.) Roem. & Schul No:2295
Common Spike-rush
Compartment 3 4 5 6 7 9 10 11 20 21 22 23 80 81 82 site Comparts: 1
records: . . + ... + Quadrats: 0%
First record: P.H.Gamble 1976 in P&E 1988. Rec code: A
'Rare.'

Carex laevigata Sm. No:2300
Smooth Sedge
Compartment 3 4 5 6 7 9 10 11 20 21 22 23 80 81 82 site Comparts: 1
records: . . . . . o . . . . o Quadrats: 0%
First record: Horwood & Gainsborough 1933. Rec code: A
'Local, one area.'

Carex sylvatica Huds. No:2310
Wood Sedge
Compartment 3 4 5 6 7 9 10 11 20 21 22 23 80 81 82 site Comparts: 7
records: . . . / / / / / / . . . . / . / Quadrats: 5%
First record: Horwood & Gainsborough 1933. Rec code: A
Common on the deeper soils.

Carex pendula Huds. No:2320
Pendulous Sedge
Compartment 3 4 5 6 7 9 10 11 20 21 22 23 80 81 82 site Comparts: 11
records: / / o / / / . / / . . . / / / / Quadrats: 8%
First record: Horwood & Gainsborough 1933. Rec code: A
Common, sometimes forming impressive stands. In marshes and ditches.

Carex pallescens L. No:2330
Pale Sedge
Compartment 3 4 5 6 7 9 10 11 20 21 22 23 80 81 82 site Comparts: 1
records: . . . . . + ... + Quadrats: 0%
First record: Horwood & Gainsborough 1933. Rec code: A
Not re-found in cmpt 9. +PHG 1976 'rare, edge of pipeline ride'.

Carex panicea L. No:2340
Carnation-grass
Compartment 3 4 5 6 7 9 10 11 20 21 22 23 80 81 82 site Comparts: 1
records: . . . . + ... + Quadrats: 0%
First record: LNC 1970. Rec code: H
+PHG 1975 'frequent'.

Carex flacca Schreb. No:2350
Carnation-grass
Compartment 3 4 5 6 7 9 10 11 20 21 22 23 80 81 82 site Comparts: 0
records: . . . . o Quadrats: 0%
First record: LNC 1970. Rec code: H
'Occasional in one area.'

Origin: * = alien, > = introduced. Records: / = SFW survey, + = post-1970, o = pre-1970. Rec code: Adequately recorded, Under-recorded, Habitat under-recorded.

Table 5.9. Systematic list of vascular plants (continued).

Carex hirta L. No:2360
Hammer Sedge

Compartment	3	4	5	6	7	9	10	11	20	21	22	23	80	81	82	site
records:	.	.	.	.	.	.	.	.	.	/	.	/	.	.	.	/

Comparts: 2
Quadrats: 0%
First record: LNC 1970. Rec code: H
Locally common in wet grassland.

Carex caryophyllea Latour. No:2370
Spring Sedge

Compartment	3	4	5	6	7	9	10	11	20	21	22	23	80	81	82	site
records:	.	.	.	.	.	.	.	.	.	+	.	.	.	.	.	+

Comparts: 1
Quadrats: 0%
First record: LNC 1970. Rec code: H
+PHG 1975 'frequent'.

Carex nigra (L.) Reichard No:2380
Common Sedge

Compartment	3	4	5	6	7	9	10	11	20	21	22	23	80	81	82	site
records:	.	.	.	.	.	.	.	.	.	+	.	.	.	.	.	+

Comparts: 1
Quadrats: 0%
First record: LNC 1970. Rec code: H
+PHG 1975 'frequent'.

Carex otrubae Podp. No:2390
False Fox-sedge

Compartment	3	4	5	6	7	9	10	11	20	21	22	23	80	81	82	site
records:	.	.	.	.	.	.	.	.	.	+	.	.	.	.	.	+

Comparts: 1
Quadrats: 0%
First record: LNC 1970. Rec code: H
+PHG 1975 'occasional'.

Carex remota L. No:2400
Remote Sedge

Compartment	3	4	5	6	7	9	10	11	20	21	22	23	80	81	82	site
records:	/	/	.	/	/	/	/	.	.	/	/	.	/	/	/	/

Comparts: 11
Quadrats: 11%
First record: Horwood & Gainsborough 1933. Rec code: A
Common in ditches and other wet places.

Festuca pratensis Huds. No:2410
Meadow Fescue

Compartment	3	4	5	6	7	9	10	11	20	21	22	23	80	81	82	site
records:	.	.	.	.	.	.	.	.	.	+	.	/	.	.	.	/

Comparts: 2
Quadrats: 0%
First record: LNC 1970. Rec code: H
Occasional in pasture.

Festuca arundinacea Schreb. No:2420
Tall Fescue

Compartment	3	4	5	6	7	9	10	11	20	21	22	23	80	81	82	site
records:	.	.	.	.	.	.	.	.	.	+	.	.	.	.	.	+

Comparts: 1
Quadrats: 0%
First record: LNC 1970. Rec code: A
+PHG 1975 'occasional'.

Festuca gigantea (L.) Vill. No:2430
Tall Brome

Compartment	3	4	5	6	7	9	10	11	20	21	22	23	80	81	82	site
records:	/	/	.	/	/	/	/	/	/	.	.	/	/	/	.	/

Comparts: 11
Quadrats: 3%
First record: LNC 1970. Rec code: A
Common in shady woodland on deeper soils.

Origin: * = alien, > = introduced. Records: / = SFW survey, + = post-1970, o = pre-1970. Rec code: Adequately recorded, Under-recorded, Habitat under-recorded.

Table 5.9. Systematic list of vascular plants (continued).

Festuca rubra ssp. *rubra* L. No:2440
Creeping Fescue

Compartment	3	4	5	6	7	9	10	11	20	21	22	23	80	81	82	site
records:	.	.	.	.	.	.	.	.	.	+	.	/	.	.	.	/

Comparts: 2 Quadrats: 0% Rec code: U
First record: LNC 1970.
Common in pasture.

Festuca rubra ssp. *commutata* Gaud. No:2450
Chewings Fescue

Compartment	3	4	5	6	7	9	10	11	20	21	22	23	80	81	82	site
records:	.	.	.	.	.	.	.	.	.	.	.	.	.	.	.	o

Comparts: 0 Quadrats: 0% Rec code: U
First record: LNC 1970.
'Frequent in field.'

Festuca ovina L. No:2460
Sheep's Fescue

Compartment	3	4	5	6	7	9	10	11	20	21	22	23	80	81	82	site
records:	.	.	+	.	.	.	.	.	.	.	.	.	.	.	.	+

Comparts: 1 Quadrats: 0% Rec code: U
First record: LNC 1970.
+PHG 1976 'locally frequent'.

Lolium perenne ssp. *perenne* L. No:2470
Rye-grass

Compartment	3	4	5	6	7	9	10	11	20	21	22	23	80	81	82	site
records:	/	/	/	/	.	/	.	.	/	/	.	/	/	/	.	/

Comparts: 10 Quadrats: 0% Rec code: A
First record: LNC 1970.
Common in pasture.

**Lolium perenne* ssp. *multiflorum* (Lam.) Husnot No:2480
Italian Rye-grass

Compartment	3	4	5	6	7	9	10	11	20	21	22	23	80	81	82	site
records:	.	.	.	.	.	/	.	.	.	.	.	.	.	.	.	/

Comparts: 1 Quadrats: 0% Rec code: A
First record: LNC 1970.
Rare, one or two plants self-sown from agricultural pasture.

Vulpia bromoides (L.) S.F.Gray No:2490
Squirrel-tail Fescue

Compartment	3	4	5	6	7	9	10	11	20	21	22	23	80	81	82	site
records:	.	.	.	.	.	.	.	.	.	.	.	.	.	.	.	o

Comparts: 0 Quadrats: 0% Rec code: H
First record: LNC 1970.
'Occasional near quarry.'

Poa annua L. No:2500
Annual Meadow-grass

Compartment	3	4	5	6	7	9	10	11	20	21	22	23	80	81	82	site
records:	/	/	/	/	/	/	/	/	/	+	.	/	/	/	/	/

Comparts: 14 Quadrats: 9% Rec code: A
First record: LNC 1970.
Very common. Forms conspicuous bright green border on most paths.

Poa nemoralis L. No:2510
Wood Meadow-grass

Compartment	3	4	5	6	7	9	10	11	20	21	22	23	80	81	82	site
records:	.	/	+	o	o	/	+	.	o	.	.	.	o	.	.	/

Comparts: 8 Quadrats: 3% Rec code: U
First record: Horwood & Gainsborough 1933.
Only two or three patches seen, although easily overlooked.

Origin: * = alien, > = introduced. Records: / = SFW survey, + = post-1970, o = pre-1970. Rec code: Adequately recorded, Under-recorded, Habitat under-recorded.

Table 5.9. Systematic list of vascular plants (continued).

```
Poa pratensis  L.                                                No:2520
Smooth Meadow-grass
Compartment 3 4 5 6 7 9 10 11 20 21 22 23 80 81 82 site   Comparts:  1
  records:  . . . . . . .  .  /  .  .  .  .  .  .   /     Quadrats:  1%
First record: LNC 1970.                                   Rec code:  U
  Occasional in open areas.

Poa trivialis  L.                                                No:2530
Rough Meadow-grass
Compartment 3 4 5 6 7 9 10 11 20 21 22 23 80 81 82 site   Comparts: 10
  records:  . / . / / /  /  /  /  +  .  /  .  /  .   /     Quadrats: 18%
First record: LNC 1970.                                   Rec code:  A
  Abundant in shady woodland, where it creeps and rarely flowers.

Dactylis glomerata  L.                                           No:2540
Cock's-foot
Compartment 3 4 5 6 7 9 10 11 20 21 22 23 80 81 82 site   Comparts: 15
  records:  / / / / / /  +  /  /  /  /  /  /  /  /   /     Quadrats:  3%
First record: LNC 1970.                                   Rec code:  A
  Common beside paths.

Cynosurus cristatus  L.                                          No:2550
Crested Dog's-tail
Compartment 3 4 5 6 7 9 10 11 20 21 22 23 80 81 82 site   Comparts:  3
  records:  . . / . . /  .  .  .  +  .  .  .  .  .   /     Quadrats:  0%
First record: LNC 1970.                                   Rec code:  A
  Occasional in grassy areas.

Briza media  L.                                                  No:2560
Quaking Grass
Compartment 3 4 5 6 7 9 10 11 20 21 22 23 80 81 82 site   Comparts:  1
  records:  . . . . . .  .  .  .  +  .  .  .  .  .   +     Quadrats:  0%
First record: LNC 1970.                                   Rec code:  H
  +PHG 1975 'frequent'.

Melica uniflora  Retz.                                           No:2570
Wood Melick
Compartment 3 4 5 6 7 9 10 11 20 21 22 23 80 81 82 site   Comparts:  4
  records:  / o . / . .  .  .  /  .  .  .  .  .  .   /     Quadrats:  1%
First record: P.H.Gamble 1965.                            Rec code:  A
  Abundant along E edge of cmpt 3, occasional elsewhere.

Glyceria fluitans  (L.) R.Br.                                    No:2580
Floating Sweet-grass
Compartment 3 4 5 6 7 9 10 11 20 21 22 23 80 81 82 site   Comparts:  7
  records:  . / . . / /  .  .  .  +  .  .  /  /  /   /     Quadrats:  0%
First record: LNC 1970.                                   Rec code:  A
  Common along the margins of wet ditches.

Glyceria declinata  Breb.                                        No:2585
Glaucous Sweet-grass
Compartment 3 4 5 6 7 9 10 11 20 21 22 23 80 81 82 site   Comparts:  2
  records:  . / . . . .  .  .  /  .  .  .  .  .  .   /     Quadrats:  0%
First record: SFW in present work 1982-86.                Rec code:  A
  A few specimens seen in muddy rides.
```

Origin: * = alien, > = introduced. Records: / = SFW survey, + = post-1970, o = pre-1970. Rec code: Adequately recorded, Under-recorded, Habitat under-recorded.

Table 5.9. Systematic list of vascular plants (continued).

Bromus sterilis L. No:2590
Barren Brome
Compartment 3 4 5 6 7 9 10 11 20 21 22 23 80 81 82 site Comparts: 1
records: . . . . + ... + Quadrats: 0%
First record: LNC 1970. Rec code: H
+PHG 1975 'locally frequent'.

Bromus ramosus Hudson No:2600
Hairy Brome
Compartment 3 4 5 6 7 9 10 11 20 21 22 23 80 81 82 site Comparts: 5
records: . . . . / / / / / . . . . . . / Quadrats: 0%
First record: LNC 1970. Rec code: A
Occasional in woodland.

Bromus hordeaceus agg. L. No:2610
Lop-grass
Compartment 3 4 5 6 7 9 10 11 20 21 22 23 80 81 82 site Comparts: 0
records: . . . . o Quadrats: 0%
First record: LNC 1970. Rec code: A
'Frequent in field.' Not seen.

Brachypodium sylvaticum (Hudson) Beauv. No:2620
Slender False-brome
Compartment 3 4 5 6 7 9 10 11 20 21 22 23 80 81 82 site Comparts: 12
records: / . / . / . / / / / / / / / / / Quadrats: 1%
First record: LNC 1970. Rec code: A
Common in woodland.

Elymus repens (L.) Gould No:2630
Couch-grass
Compartment 3 4 5 6 7 9 10 11 20 21 22 23 80 81 82 site Comparts: 1
records: . . . . . / . . . . / Quadrats: 0%
First record: LNC 1970. Rec code: A
One or two small patches, an arable weed.

Hordeum secalinum Schreber No:2635
Meadow Barley
Compartment 3 4 5 6 7 9 10 11 20 21 22 23 80 81 82 site Comparts: 1
records: . . . . / . . . / Quadrats: 0%
First record: SFW in present work 1982-86. Rec code: A
A small patch appeared in 1985 at SK53961277. Not seen since.

Avenula pubescens (Hudson) Dumort. No:2640
Hairy Oat-grass
Compartment 3 4 5 6 7 9 10 11 20 21 22 23 80 81 82 site Comparts: 1
records: . . . . + ... + Quadrats: 0%
First record: LNC 1970. Rec code: H
+PHG 1975 'occasional'.

Arrhenatherum elatius (L.)Beauv.ex J&C P No:2650
False Oat-grass
Compartment 3 4 5 6 7 9 10 11 20 21 22 23 80 81 82 site Comparts: 12
records: / / / / . / . . / / / / / / / / Quadrats: 3%
First record: LNC 1970. Rec code: A
Common in woodland edge situations.

Origin: * = alien, > = introduced. Records: / = SFW survey, + = post-1970, o = pre-1970. Rec code: Adequately recorded, Under-recorded, Habitat under-recorded.

Table 5.9. Systematic list of vascular plants (continued).

Trisetum flavescens (L.) Beauv. No:2660
Yellow Oat-grass
Compartment 3 4 5 6 7 9 10 11 20 21 22 23 80 81 82 site Comparts: 2
records: . . / . . . . . + ... / Quadrats: 0%
First record: LNC 1970. Rec code: H
Rare.

Deschampsia cespitosa (L.) Beauv. No:2670
Tufted Hair-grass
Compartment 3 4 5 6 7 9 10 11 20 21 22 23 80 81 82 site Comparts: 15
records: / / / / / / / / / / / / / / / / Quadrats: 41%
First record: P.H.Gamble 1965. Rec code: A
Abundant, especially in waterlogged places.

Deschampsia flexuosa (L.) Trin. No:2680
Wavy Hair-grass
Compartment 3 4 5 6 7 9 10 11 20 21 22 23 80 81 82 site Comparts: 13
records: / / / / / . + / / / / . / / / / Quadrats: 27%
First record: LNC 1970. Rec code: A
Locally abundant, an important constituent of spoil-heap and outcrop vegetation.

Aira praecox L. No:2690
Early Hair-grass
Compartment 3 4 5 6 7 9 10 11 20 21 22 23 80 81 82 site Comparts: 4
records: / o / . . . . . / . . . . . . / Quadrats: 1%
First record: LNC 1970. Rec code: A
Occasional plants in open, rocky situations.

Anthoxanthum odoratum L. No:2700
Sweet Vernal-grass
Compartment 3 4 5 6 7 9 10 11 20 21 22 23 80 81 82 site Comparts: 7
records: . / / . . . . . / / . / / . / / Quadrats: 1%
First record: LNC 1970. Rec code: A
Common in grassland.

Holcus lanatus L. No:2710
Yorkshire Fog
Compartment 3 4 5 6 7 9 10 11 20 21 22 23 80 81 82 site Comparts: 13
records: / / / / / / + . / / . / / / / / Quadrats: 8%
First record: Horwood & Gainsborough 1933. Rec code: A
Common.

Holcus mollis L. No:2720
Creeping Soft-grass
Compartment 3 4 5 6 7 9 10 11 20 21 22 23 80 81 82 site Comparts: 15
records: / / / / / / / / / / / / / / / / Quadrats: 46%
First record: LNC 1970. Rec code: A
Abundant, especially in more open woodland. Characteristic or paths beyond Poa annua zone.

Agrostis canina L. No:2730
Brown Bent-grass
Compartment 3 4 5 6 7 9 10 11 20 21 22 23 80 81 82 site Comparts: 1
records: . . . . + ... + Quadrats: 0%
First record: LNC 1970. Rec code: U
+PHG 1975 'occasional'.

Origin: * = alien, > = introduced. Records: / = SFW survey, + = post-1970, o = pre-1970. Rec code: Adequately recorded, Under-recorded, Habitat under-recorded.

Table 5.9. Systematic list of vascular plants (continued).

Agrostis vinealis Schreber No:2735
Brown Bent
Compartment 3 4 5 6 7 9 10 11 20 21 22 23 80 81 82 site Comparts: 1
records: . . . . / . . . / Quadrats: 0%
First record: SFW in present work 1982-86. Rec code: U
Occasional in pasture.

Agrostis capillaris L. No:2740
Common Bent-grass
Compartment 3 4 5 6 7 9 10 11 20 21 22 23 80 81 82 site Comparts: 14
records: / / / / / / + / / / . / / / / / Quadrats: 16%
First record: LNC 1970. Rec code: A
Common in pasture an along rides.

Agrostis stolonifera L. No:2745
Creeping Bent
Compartment 3 4 5 6 7 9 10 11 20 21 22 23 80 81 82 site Comparts: 1
records: . . . . / . . . / Quadrats: 0%
First record: SFW in present work 1982-86. Rec code: A
Around puddles in the track through cmpt 23.

Phleum pratense ssp. *pratense* L. No:2750
Timothy
Compartment 3 4 5 6 7 9 10 11 20 21 22 23 80 81 82 site Comparts: 5
records: / . / / . / . . . . . / . . . / Quadrats: 0%
First record: LNC 1970. Rec code: A
Common in the pastures, occasional beside rides and woodland edges.

Phleum pratense ssp. *bertolonii* (DC)Serb.&E.I.Nyar No:2760
Cat's-tail
Compartment 3 4 5 6 7 9 10 11 20 21 22 23 80 81 82 site Comparts: 3
records: . . . / . . . . / . . / . . . / Quadrats: 0%
First record: LNC 1970. Rec code: A
Occasional.

Alopecurus pratensis L. No:2770
Meadow Fox-tail
Compartment 3 4 5 6 7 9 10 11 20 21 22 23 80 81 82 site Comparts: 3
records: . . . . . / . . . / . / . . . / Quadrats: 0%
First record: LNC 1970. Rec code: A
Woodland edges.

Alopecurus geniculatus L. No:2780
Marsh Fox-tail
Compartment 3 4 5 6 7 9 10 11 20 21 22 23 80 81 82 site Comparts: 2
records: . . . . / + ... / Quadrats: 0%
First record: LNC 1970. Rec code: A
Along a very wet ride.

Alopecurus aequalis Sobol. No:2782
Orange Fox-tail
Compartment 3 4 5 6 7 9 10 11 20 21 22 23 80 81 82 site Comparts: 1
records: . . . . . / . . . . / Quadrats: 0%
First record: SFW in present work 1982-86. Rec code: A
Appeared on soil disturbed by excavators 1986. Not expected to persist.

Origin: * = alien, > = introduced. Records: / = SFW survey, + = post-1970, o = pre-1970. Rec code: Adequately recorded, Under-recorded, Habitat under-recorded.

Table 5.9. Systematic list of vascular plants (continued).

Phalaris arundinacea L. No:2785
Reed-grass
Compartment 3 4 5 6 7 9 10 11 20 21 22 23 80 81 82 site Comparts: 1
records: . . . . . / . . . . / Quadrats: 0%
First record: SFW in present work 1982-86. Rec code: A
A small stand grows at SK53741174.

Milium effusum L. No:2790
Wood Millet
Compartment 3 4 5 6 7 9 10 11 20 21 22 23 80 81 82 site Comparts: 7
records: / . . / . . / / / . . . / . / / Quadrats: 12%
First record: Horwood & Gainsborough 1933. Rec code: A
Locally common in woodland.

Danthonia decumbens (L.) DC No:2800
Heath grass
Compartment 3 4 5 6 7 9 10 11 20 21 22 23 80 81 82 site Comparts: 2
records: . . + ... + ... + Quadrats: 0%
First record: LNC 1970. Rec code: H
+PHG 1975 'occasional in cmpt 21'; +PHG 1976 'rare in cmpt 5'.

Molinia caerulea (L.) Moench No:2810
Purple Moor-grass
Compartment 3 4 5 6 7 9 10 11 20 21 22 23 80 81 82 site Comparts: 1
records: / . . . . / Quadrats: 0%
First record: SFW in present work 1982-86. Rec code: A
A single tuft on the bank between cmpts 21 and 3 at SK53791266.

Nardus stricta L. No:2820
Mat-grass
Compartment 3 4 5 6 7 9 10 11 20 21 22 23 80 81 82 site Comparts: 1
records: . . . . + ... + Quadrats: 0%
First record: LNC 1970. Rec code: H
+PHG 1975 'locally frequent'.

Origin: * = alien, > = introduced. Records: / = SFW survey, + = post-1970, o = pre-1970. Rec code: Adequately recorded, Under-recorded, Habitat under-recorded.

Table 5.10. Alphabetical list of vascular plants. The *Abbreviated names* are those that appear on some figures and tables. *Species number* allows cross-reference to table 5.9. *Preferred habitats* and *Layer* are decoded at the bottom of the table, see section 5.1.3 for further information. Names used in the *Flora of Leicestershire* (Primavesi & Evans 1988) are also given where they differ from those used in this report.

Scientific name	Abbrev. name	Species number	Pref. habs	Layer
Abies grandis	Abie gran	101	F	C
Acer campestre	Acer camp	453	EF	C
Acer platanoides	Acer plat	452	FE	C
Acer pseudoplatanus	Acer pseu	451	EF	C
Achillea millefolium	Achi mill	1840	GH	F
Achillea ptarmica	Achi ptar	1850	MH	F
Aegopodium podagraria	Aego poda	1110	EA	F
Aesculus hippocastanum	Aesc hipp	454	AE	C
Aethusa cynapium	Aeth cyna	1115	AR	F
Agrimonia eupatoria	Agri eupa	850	GE	F
Agrimonia procera	Agri proc	860	E	F
Agrostis canina	Agro cani	2730	HM	F
Agrostis capillaris	Agro capi	2740	GH	F
Agrostis stolonifera	Agro stol	2745	GH	F
Agrostis vinealis	Agro vine	2735	HM	F
(not distinguished from *A. canina* in P & E 1988.)				
Aira praecox	Aira prae	2690	HG	F
Ajuga reptans	Ajug rept	1630	FE	F
Alchemilla filicaulis ssp. *vestita*	Alch fili	870	GM	F
Alchemilla xanthochlora	Alch xant	880	GM	F
Alliaria petiolata	Alli peti	250	FE	F
Alnus glutinosa	Alnu glut	1282	EW	C
Alopecurus aequalis	Alop aequ	2782	WE	F
Alopecurus geniculatus	Alop geni	2780	MW	F
Alopecurus pratensis	Alop prat	2770	GH	F
Anemone apennina	Anem apen	125		F
Anemone nemorosa	Anem nemo	120	F	F
Angelica sylvestris	Ange sylv	1130	FE	F
Anthoxanthum odoratum	Anth odor	2700	GH	F
Anthriscus sylvestris	Anth sylv	1080	EF	F
Aphanes arvensis agg.	Apha arve	890	HA	F
Apium nodiflorum	Apiu nodi	1120	WE	F
Arctium minus agg.	Arct minu	1880	FE	F
Arrhenatherum elatius	Arrh elat	2650	GH	F
Arum maculatum	Arum macu	2290	F	F
Asplenium adiantum-nigrum	Aspl adia	33	S	F
Asplenium trichomanes	Aspl tric	35	SE	F
Athyrium filix-femina	Athy f-f	50	FE	F
Avenula pubescens	Aven pube	2640	GH	F
Bellis perennis	Bell pere	1830	GH	F
Betula pendula	Betu pend	1279	FH	C
Betula pubescens	Betu pube	1280	FH	C
Betula sp.	Betu sp.	1281	FH	C
Brachypodium sylvaticum	Brac sylv	2620	FE	F
Briza media	Briz medi	2560	GM	F
Bromus hordeaceus agg.	Brom hord	2610	GH	F
Bromus ramosus	Brom ramo	2600	FE	F
Bromus sterilis	Brom ster	2590	EA	F
Callitriche stagnalis	Call stag	1060	WM	F
Calluna vulgaris	Call vulg	1330	HF	S
Caltha palustris	Calt palu	110	ME	F

Habitats: Arable, Grassland, Heathland, F = woodland, W = aquatic, Marsh, Edge, Ruderal, Saxicole. **Layers**: Field, Shrub, Canopy.

Table 5.10. Alphabetical list of vascular plants (continued).

Scientific name	Abbrev. name	Species number	Pref. habs	Layer
Calystegia sepium	Caly sepi	1385	EF	F
Capsella bursa-pastoris	Caps burs	192	AR	F
Cardamine amara	Card amar	210	WE	F
Cardamine flexuosa	Card flex	220	ME	F
Cardamine hirsuta	Card hirs	230	ES	F
Cardamine pratensis	Card prat	200	MG	F
Carex caryophyllea	Care cary	2370	GH	F
Carex flacca	Care flac	2350	MG	F
Carex hirta	Care hirt	2360	MG	F
Carex laevigata	Care laev	2300	ME	F
Carex nigra	Care nigr	2380	MH	F
Carex otrubae	Care otru	2390	MW	F
Carex pallescens	Care pall	2330	MH	F
Carex panicea	Care pani	2340	MH	F
Carex pendula	Care pend	2320	FE	F
Carex remota	Care remo	2400	FE	F
Carex sylvatica	Care sylv	2310	FE	F
Carpinus betulus	Carp betu	1284	FA	C
Castanea sativa	Cast sati	1290	FE	C
Centaurea nigra	Cent nigr	1920	GH	F
Cerastium fontanum ssp. *glabrescens* (*C. f.* ssp. *triviale* in P & E 1988.)	Cera font	360	GM	F
Cerastium glomeratum	Cera glom	361	GH	F
Cerastium semidecandrum	Cera semi	364	HG	F
Chamerion angustifolium (*Epilobium angustifolium* L. in P & E 1988.)	Cham angu	1040	FE	F
Chrysosplenium oppositifolium	Chry oppo	987	FE	F
Circaea lutetiana	Circ lute	1050	FE	F
Cirsium arvense	Cirs arve	1910	GE	F
Cirsium palustre	Cirs palu	1900	MG	F
Cirsium vulgare	Cirs vulg	1890	GH	F
Conopodium majus	Cono maju	1090	GH	F
Convallaria majalis	Conv maja	2080	FE	F
Convolvulus arvensis	Conv arve	1380	AE	F
Corydalis lutea	Cory lute	185	SE	F
Corylus avellana	Cory avel	1286	FE	S
Cotoneaster sp.	Coto sp.	950	G	S
Crataegus monogyna	Crat mono	960	EF	S
Crataegus monogyna x *laevigata*	Crat x	956	FE	S
Crepis capillaris	Crep capi	2050	GE	F
Cynosurus cristatus	Cyno cris	2550	GM	F
Cytisus scoparius	Cyti scop	480	HG	S
Dactylis glomerata	Dact glom	2540	GM	F
Dactylorhiza fuchsii	Dact fuch	2270	GH	F
Dactylorhiza maculata ssp. *ericetorum* (*D. m.* (L.) Soo ssp. *maculata* in P & E 1988.)	Dact macu	2280	HM	F
Danthonia decumbens	Dant decu	2800	HG	F
Deschampsia cespitosa	Desc cesp	2670	MG	F
Deschampsia flexuosa	Desc flex	2680	HG	F
Digitalis purpurea	Digi purp	1420	FE	F

Habitats: Arable, Grassland, Heathland, F = woodland, W = aquatic, Marsh, Edge, Ruderal, Saxicole. **Layers:** Field, Shrub, Canopy.

Table 5.10. Alphabetical list of vascular plants (continued).

Scientific name	Abbrev. name	Species number	Pref. habs	Layer
Dryopteris affinis	Dryo affi	60	FE	F
(*D. borreri* Newman in P & E 1988.)				
Dryopteris carthusiana	Dryo cart	90	FH	F
Dryopteris dilatata	Dryo dila	80	FE	F
Dryopteris filix-mas	Dryo f-m	70	FE	F
Eleocharis palustris	Eleo palu	2295	MW	F
Elymus repens	Elym repe	2630	EA	F
Epilobium ciliatum	Epil cili	1010	RE	F
(*E. adenocaulon* Hausskn. in P & E 1988.)				
Epilobium hirsutum	Epil hirs	992	WM	F
Epilobium montanum	Epil mont	996	FE	F
Epilobium obscurum	Epil obsc	1020	MH	F
Epilobium palustre	Epil palu	1030	ME	F
Epilobium roseum	Epil rose	1000	EF	F
Epilobium sp.	Epil sp.	1035		F
Epipactis helleborine	Epip hell	2240	FE	F
Equisetum palustre	Equi palu	10	MW	F
Equisetum telmateia	Equi telm	15	MF	F
Erophila verna	Erop vern	197	ES	F
Euphrasia officinalis agg.	Euph offi	1520	GH	F
Fagus sylvatica	Fagu sylv	1288	FE	C
Festuca arundinacea	Fest arun	2420	ME	F
Festuca gigantea	Fest giga	2430	FE	F
Festuca ovina	Fest ovin	2460	HG	F
Festuca pratensis	Fest prat	2410	GH	F
Festuca rubra ssp. *commutata*	Fest ruco	2450	EG	F
Festuca rubra ssp. *rubra*	Fest ruru	2440	EG	F
(sspp. not distinguished in P & E 1988.)				
Filipendula ulmaria	Fili ulma	590	MW	F
Fragaria vesca	Frag vesc	830	FE	F
Frangula alnus	Fran alnu	458	FE	S
Fraxinus excelsior	Frax exce	1345	FE	C
Galeopsis ladanum	Gale lada	1585	A	F
(*G. angustifolia* Enhr. ex Hoffm. in P & E 1988.)				
Galeopsis tetrahit agg.	Gale tetr	1590	AE	F
Galium aparine	Gali apar	1710	EF	F
Galium mollugo	Gali moll	1660	EF	F
Galium palustre agg.	Gali palu	1690	MW	F
Galium saxtile	Gali saxa	1680	HG	F
Galium sp.	Gali sp.	1712	M	F
Galium uliginosum	Gali ulig	1700	MH	F
Galium verum	Gali veru	1670	GH	F
Genista tinctoria	Geni tinc	460	GE	F
Geranium dissectum	Gera diss	438	AE	F
Geranium molle	Gera moll	439	ER	F
Geranium robertianum	Gera robe	440	FE	F
Geum urbanum	Geum urba	840	FE	F
Glechoma hederacea	Glec hede	1600	FE	F
Glyceria declinata	Glyc decl	2585	MW	F
Glyceria fluitans	Glyc flui	2580	WE	F
Gnaphalium uliginosum	Gnap ulig	1820	MG	F
(*Filaginella uliginosa* (L.) Opiz in P & E 1988.)				
Hedera helix	Hede heli	1065	FE	F
Heracleum sphondylium	Hera spho	1140	EF	F

Habitats: Arable, Grassland, Heathland, F = woodland, W = aquatic, Marsh, Edge, Ruderal, Saxicole. **Layers**: Field, Shrub, Canopy.

Table 5.10. Alphabetical list of vascular plants (continued).

Scientific name	Abbrev. name	Species number	Pref. habs	Layer
Hieracium diaphanum	Hier diap	2001	EG	F
Hieracium maculatum	Hier macu	2000	EG	F
Hieracium perpropinquum	Hier perp	2030	EF	F
Hieracium rigens	Hier rige	2035	AF	F
Hieracium salticola	Hier salt	2002	EF	F
Hieracium sp.	Hier sp.	1999	EF	F
Hieracium strumosum	Hier stru	2010	EF	F
Hieracium vagum	Hier vagu	2004	EF	F
Hieracium vulgatum	Hier vulg	2003	ER	F
Holcus lanatus	Holc lana	2710	GH	F
Holcus mollis	Holc moll	2720	HG	F
Hordeum secalinum	Hord seca	2635	GM	F
Hyacinthoides non-scripta	Hyac nons	2100	F	F
Hypericum hirsutum	Hype hirs	330	GE	F
Hypericum humifusum	Hype humi	310	GH	F
Hypericum perforatum	Hype perf	290	GH	F
Hypericum pulchrum	Hype pulc	320	FE	F
Hypericum tetrapterum	Hype tetr	300	MH	F
Hypochaeris radicata (*Hypochoeris* in P & E 1988.)	Hypo radi	1950	GH	F
Ilex aquifolium	Ilex aqui	456	FE	S
Impatiens glandulifera	Impa glan	449	EW	F
Iris pseudacorus	Iris pseu	2210	WE	F
Jasione montana	Jasi mont	1655	G	F
Juncus acutiflorus	Junc acut	2150	MH	F
Juncus articulatus	Junc arti	2160	MH	F
Juncus bufonius	Junc bufo	2120	ME	F
Juncus conglomeratus	Junc cong	2140	MH	F
Juncus effusus	Junc effu	2130	MW	F
Juncus inflexus	Junc infl	2125	MH	F
Juncus kochii (not distinguished from *J. bulbosus* in P & E 1988.)	Junc koch	2121	ME	F
Lamiastrum galeobdolon	Lami gale	1570	FE	F
Lamium album	Lami albu	1580	EG	F
Lapsana communis	Laps comm	1940	EA	F
Larix decidua	Lari deci	104	FE	C
Lathyrus montanus	Lath mont	580	HG	F
Lathyrus pratensis	Lath prat	570	GH	F
Leontodon autumnalis	Leon autu	1960	GH	F
Leucanthemum vulgare	Leuc vulg	1870	GH	F
Listera ovata	List ovat	2250	FE	F
Lolium perenne ssp. *multiflorum* (*L. multiflorum* Lam. in P & E 1988.)	Loli pemu	2480	GM	F
Lolium perenne ssp. *perenne* (*L. perenne* L. in P & E 1988.)	Loli pepe	2470	GM	F
Lonicera periclymenum	Loni peri	1720	FE	F
Lotus corniculatus	Lotu corn	530	GH	F
Lotus uliginosus	Lotu ulig	540	MH	F
Lunaria annua	Luna annu	195	ER	F
Luzula campestris	Luzu camp	2190	GH	F
Luzula multiflora	Luzu mult	2200	HM	F
Luzula pilosa	Luzu pilo	2170	FE	F
Luzula sylvatica	Luzu sylv	2180	FE	F
Lychnis flos-cuculi	Lych flos	350	ME	F

Habitats: Arable, Grassland, Heathland, F = woodland, W = aquatic, Marsh, Edge, Ruderal, Saxicole. **Layers**: Field, Shrub, Canopy.

Table 5.10. Alphabetical list of vascular plants (continued).

Scientific name	Abbrev. name	Species number	Pref. habs	Layer
Lysimachia nemorum	Lysi nemo	1340	FE	F
Lysimachia punctata	Lysi punc	1342	RE	F
Malus sylvestris	Malu sylv	980	EF	S
Matricaria matricarioides	Matr matr	1860	RA	F
(*Chamomilla suaveolens* (Pursh) Rydb. in P & E 1988.)				
Melampyrum pratense	Mela prat	1510	FE	F
Melica uniflora	Meli unif	2570	FE	F
Mentha aquatica	Ment aqua	1530	WE	F
Mentha sp.	Ment sp.	1535	WE	F
Mercurialis perennis	Merc pere	1160	FE	F
Milium effusum	Mili effu	2790	FE	F
Moehringia trinervia	Moeh trin	430	FE	F
Moenchia erecta	Moen erec	405	H	F
Molinia caerulea	Moli caer	2810	HG	F
Muscari neglectum	Musc negl	2105	E	F
Mycelis muralis	Myce mura	1965	SE	F
Myosotis arvensis	Myos arve	1370	FE	F
Myosotis laxa ssp. *caespitosa*	Myos laxa	1360	ME	F
Myosoton aquaticum	Myos aqua	367	EW	F
Narcissus sp.	Narc sp.	2205	G	F
Nardus stricta	Nard stri	2820	HM	F
Nasturtium officinale	Nast offi	240	WM	F
Ophioglossum vulgatum	Ophi vulg	20	GH	F
Orchis mascula	Orch masc	2260	FE	F
Ornithogalum umbellatum	Orni umbe	2090	FE	F
Oxalis acetosella	Oxal acet	450	FE	F
Pastinaca sativa	Past sati	1135	G	F
Pedicularis sylvatica	Pedi sylv	1490	HM	F
Phalaris arundinacea	Phal arun	2785	WE	F
Phleum pratense ssp. *bertolonii*	Phle prbe	2760	GE	F
Phleum pratense ssp. *pratense*	Phle prpr	2750	GE	F
Phyllitis scolopendrium	Phyl scol	40	FE	F
Picea abies	Pice abie	103	FE	C
Pilosella officinarum	Pilo offi	2040	ER	F
Pimpinella major	Pimp majo	1100	EG	F
Pinus nigra var. *maritima*	Pinu nigr	106	FE	C
(varieties not distinguished in P & E 1988.)				
Pinus sylvestris	Pinu sylv	105	FE	C
Plantago lanceolata	Plan lanc	1650	GH	F
Plantago major	Plan majo	1640	GH	F
Poa annua	Poa annu	2500	GA	F
Poa nemoralis	Poa nemo	2510	F	F
Poa pratensis	Poa prat	2520	GM	F
Poa trivialis	Poa triv	2530	GM	F
Polygonatum multiflorum	Poly mult	2085	FE	F
Polygonum amphibium	Poly amph	1175	ME	F
Polygonum aviculare agg.	Poly avic	1170	AR	F
Polygonum hydropiper	Poly hydr	1200	EF	F
Polygonum lapathifolium	Poly lapa	1190	AE	F
Polygonum persicaria	Poly pers	1180	AE	F
Polypodium interjectum	Poly inte	100	FE	F
Polystichum aculeatum	Poly acul	96	FE	F

Habitats: Arable, Grassland, Heathland, F = woodland, W = aquatic, Marsh, Edge, Ruderal, Saxicole. **Layers**: Field, Shrub, Canopy.

Table 5.10. Alphabetical list of vascular plants (continued).

Scientific name	Abbrev. name	Species number	Pref. habs	Layer
Polystichum setiferum	Poly seti	94	FE	F
Populus alba	Popu alba	1298	AE	C
Populus canescens	Popu cane	1299	FE	C
Populus tremula	Popu trem	1300	FE	C
Populus x *canadensis*	Popu xcan	1305	FE	C
Potentilla anserina	Pote anse	810	MG	F
Potentilla erecta	Pote erec	820	HM	F
Potentilla reptans	Pote rept	825	EG	F
Potentilla sterilis	Pote ster	800	GH	F
Primula veris	Prim veri	1336	GM	F
Primula vulgaris	Prim vulg	1338	FE	F
Prunella vulgaris	Prun vulg	1540	GH	F
Prunus avium	Prun aviu	940	FE	C
Prunus domestica ssp. *insititia*	Prun dome	937	EF	S
Prunus laurocerasus	Prun laur	945	FE	S
Prunus spinosa	Prun spin	935	FE	S
Pseudotsuga taxifolia	Pseu taxi	102	F	C
Pteridium aquilinum	Pter aqui	30	HF	F
Pulicaria dysenterica	Puli dyse	1810	ME	F
Quercus cerris	Quer cerr	1291	FE	C
Quercus coccinea	Quer cocc	1296		C
Quercus maxima	Quer maxi	1295		C
Quercus petraea	Quer petr	1294	FE	C
Quercus petraea x *robur*	Quer x	1293	FE	C
Quercus robur	Quer robu	1292	FE	C
Quercus sp.	Quer sp.	1297	FE	C
Ranunculus acris	Ranu acri	130	GH	F
Ranunculus auricomus	Ranu auri	150	FE	F
Ranunculus bulbosus	Ranu bulb	145	GM	F
Ranunculus ficaria	Ranu fica	180	FG	F
Ranunculus flammula	Ranu flam	160	MW	F
Ranunculus repens	Ranu repe	140	GH	F
Ranunculus sceleratus	Ranu scel	170	WE	F
Ranunculus trichophyllus	Ranu tric	175	W	F
Rhinanthus minor	Rhin mino	1500	GH	F
Rhododendron ponticum	Rhod pont	1327	FA	S
Ribes nigrum	Ribe nigr	990	FE	S
Ribes rubrum	Ribe rubr	989	FE	S
Ribes uva-crispa	Ribe uvac	991	FE	S
Rorippa palustris	Rori palu	245	EW	F
(*R. islandica* (Oeder) Borbas in P & E 1988.)				
Rosa arvensis	Rosa arve	902	EF	S
Rosa canina agg.	Rosa cani	904	EF	S
Rosa tomentosa	Rosa tome	920	EF	S
Rubus bloxamianus	Rubu blox	757	FE	F
Rubus caesius	Rubu caes	650	F	S
Rubus cardiophyllus	Rubu card	725	FE	F
Rubus dasyphyllus	Rubu dasy	768	FE	F
Rubus diversus	Rubu dive	746	FE	F
Rubus eboracensis	Rubu ebor	778	FE	F
Rubus echinatus	Rubu echi	759	FE	F
Rubus flexuosus	Rubu flex	760	FE	F
Rubus fruticosus agg.	Rubu frut	700	FE	F
Rubus hylocharis	Rubu hylo	769	FE	F

Habitats: Arable, Grassland, Heathland, F = woodland, W = aquatic, Marsh, Edge, Ruderal, Saxicole. **Layers**: Field, Shrub, Canopy.

Table 5.10. Alphabetical list of vascular plants (continued).

Scientific name	Abbrev. name	Species number	Pref. habs	Layer
Rubus hystrix	Rubu hyst	790	FE	F
Rubus idaeus	Rubu idae	600	FE	S
Rubus lindebergii	Rubu linb	728	FE	F
Rubus lindleianus	Rubu linl	717	FE	F
Rubus pallidus	Rubu pall	762	FE	F
Rubus platyacanthus	Rubu plat	719	FE	F
Rubus polyanthemus	Rubu poly	730	FE	F
Rubus pyramidalis	Rubu pyra	721	FE	F
Rubus rudis	Rubu rudi	764	FE	F
Rubus rufescens	Rubu rufe	766	FE	F
Rubus watsonii	Rubu wats	773	FE	F
Rumex acetosa	Rume acet	1220	GM	F
Rumex acetosella agg.	Rume acla	1210	HG	F
Rumex conglomeratus	Rume cong	1260	MW	F
Rumex crispus	Rume cris	1230	GE	F
Rumex obtusifolius	Rume obtu	1240	EG	F
Rumex sanguineus	Rume sang	1250	FE	F
Rumex sp.	Rume sp.	1265		F
Sagina apetala	Sagi apet	410	HG	F
Sagina procumbens	Sagi proc	420	RS	F
Salix aurita	Sali auri	1319	EF	S
Salix aurita x *cinerea*	Sali xac	1322	EW	S
Salix caprea	Sali capr	1312	EF	S
Salix cinerea ssp. *oleifolia*	Sali cine	1315	EW	S
Sambucus nigra	Samb nigr	1715	FE	S
Sanguisorba officinalis	Sang offi	900	MG	F
Sanicula europaea	Sani euro	1070	FE	F
Scrophularia auriculata	Scro auri	1410	WM	F
Scrophularia nodosa	Scro nodo	1400	FE	F
Scutellaria galericulata	Scut gale	1610	WE	F
Senecio aquaticus	Sene aqua	1770	ME	F
Senecio jacobaea	Sene jaco	1760	GH	F
Senecio sylvaticus	Sene sylv	1780	HG	F
Senecio vulgaris	Sene vulg	1790	AE	F
Serratula tinctoria	Serr tinc	1930	HG	F
Silene dioica	Sile dioi	340	FE	F
Solanum dulcamara	Sola dulc	1390	WE	F
Solidago virgaurea	Soli virg	1825	RH	F
Sonchus arvensis	Sonc arve	1970	AE	F
Sonchus asper	Sonc aspe	1990	AE	F
Sonchus oleraceus	Sonc oler	1980	AE	F
Sorbus aucuparia	Sorb aucu	970	FE	C
Sorbus intermedia	Sorb inte	976	EF	C
Stachys officinalis	Stac offi	1560	HG	F
Stachys sylvatica	Stac sylv	1550	EF	F
Stellaria alsine	Stel alsi	400	ME	F
Stellaria graminea	Stel gram	390	GH	F
Stellaria holostea	Stel holo	380	FE	F
Stellaria media	Stel medi	370	FE	F
Succisa pratensis	Succ prat	1750	GH	F
Tamus communis	Tamu comm	2230	EF	F
Taraxacum section Erythrosperma	Tara eryt	2070	G	F
Taraxacum section Vulgaria	Tara vulg	2060	G	F

Habitats: Arable, Grassland, Heathland, F = woodland, W = aquatic, Marsh, Edge, Ruderal, Saxicole. **Layers**: Field, Shrub, Canopy.

Table 5.10. Alphabetical list of vascular plants (continued).

Scientific name	Abbrev. name	Species number	Pref. habs	Layer
Taxus baccata	Taxu bacc	107	FE	C
Teesdalia nudicaulis	Tees nudi	190	R	F
Teucrium scorodonia	Teuc scor	1620	HG	F
Tilia cordata	Tili cord	433	FE	C
Tilia x *europaea* (*T.* x *vulgaris* Hayne in P & E 1988.)	Tili x	436	AE	C
Torilis japonica	Tori japo	1150	EG	F
Trifolium dubium	Trif dubi	490	GM	F
Trifolium medium	Trif medi	510	GH	F
Trifolium pratense	Trif prat	520	GE	F
Trifolium repens	Trif repe	500	GH	F
Tripleurospermum inodorum (*Matricaria perforata* Merat in P & E 1988.)	Trip inod	1855	AE	F
Trisetum flavescens	Tris flav	2660	GE	F
Tritonia x *crocosmiflora*	Trit xcro	2220	RE	F
Tussilago farfara	Tuss farf	1800	MG	F
Ulex europaeus	Ulex euro	470	HG	S
Ulex gallii	Ulex gall	475	HG	S
Ulmus glabra	Ulmu glab	1275	AE	C
Umbilicus rupestris	Umbi rupe	983	R	F
Urtica dioica	Urti dioi	1270	FE	F
Vaccinium myrtillus	Vacc myrt	1332	HF	S
Valeriana dioica	Vale dioi	1740	MF	F
Valeriana officinalis	Vale offi	1730	MF	F
Veronica arvensis	Vero arve	1480	AE	F
Veronica beccabunga	Vero becc	1430	WE	F
Veronica chamaedrys	Vero cham	1460	GH	F
Veronica hederifolia ssp. *hederifolia* (ssp. not recognised in P & E 1988.)	Vero hede	1485	AR	F
Veronica montana	Vero mont	1450	FE	F
Veronica officinalis	Vero offi	1440	HG	F
Veronica serpyllifolia	Vero serp	1470	GH	F
Viburnum opulus	Vibu opul	1717	FE	S
Vicia cracca	Vici crac	550	EG	F
Vicia sepium	Vici sepi	560	EG	F
Viola canina	Viol cani	280	GW	F
Viola reichenbachiana	Viol reic	270	FE	F
Viola riviniana	Viol rivi	260	FE	F
Viola sp.	Viol sp.	285	FE	F
Vulpia bromoides	Vulp brom	2490	ER	F

Habitats: Arable, Grassland, Heathland, F = woodland, W = aquatic, Marsh, Edge, Ruderal, Saxicole. **Layers**: Field, Shrub, Canopy.

Table 5.11. Alphabetical list of bryophytes. The species numbers are those of Corley & Hill 1981. For a full explanation see section 5.2.2.

Liverworts

Aneura pinguis (L.) Dum. 15/1
First record: Horwood 1909.
Latest record: Sowter 1941.

Barbilophozia attenuata (Mart.) Loeske. 26/5
Only record: Sowter 1969.

B. barbata (Schmid ex. Schreb.) Loeske 26/8
Only record: [*Lophozia barbata* (Schmid.) Dum.] Sowter 1941.

Calypogeia arguta Nees & Mont. 69/8
First record: [*Kantia arguta*] Horwood 1909.
Latest record: Sowter 1941.

C. fissa (L.) Raddi. 69/5
Only record: Sowter 1941.

Cephalozia bicuspidata (L.) Dum. 59/1a
First record: Mott 1886.
Latest record: Sowter 1941.

Cephaloziella divaricata (Sm.) Schiffn. 58/6
First record: [*Cephalozia byssacea* Dum.] Coleman in Mott 1886.
Latest record: [*C. starkii* (Funck.) Schiffn.] Sowter 1941.

Chiloscyphus polyanthos (L.) Corda. 49/1
First record: Reader in Mott 1886.
Latest record: Sowter 1941.

Conocephalum conicum (L.) Dum. 6/1
First record: Horwood 1909.
Latest record: Sowter 1941.

Diplophyllum albicans (L.) Dum. 54/1
First record: Coleman and Reader in Mott 1886.
Latest record: Sowter 1941.

Frullania tamarisci (L.) Dum. 78/2
First record: Horwood 1909.
Latest record: Sowter 1941 'Slate pits, extinct'.

Lepidozia reptans Dum. 67/1
Only record: Mott 1886.

Lophocolea bidentata (L.) Dum. 48/1
L. cuspidata (Nees) Limpr. 48/2
Only record: SFW/DWB in present work 1984-87.
These very similar spp. were not always distinguished. They are collectively abundant on soil and rotting wood.

L. heterophylla (Schrad.) Dum. 48/4
Only record: SFW/DWB in present work 1984-87.

Table 5.11. Alphabetical list of bryophytes (continued).

Lophozia bicrenata (Schmid. ex Hoffm.) Dum. 28/10
First record: [*Jungermannia bicrenata* Lindb.] Bloxam in Mott 1886.
Latest record: Sowter 1941.

Lophozia ventricosa (Dicks.) Dum. 28/1a
First record: Horwood 1909.
Latest record: SFW/DWB in present work 1984-87.
On slate spoil heaps.

Marchantia polymorpha L. 9/1
Only record: SFW/DWB in present work 1984-87.
Found only once, on soil in cmpt. 9.

Nardia scalaris (Schrad.) Gray 39/2
Only record: Horwood 1909.

Pellia endiviifolia (Dicks) Dum. 18/3
Only record: [*Pellia endiviaefolia*] Horwood 1909.

P. epiphylla (L.) Dum. 18/1
First record: Horwood 1909.
Latest record: SFW/DWB in present work 1984-87.
Common on stream banks.

Porella platyphylla (L.) Pfeiff. 77/3
Only record: Bloxam in Mott 1886.

Ptilidium ciliare (L.) Hampe. 72/1
First record: Sowter 1941.
Latest record: SFW/DWB in present work 1984-87.
Among slate spoil in cmpt 20.

Radula complanata Dum. 75/1
Only record: Mott 1886.

Mosses

Aloina aloides (Schultz) Kindb. var. *ambigua* 41/3b
Only record: [*Barbula ambigua* B. & S.] Bloxam in Mott 1886.

A. rigida (Hedw.) Limpr. 41/2
Only record: [*Tortula rigida* Schrad.] Jackson 1905.

Amblystegium serpens (Hedw.) B. S. & G. 141/1a
Only record: SFW/DWB in present work 1984-87.
On soil.

A. tenax (Hedw.) C.Jens. 141/3
First record: Reader in Mott 1886 'in brook'.
Latest record: [*Amblystegium tenax* (Hedw.) Dix. comb. nov. (*A. irriguum* B & S)] Sowter 1941.

A. varium (Hedw.) Lindb. 141/4
Only record: D.W.Ballard 1985.
On wood-bank in shade.

Atrichum undulatum (Hedw.) P. Beauv. 8/3a
Only record: SFW/DWB in present work 1984-87.
Common on damp soil.

Table 5.11. Alphabetical list of bryophytes (continued).

Aulocomnium androgynum (Hedw.) Schwaegr. 96/3
Only record: SFW/DWB in present work 1984-87.
On rotting logs.

Barbula cylindrica (Tayl.) Schimp. 49/20
First record: Reader in Mott 1886.
Latest record: Horwood 1909.

B. rigidula (Hedw.) Mitt. 49/14
Only record: Sowter 1941 'Slate quarry'.

Bartramia ithyphylla Brid. 102/4
Only record: Sowter 1941 'Slate pits, extinct'.

B. pomiformis Hedw. 102/2
First record: Coleman in Mott 1886.
Latest record: Sowter 1941 'Slate pits'.

Brachythecium albicans Neck. 150/1
Only record: Bloxam in Mott 1886 'Slate quarry'.

B. glareosum (Spruce) Br. Eur. 150/2
Only record: Sowter 1941.

B. plumosum (Hedw.) Br. Eur. 150/13
Only record: D.W.Ballard 1985-87.

B. rivulare Br. Eur. 150/7
Only record: D.W.Ballard 1985.
On trunk of fallen tree.

B. rutabulum (Hedw.) Br. Eur. 150/6
Only record: SFW/DWB in present work 1984-87.
Very common on stumps, twigs, etc.

Bryum capillare Hedw. 89/20
Only record: SFW/DWB in present work 1984-87.

Campylopus paradoxus Wils. 34/6
Only record: D.W.Ballard 1984.
Around outcrops.

Ceratodon purpureus (Hedw.) Brid. 21/1a
Only record: SFW/DWB in present work 1984-87.
On soil.

Cirriphyllum piliferum (Hedw.) Grout 153/1
Only record: D.W.Ballard 1985-87.

Ctenidium molluscum (Hedw.) Mitt. 170/1a
Only record: [*Hypnum molluscum*] Horwood 1909.

Dicranella heteromalla (Hedw.) Schimp. 28/10
Only record: SFW/DWB in present work 1984-87.
Abundant on tree bases and on the ground.

D. varia (Hedw.) Schimp. 28/7
Only record: D.W.Ballard 1985-87.

Dicranoweisia cirrata (Hedw.) Lindb. ex Milde 29/1
Only record: D.W.Ballard 1985-87.
On trunks and low branches.

Table 5.11. Alphabetical list of bryophytes (continued).

Dicranum majus Sm. 32/6
Only record: Sowter 1941.

D. montanum Hedw. 32/12
Only record: D.W.Ballard 1985-87.

D. scoparium Hedw. 32/5
Only record: SFW/DWB in present work 1984-87.
Locally abundant on slate spoil and heathy places.

Eurhynchium praelongum (Hedw.) Br. Eur. 155/5a
Only record: SFW/DWB in present work 1984-87.
Common on the ground.

Fissidens incurvus Starke ex Roehl. 37/3
Only record: Sowter 1941.

F. taxifolius Hedw. 37/14a
Only record: SFW/DWB in present work 1984-87.
On wet soil.

Funaria hygrometrica Hedw. 71/1
Only record: D.W.Ballard 1985-87.
On bonfire-sites.

F. muhlenbergii Turn. 71/2
Only record: [*Funaria calcarea* Wahl.] Sowter 1941.

Grimmia ovalis (Hedw.) Lindb. 64/9
First record: [*Grimmia ovata* (W. & M.)] Bloxam in Mott 1886.
'Slate pits'.
Last record: Sowter 1945 'extinct'.

Hedwigia ciliata (Hedw.) P.Beauv. 112/1
First record: Horwood 1909.
Latest record: Sowter 1941 'extinct'.

Homalothecium lutescens (Hedw.) Robins. 149/2
Only record: [*Camptothecium lutescens* B. & S.] Sowter 1941
'Slate pits'.

H. sericeum (Hedw.) Br. Eur. 149/1
Only record: D.W.Ballard 1985-87.

Hylocomium splendens (Hedw.) Br. Eur. 175/4
Only record: Jackson 1905.

Hypnum cupressiforme Hedw. 168/3a
First record: Bloxam 1831.
Latest record: D.W.Ballard 1987.
Common everywhere.

H. cupressiforme Hedw. var. *lacunosum* Brid. 168/3c
Only record: [*Hypnum cupressiforme* L. var. *elatum* B. & S.]
Sowter 1941.

H. cupressiforme Hedw. var. *resupinatum* (Tayl.) Schimp. 168/3b
Only record: D.W.Ballard 1985-87.

Table 5.11. Alphabetical list of bryophytes (continued).

Hypnum jutlandicum Holmen & Warncke 168/5
First record: ? [*H. denticulatum*] Potter 1842; or [*H. cupressiforme* var. *ericetorum* B. & S.] Sowter 1941.
Latest record: D.W.Ballard 1985-87.

H. mammilatum (Brid.) Loeske 168/4
Only record: D.W.Ballard 1985-87.

Isopterygium elegans (Brid.) Lindb. 161/2
First record: Sowter 1972.
Latest record: SFW/DWB in present work 1984-87.
On tree bases.

Isothecium myosuroides Brid. 147/2a
First record: [*Eurhynchium myosuroides* Schp.] Coleman in Mott 1886.
Latest record: SFW/DWB in present work 1984-87.
On shaded rock.

Leucobryum glaucum (Hedw.) Angstr. 36/1
First record: Sowter 1941
Latest record: SFW/DWB in present work 1984-87.
A few depauperate plants on the ground in cmpt 20.

Mnium hornum Hedw. 91/1
Only record: SFW/DWB in present work 1984-87.
Generally abundant on soil, rocks and tree bases.

Orthodontium lineare Schwaegr. 83/1
Only record: SFW/DWB in present work 1984-87.
Abundant on tree bases. Recent colonist from the southern hemisphere.

Philonotis fontana (Hedw.) Brid. 105/5
Only record: Sowter 1941.

Plagiomnium affine (Funck) Kop. 94/2
Only record: [*Mnium affine* Bland.] Sowter 1941.

P. rostratum (Schrad.) Kop. 94/7
Only record: D.W.Ballard 1985-87.

P. undulatum (Hedw.) Kop. 94/6
Only record: SFW/DWB in present work 1984-87.
Common on damp shady ground.

Plagiothecium denticulatum (Hedw.) Br. Eur. 159/3a
First record: Bloxam 1831.
Latest record: D.W.Ballard 1985-87.

P. nemorale (Mitt.) Jaeg. 159/10
Only record: [*P. sylvaticum* (Brid.) B., S. & G.] Sowter 1969.

P. undulatum (Hedw.) Br. Eur. 159/11
Only record: Jackson 1905.

Pleurozium schreberi (Brid.) Mitt. 174/1
Only record: [*Hypnum schreberi* Willd.] Sowter 1941.

Pogonatum aloides (Hedw.) P. Beauv. 6/2a
Only record: [*Polytrichum aloides* Hedw.] Sowter 1941.

Table 5.11. Alphabetical list of bryophytes (continued).

Pogonatum urnigerum (Hedw.) P.Beauv. 6/3
Only record: D.W.Ballard 1985-87.

Pohlia nutans (Hedw.) Lindb. 85/4
Only record: SFW/DWB in present work 1984-87.

P. proligera (Kindb. ex Breidl.) Lindb. ex Arnell 85/10
Only record: [*Pohlia annotina* (Hedw.) Loeske.] Sowter 1969 'Amongst slate debris'.

Polytrichum formosum Hedw. 5/3
Only record: SFW/DWB in present work 1984-87.
On thin, well-drained soil.

P. juniperinum Hedw. 5/7
First record: Jackson 1905.
Latest record: SFW/DWB in present work 1984-87.
In exposed sites on thin, acid soil.

P. piliferum Hedw. 5/6
Only record: SFW/DWB in present work 1984-87.
In similar sites to the previous species.

Pottia starkeana (Hedw.) C.Muell. ssp. *minutula* (Schleich. ex Schwaegr.) 45/2d
Only record: [*Pottia minutula* Furnr.] Jackson 1905.

Pseudoscleropodium purum (Limpr.) Fleisch. 151/1
Only record: D.W.Ballard 1985.
Bank of quarry, among grass.

Ptychomitrium polyphyllum Fuern. 67/1
First record: Bloxam in Mott 1886.
Latest record: Sowter 1941 'Slate pits, extinct'.

Racomitrium aciculare (Hedw.) Brid. 66/2
First record: [*Rhacomitrium aciculare* Brid.] Bloxam in Mott 1886.
Latest record: Sowter 1941 'Slate pits, extinct'.

R. canescens (Hedw.) Brid. 66/9a
First record: [*Rhacomitrium canescens* Brid.] Coleman in Mott 1886.
Latest record: Sowter 1941 'Slate pits, extinct'.

R. lanuginosum (Hedw.) Brid. 66/8
First record: [*Trichostomum lanuginosum* Hedw.] Bloxam in Potter 1842 'slate pits'.
Latest record: Sowter 1941 'slate pits'.

Rhizomnium punctatum (Hedw.) Kop. 93/1
Only record: SFW/DWB in present work 1984-87.
On shady stream-banks.

Rhynchostegium confertum (Dicks.) Br. Eur. 154/4
Only record: D.W.Ballard 1985.
On trunk of fallen birch.

Rhynchostegium riparioides (Hedw.) C. Jens. 154/1
Only record: D.W.Ballard 1987.
Bank of stream, cmpt 9.

Table 5.11. Alphabetical list of bryophytes (continued).

Schistidium apocarpum (Hedw.) Br. Eur. 63/4a
Only record: SFW/DWB in present work 1984-87.
On top of stone wall.

Sphagnum capillifolium (Ehrh.) Hedw. 1/12
Only record: [*S. acutifolium* Ehrh.] Sowter 1941.

Tetraphis pellucida Hedw. 3/1
Only record: SFW/DWB in present work 1984-87.
On rotten stumps.

Thuidium tamariscinum (Hedw.) Br. Eur. 137/2
First record: Hesselgreaves 1970.
Latest record: SFW/DWB in present work 1984-87.
Uncommon, on soil.

Tortula muralis Hedw. 40/8a
Only record: SFW/DWB in present work 1984-87.
On a stone wall.

Ulota crispa (Hedw.) Brid. 111/3a
First record: Coleman in Mott 1886.
Latest record: Sowter 1941 'extinct'.

Table 5.12. Alphabetical list of lichens. Refer to section 5.3.2 for a full explanation.

Acarospora fuscata (Nyl.) Arnold
Only record: A. Fletcher 1989-90. Site B13.
Common on well-lit acid rocks.

Baeomyces rufus (Huds.) Rebent.
Only record: Hawksworth 1966.
Common in Charnwood Forest.

Buellia griseovirens (Turner ex Borrer ex Sm.) Almb.
Only record: A. Fletcher 1989-90. Site C3.
On stumps.

Caloplaca citrina (Hoffm.) Th.Fr.
Only record: Hawksworth 1966.
Very common on mortar, cement, etc.

Candelariella vitellina (Hoffm.) Mull.Arg.
Only record: Hawksworth 1966.
Common on mortar, cement and tree-bases.

Cetraria chlorophylla (Willd.) Vainio
First record: Hawksworth 1967.
Latest record: A. Fletcher 1989-90. Sites B3, B9, B10.
On stumps and bark, well-lit.

Chaenotheca ferruginea (Turner ex Sm.) Mig.
Only record: A. Fletcher 1989-90. Sites B1, B7, C3.
On large ash and lime in crevices, fertile; possibly an old woodland indicator, now spreading rapidly in the county.

Cladonia caespiticia (Pers.) Florke
Only record: Horwood 1904.
A doubtful record, possibly a mis-identified specimen of *C. coniocraea*.

C. cervicornis (Ach.) Flotow
Only record: Hawksworth 1967.
Common in Charnwood Forest on rocks.

C. chlorophaea (Florke ex Sommerf.) Sprengel
Only record: Hawksworth 1966.
Common eveywhere.

C. coccifera (L.) Willd.
Only record: Fletcher 1989-90. Site B13.
Common acid heath species.

C. coniocraea auct.
First record: Hawksworth 1969.
Latest record: Fletcher 1989-90. Site C3.
Common on stumps.

C. digitata (L.) Hoffm.
Only record: Fletcher 1989-90. Sites B3, B10, C3.
Very common, especially on stumps and acid bark.

C. fimbriata (L.) Fr.
First record: Hawksworth 1966.
Latest record: Fletcher 1989-90. Site C3.
On stumps.

Table 5.12. Alphabetical list of lichens (continued).

Cladonia furcata (Huds.) Schrader
Only record: Fletcher 1989-90. Site B13.
Common heath species.

C. macilenta Hoffm.
First record: Hawksworth 1966.
Latest record: Fletcher 1989-90. Sites B2, B8, B9, C3.
Common on stumps and tree bases.

C. ochrochlora Florke
Only record: Fletcher 1989-90. Site C3.
On stumps and tree bases. Frequent but overlooked as *C. coniocraea*.

C. parasitica (Hoffm.) Hoffm.
Only record: Fletcher 1989-90. Site B8.
Rare in county, on stumps.

C. polydactyla (Florke) Sprengel
First record: Hawksworth 1967.
Latest record: Fletcher 1989-90. Sites B3, B10.
Common bark and stump species.

?*C. rangiferina* (L) Wigg.
Only record: Horwood 1909.
Doubtful determination; Swithland Wood is well outside present range of this sp.

C. subulata (L.) Wigg.
Only record: Hawksworth 1967.

C. uncialis ssp. *biuncialis* (Hoffm.) Choisy
First record: Hawksworth 1967.
Latest record: Fletcher 1989-90. Site B13.
Rare Charnwood speciality, on acid, wet heaths; here on spoil heap.

Coelocaulon aculeatum (Schreber) Link
Only record: Fletcher 1989-90. Site B13.
Acid heathland species, confined in county to Charnwood Forest.

Diploschistes scruposus (Schreber) Norman
Only record: Hawksworth 1966.
On rocks in Charnwood Forest.

Gyalideopsis anastomosans P.James & Vezda
Only record: Fletcher 1989-90. Site C1.
On shaded hazel, old forest species in Leicestershire.

Huilia tuberculosa (Sm.) P.James
First record: Hawksworth 1967.
Latest record: Fletcher 1989-90. Site B13.
Common acid rock species.

Hypocenomyce scalaris (Ach.) Choisy
First record: Davey & Dove 1972.
Latest record: Fletcher 1989-90. Sites B3, B9, C3.
Common on stumps.

Hypogymnia physodes (L.) Nyl.
First record: Davey & Dove 1972.
Latest record: Fletcher 1989-90. Sites B3, B10, C3.
Very common, acid bark and stumps.

Table 5.12. Alphabetical list of lichens (continued).

Lecanactis abietina (Ach.) Korber
Only record: Fletcher 1989-90. Sites B5, B6, B7.
Rare, old forest species, especially in light shade.

?*Lecanora allophana* (Ach.) Nyl.
Only record: Horwood 1909.
Not correctly recorded from Britain. Probably *L. dispersa*.

L. atra (Huds.) Ach.
Only record: Hawksworth 1966.
Common on acid rocks in Leicestershire.

L. conizaeoides Nyl. ex Crombie
First record: Hawksworth 1966.
Latest record: Fletcher 1989-90. Sites B1, B6, B7, C3.
Common on all bark, rarer on rock.

L. expallens Ach.
Only record: Fletcher 1989-90. Site B11.
Common on bark.

L. soralifera (Suza) Rasanen
Only record: Hawksworth 1966.

Lecidea orosthea (Ach.) Ach.
Only record: Fletcher 1989-90. Site B13.
Common acid rock species.

Lepraria 'incana' sensu lat.
First record: Davey & Dove 1972.
Latest record: Fletcher 1989-90. Sites B1, B6, B7, B13.
Common everywhere.

?*Leptogium palmatum* (Huds.) Mont.
Only record: Hawksworth 1967.
Unlikely record, needs checking.

Lobaria scrobiculata (Scop.) DC
Only record: Potter 1842.
No specimen in Leicestershire Museum herbarium.

Micarea prasina Fr.
Only record: Fletcher 1989-90. Site B3.
Common but overlooked, on shaded bark and stumps.

Ochrolechia androgyna (Hoffm.) Arnold
Only record: Fletcher 1989-90. Sites B3, B12.
Frequent on acid substrata and acid bark.

Opegrapha varia Pers.
Only record: Hawksworth 1967.
Rare in Leicestershire, on old trees.

Parmelia glabratula ssp. *fuliginosa* (Fr. ex Duby) Laundon
Only record: Hawksworth 1966.
Very common an acid rocks.

P. omphalodes (L.) Ach.
Only record: Hawksworth 1967.
Occasional in Charnwood Forest.

Table 5.12. Alphabetical list of lichens (continued).

Parmelia saxatilis (L.) Ach.
First record: Hawksworth 1966.
Latest record: Fletcher 1989-90. Sites B3, B10, C3.
Common acid-loving species.

P. sulcata T. Taylor
First record: Hawksworth 1966.
Latest record: Fletcher 1989-90. Site B5.
Common bark species where well-lit.

?*P. tiliaceae* (Hoffm.) Ach.
Only record: Hawksworth 1967.
Probably *P. pastillifera* (Harm.) R. Schubert & Klem., though not recorded so far for Leicestershire.

Parmeliopsis ambigua (Wulfen) Nyl.
First record: Davey & Dove 1972.
Latest record: Fletcher 1989-90. Sites B3, B9, B10, C3.
On stumps and palings.

Pertusaria albescens var. *corallina* (Zahlbr.) Laundon
Only record: Fletcher 1989-90. Site C3.
On oak stump, frequent.

Placynthiella icmalea (Ach.) Coppins & P.James
Only record: Fletcher 1989-90. Site B12.
Common stumps and bark species.

Platismatia glauca (L.) Culb. & C.Culb.
Only record: Fletcher 1989-90. Site C3.
On oak stump, well-lit. Common on old trees and rocks in Leicestershire.

Psilolechia lucida (Ach.) M.Choisy
Only record: Fletcher 1989-90. Site B13.
Shaded acid crevices, common.

Rhizocarpon obscuratum (Ach.) Massal.
Only record: Fletcher 1989-90. Site B13.
Common, well-lit acid rocks.

Schismatomma decolorans (Turner & Borrer ex Sm.) Clauz. & Vezda
Only record: Fletcher 1989-90. Site B4.
Old forest indicator in Leicestershire, in lime bark crevices.

Trapeliopsis granulosa (Hoffm.) Lumbsch
Only record: Fletcher 1989-90. Site C3.
On oak stump. Common in Leicestershire.

Verrucaria aethiobola Wahlenb.
Only record: Fletcher 1989-90. Site C2.
Shaded stream bed on rock, rare in the county, Charnwood only.

V. aquatilis Mudd.
Only record: Fletcher 1989-90. Site C2.
Shaded stream bed on rock, rare in the county, Charnwood only.

V. hydrela Ach.
Only record: Hawksworth 1967.

Chapter 6

Vegetation: Field Layer

6.1 Scope and Objective

The woodland field layer has been defined in chapter 4 as all herbaceous plants, together with woody plants of less than one metre in height. Bryophytes have been ignored and a ground layer has not been distinguished from the field layer. The purpose of this part of the survey is to assess the distribution and abundance of the most important field layer species in each compartment, and to identify recurring plant communities. In addition to describing the field layer vegetation, the present chapter explains the recording procedure for saplings and young re-growth of woody plants. The latter groups of plants (taller than one metre but less than 15 cm girth) belong to the shrub layer, but were, for convenience, recorded alongside the field layer plants.

6.2 Method

A sampling method was adopted, whereby detailed studies were made of small plots or quadrats.

6.2.1 Minimal area and quadrat size

Purpose

A pilot study was undertaken to establish an appropriate size for the quadrats of the main field layer survey. The scale of pattern in the field layer is generally much smaller than a whole compartment, and it was intended that individual quadrats be representative of the various types of vegetation within a compartment (see section 4.3.4). The optimum quadrat size is just greater than that necessary to ensure all but the rarer species are sampled. The *nested quadrat* procedure was used to determine this *minimal area* (Kershaw 1964).

Procedure

A one metre square was measured out in an area of woodland in which the field layer vegetation seemed, by eye, to be homogeneous. The species present were listed. Then the area was doubled by setting out a second square alongside the first, and additional species were recorded (figure 6.1). The area was again doubled to four square metres, then eight, and so on, up to 256, each time recording new species. This was done in six places throughout the wood (see solid squares in figure 6.3).

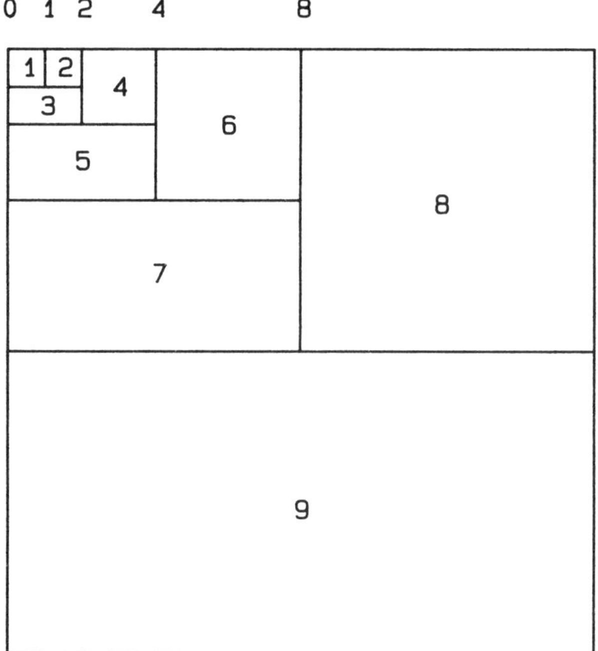

Figure 6.1. Layout of plots to establish the minimal area for quadrats. Across the top is a scale in metres; the numbers 1-9 within the plots give the sequence of recording.

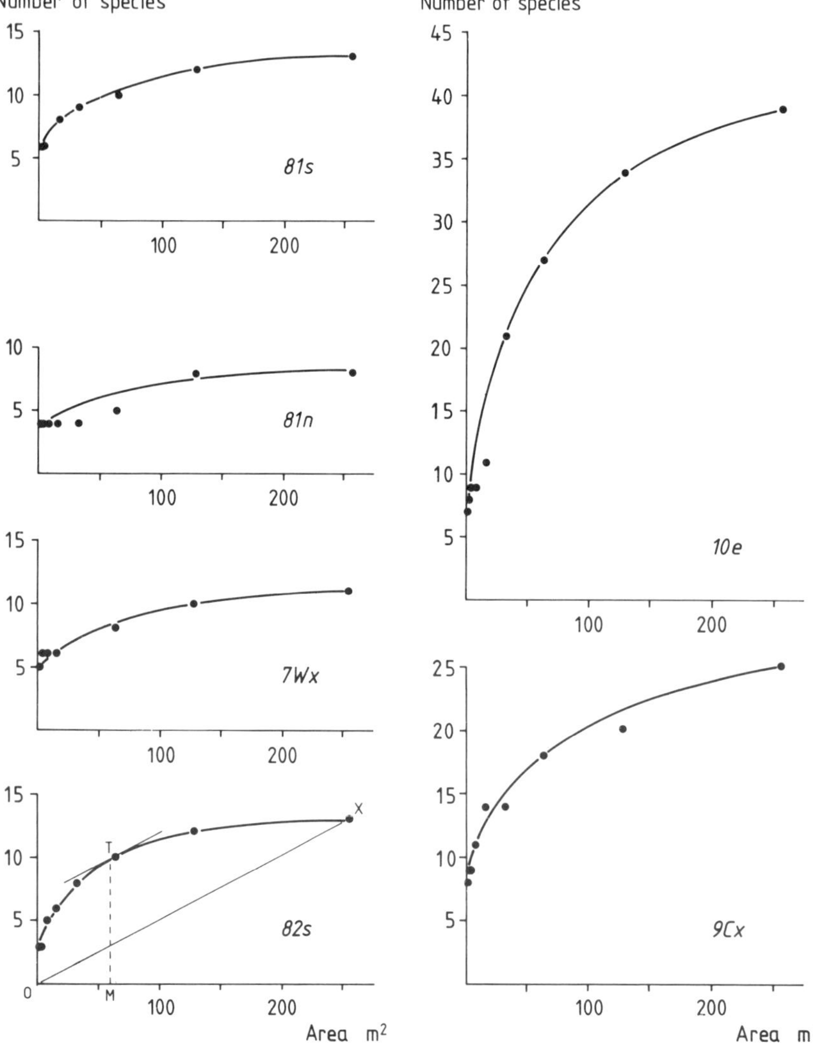

Figure 6.2. Results of the minimal area pilot study. Each curve shows how the number of species increases as the sampling area is repeatedly doubled from 1 to 256 square metres. Six sampling areas were recorded, whose identities are shown in italics. The result for 82s includes the geometrical construction used to establish the minimal area *M*.

Results

The results are shown in figure 6.2. Doubling the area does not double the number of species; there is a law of diminishing returns, such that fewer species are added as the area increases. With the exception of compartment 10, all curves are nearly level at a plot area of 256 square metres. The plot in compartment 10 was, in retrospect, badly sited. It was found to extend across a bank, and into a ditch at the boundary with compartment 11. Plots should be confined to one vegetation type for the procedure to be meaningful, so the results for this plot must be rejected.

Analysis and conclusion

The curves are more or less smooth, and it is difficult to decide precisely which point corresponds to the minimal area. The advice of Mueller-Dombois & Ellenberg (1974) was followed. As shown on the curve for 82s in figure 6.2, a line is drawn from the origin *O* to the top right of the curve *X*. Then the point on the curve *T* where the slope equals that of the line *OX* gives the minimal area *M*. The range of minimal areas so obtained was 30 to 60 square metres. Thus a quadrat area of 100 square metres is both convenient to set out (a square with 10 m sides), and large enough to ensure that all the important species are sampled.

6.2.2 Placing of quadrats

Between two and twelve quadrats were placed in each compartment, depending on its size. In varied compartments such as those containing a marsh, quadrats were placed in each vegetation type. In homogeneous compartments, 100 m National Grid squares were used as a guide to distribute the quadrats more or less evenly, with one quadrat for each grid square. Care was taken not to include an obvious community boundary within a quadrat, nor any atypical areas. In most parts of the wood minor footpaths were regarded as typical, and no precautions were taken to avoid them.

The total number of quadrats examined was 74. Figure 6.3 shows their locations. To save time, the grid squares surveyed for the minimal area pilot study were not re-surveyed with 10 x 10 m quadrats. Instead, the minimal area result for 128 square metres was used. Strictly, these plots are too large, but it will be seen from the shape of the curves that the extra 28 square metres would have affected the result very little.

6.2.3 Recording procedure

All vascular plants rooted within each quadrat were recorded, except woody plants large enough to be included in the point centred quarter survey (chapter 7). After about ten minutes of searching, usually by two recorders, each species in the list was assigned a score, according to the Braun-Blanquet scale (table 6.1). This semi-quantitative scale makes use of the concept of *cover*, which is the area on a horizontal surface occupied by a vertical projection of all parts of the species concerned, expressed as a percentage. In other words, it is the area of ground covered, assuming the ground to be level. Since plants frequently overlap one another, the total cover may exceed 100%. The lower scores (+ and 1) incorporate assessments of numerical abundance as well as cover, so the scale is most accurately described as one of cover-abundance. Being based on subjective estimates, the method is inevitably prone to personal bias. There is a tendency for some recorders to assign consistently too high a score, and others too low (Sykes *et. al.* 1983). However, as the same recorders surveyed all the quadrats, comparisons between them should be valid.

6. Field Layer

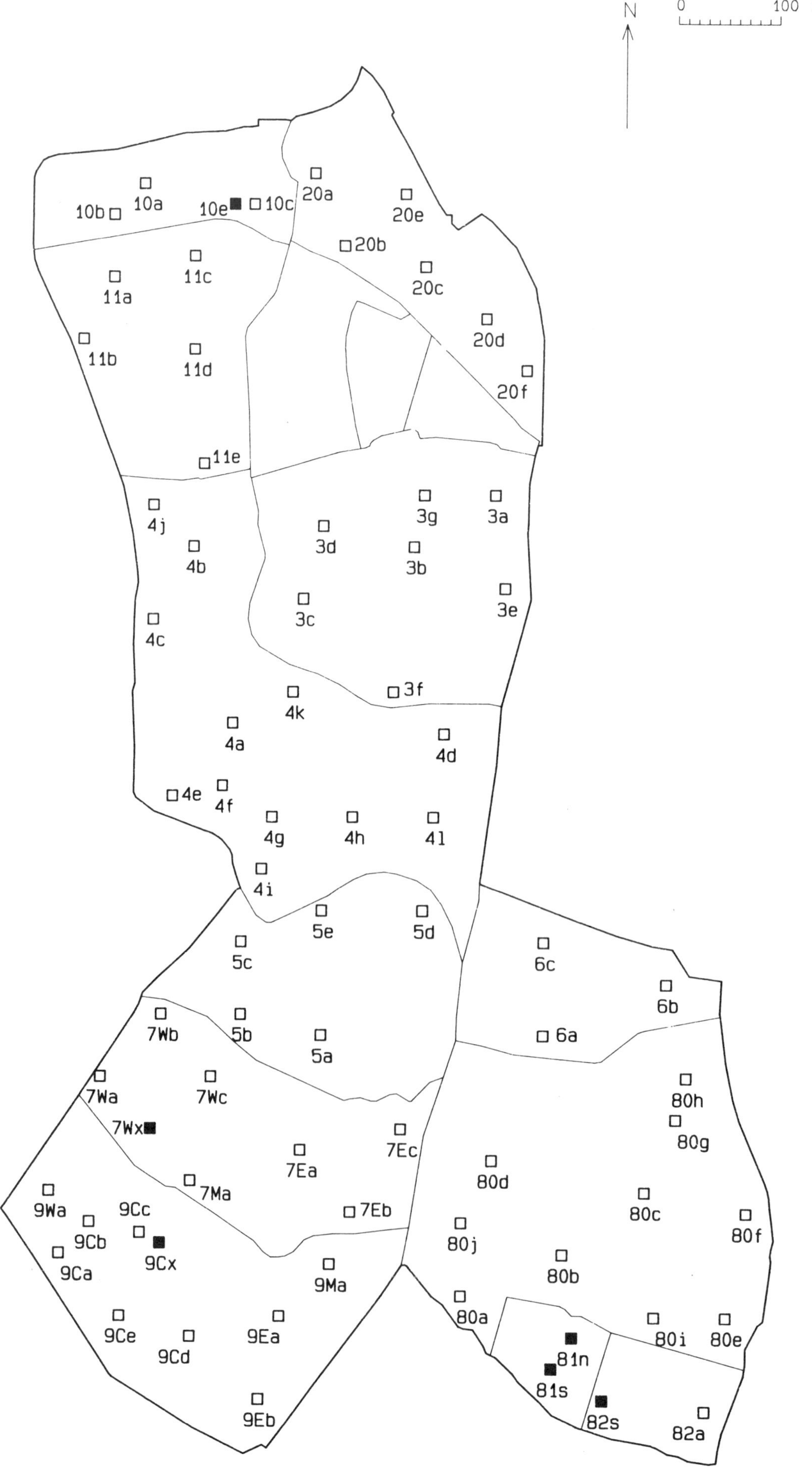

Table 6.1. The Braun-Blanquet cover-abundance scale. *Cover* means the percentage of the ground area covered by the species concerned. The typical cover values will be used in section 6.3.1.

Score	Meaning	Typical cover (%)
+	sparse or very sparse, cover small	0.1
1	plentiful, cover small	1
2	cover 5-25%	15
3	cover 25-50%	37.5
4	cover 50-75%	62.5
5	cover >75%	87.5

Finally, a tally was kept of the number of each species of sapling present, that is to say trees or shrubs taller than one metre but too small in girth for the survey of shrub and canopy layers. Two species, blackthorn *Prunus spinosa* and guelder rose *Viburnum opulus,* occurred as groups of innumerable individual stems that were clearly connected below ground level. These were tallied as so many *groups.* The results of the sapling survey are presented and discussed along with the shrub and canopy survey in the following chapter, where they may be more conveniently related to the older members of their respective populations.

The recording work was restricted to a seven week period between 25 May and 15 July. To start any earlier would have risked not finding late species such as enchanter's nightshade *Circaea lutetiana,* whereas plants like *Anemone nemorosa,* whose leaves soon wither, might have been missed had recording continued beyond mid July. During this seven week period, growth of most woodland herbs is, of course, very considerable. Recorded cover value thus depends to some extent on date of survey, but the species lists at least should be reasonably complete and comparable (Kirby *et. al.* 1986). From the point of view of comparing species cover between quadrats, a shorter fieldwork season would have been preferable, but this would have delayed completion of the work by at least another year.

6.3 Results and Analysis

Table 6.2 gives details of each of the 74 quadrats examined, including the results of analyses to be discussed shortly. Table 6.3 shows the Braun-Blanquet scores for the 49 species that were found in five or more quadrats. A further 61 species were found less frequently. Being generally unimportant as components of the field layer, these latter species are excluded from the analyses that follow. All plants found in the quadrats, however, may be identified by referring to the *quadrats* entry in table 5.9. Occasionally, plant specimens could not be identified to species, usually because they were too young or else not in flower. This accounts for generic entries such as *Viola* sp.. For the sake of brevity, all records including subspecies, hybrids and genera, will be treated as though they were species.

< **Figure 6.3.** Locations of the field layer quadrats. The six plots of the pilot study, used to establish minimal area, are shown solid.

Table 6.2. Details of the 74 field layer quadrats. They are identified by a compartment number and a lower case letter. Compartments 7 and 9 are subdivided by means of upper case letters, interpreted as follows: M = marsh, E = east, W = west, C = central. Figure 6.3 shows their locations. All quadrats were 10 x 10 = 100 m^2, except 7Wx, 9Cx, 10e, 81n, 81s and 82s which were 16 x 8 = 128 m^2. *Soil pH* was measured in the centre of each quadrat; refer to section 2.3.5 for details. *Shannon diversity* is an index of species diversity which takes into account the proportion of each species; refer to section 6.3.2. *Total cover* is the sum of the estimated ground area covered by each species expressed as a percentage; refer to section 6.3.2.

Ident.	Grid reference	Date surveyed	Soil pH	Number of spp	Shannon diversity	Total cover %
3 a	54011264	4 June 85	5.0	16	1.022	58
3 b	53931259	4 June 85	5.0	9	1.114	92
3 c	53821254	25 June 85	4.5	9	1.342	36
3 d	53841261	25 June 85	5.0	12	1.323	73
3 e	54021255	27 June 85	4.3	15	1.303	72
3 f	53911245	27 June 85	4.7	8	1.295	47
3 g	53941264	12 July 85	4.8	9	0.983	95
4 a	53751242	17 July 84	6.8	24	1.682	25
4 b	53711259	25 June 85	4.5	18	1.744	54
4 c	53671252	25 June 85	4.8	8	1.417	49
4 d	53961241	27 June 85	4.6	19	1.427	75
4 e	53691235	9 July 85	4.4	9	1.034	117
4 f	53741236	9 July 85	4.5	12	1.666	101
4 g	53791233	9 July 85	6.2	24	2.128	47
4 h	53871233	9 July 85	4.3	14	1.099	97
4 i	53781228	10 July 85	4.7	11	1.047	144
4 j	53671263	12 July 85	5.0	9	1.202	71
4 k	53811245	12 July 85	4.6	13	1.048	58
4 l	53951233	12 July 85	4.6	11	1.117	98
5 a	53841212	4 July 85	4.8	10	0.944	32
5 b	53761214	4 July 85	4.5	10	0.716	81
5 c	53761221	10 July 85	4.7	8	0.706	108
5 d	53941224	10 July 85	5.0	15	0.900	84
5 e	53841224	13 July 85	4.3	12	1.094	59
6 a	54061212	2 July 85	4.4	8	0.807	55
6 b	54181217	2 July 85	4.7	6	1.506	62
6 c	54061221	2 July 85	4.5	7	1.282	47
7Ea	53821201	12 June 85	4.5	11	1.026	58
7Eb	53871195	12 June 85	4.1	16	2.180	5
7Ec	53921203	4 July 85	4.6	11	0.842	19
7Ma	53711198	13 July 85	7.2	23	2.232	89
7Wa	53621208	12 June 85	4.3	11	1.435	124
7Wb	53681214	12 June 85	4.2	8	1.193	71
7Wc	53731208	12 June 85	4.2	11	1.393	49
7Wx	53671203	19 June 84	4.5	10	1.108	118
9Ca	53581191	25 May 85	7.1	33	1.413	63
9Cb	53611194	25 May 85	4.7	24	1.347	124
9Cc	53661193	25 May 85	6.9	19	1.492	37
9Cd	53711183	25 May 85	7.1	14	1.230	94
9Ce	53641185	4 July 85	7.5	22	1.834	55
9Cx	53681192	19 June 84	5.5	20	1.896	69
9Ea	53801185	3 July 84	4.2	16	1.351	112
9Eb	53781177	4 July 85	6.1	15	1.498	50

Table 6.2. Details of the 74 field layer quadrats (continued).

Ident.	Grid reference	Date surveyed	Soil pH	Number of spp	Shannon diversity	Total cover %
9Ma	53851190	3 July 84	5.9	26	2.198	31
9Wa	53571197	12 June 85	4.8	22	1.631	51
10 a	53661294	24 June 84	4.7	10	0.728	128
10 b	53631291	24 June 84	5.0	10	0.765	82
10 c	53771292	10 June 85	5.4	14	1.054	20
10 e	53751292	12 June 84	5.3	33	1.413	63
11 a	53631285	24 June 84	5.2	16	1.217	71
11 b	53601279	24 June 84	4.9	25	1.664	52
11 c	53711287	17 July 84	4.8	24	1.594	88
11 d	53711278	17 July 84	4.2	15	1.284	35
11 e	53721267	17 July 84	4.8	12	0.782	82
20 a	53831295	15 July 84	6.5	22	1.407	64
20 b	53861288	15 July 84	5.3	11	0.777	54
20 c	53941286	4 June 85	4.7	19	1.492	37
20 d	54001281	4 June 85	4.8	13	1.475	50
20 e	53921293	10 June 85	4.9	20	1.338	62
20 f	54041276	10 June 85	4.9	15	1.066	96
80 a	53981187	28 May 85	4.4	14	0.799	82
80 b	54081191	28 May 85	5.1	11	0.905	56
80 c	54161197	28 May 85	4.7	12	1.313	36
80 d	54011200	28 May 85	4.8	15	1.360	36
80 e	54241185	23 June 85	4.2	7	1.100	91
80 f	54261195	23 June 85	4.2	6	0.783	55
80 g	54191204	2 July 85	4.7	6	0.820	128
80 h	54201208	2 July 85	4.8	11	1.138	34
80 i	54171185	13 July 85	4.6	7	0.711	127
80 j	53981194	13 July 85	5.0	7	1.009	96
81 n	54091183	10 June 84	4.6	8	1.107	91
81 s	54071180	10 June 84	4.5	11	1.383	84
82 a	54221176	23 June 85	4.8	8	1.144	70
82 s	54121177	10 June 84	4.3	12	1.037	58

6.3.1 Species frequency, abundance and distribution

Frequency

Table 6.4 summarises the behaviour of the species that were found in at least five quadrats. *Frequency* is defined as the probability that a species will be found in a random quadrat. An important property of frequency, as an ecological parameter, is its dependence on the quadrat size; most species would be found less frequently in smaller quadrats. The ten most frequent species are included on figure 6.4. *Rubus fruticosus, Pteridium aquilinum,* honeysuckle *Lonicera periclymenum,* broad buckler-fern *Dryopteris dilatata* and seedlings of oak *Quercus* sp. and ash *Fraxinus excelsior* are each more likely than not to be found in a quadrat.

Table 6.3. Braun-Blanquet cover-abundance scores for species found in five or more quadrats. Quadrats are identified across the top of the table (to be read vertically). Species names are given in an abbreviated form down the left side; they may be expanded with the aid of table 5.10.

	3333333	444444444444	55555	666	777	7	7777	999999	99	9	9	1111	11111	222222	8888888888	88	88
					EEE	M	WWWW	CCCCCC	EE	M	W	0000	11111	000000	0000000000	11	22
	abcdefg	abcdefghijkl	abcde	abc	abc	a	abcx	abcdex	ab	a	a	abce	abcde	abcdef	abcdefghij	ns	as
Pter aqui	+312224	.21243.45321	245.2	322	312	.	2224	22+222	22	.	2	32..	2+222	..2212	.22.334254	31	33
Athy f-f	....	+.....1+...1	.....	...	...	.	....	++1..1	..	.	.	....	.....	.....+	..1.+.....	..	..
Dryo f-m	1+.11..	+....2+.+1..	...+.	+..	++.	.	.+1.	......	..	.	.	11.1	++++1	......	.1.+......	..	..
Dryo dila	++11+21	11+1+21111+1	+.111	+.+	1.+	1	...+	.++..+	1.	+	+	+++1	+.+++	.+.+++	.+++.+....	+.	++
Dryo cart	....	+....1......	+....	...	...	.	....	......	.+	.	.	.+.+	+++..	......	....	..	..
Anem nemo	1......	.1..........	.....	...	1..	+	.+11	342.11	+1	+	1	+1..	++...	.+++..	+.........	..	..
Ranu repe	....	......1.....	.....	...	...	1	....	+.....	..	+	.	....	.....	..+...	....	..	..
Card flex	....	1..+........	.....	...	...	+	....	......	..	+	+	...+	.....	1.....	....	..	..
Viol sp.	....	....	.....	...	...	+	....	12	+.	.	.	...+	+1...	......	....	..	..
Moeh trin	....	....	.....	...	...	.	....	......	..	.	.	+.++	+.+..	..+...	....	..	..
Tili cord	+......	....	.....	...	...	.	....	......	..	.	.	11++	.+...	......	....	..	..
Oxal acet	....+.+	+....+.1..+.	.....	...	...	.	....	..1..1	+.	+	.	..++	+++++	.++...	...+......	.+	..
Acer pseu	.+.+...	+...+..++..+	...1.	...	..+	.	....	..+.1.	..	.	+	.11+	12111	.+++1.	+..2......	..	..
Ilex aqui	+...+..	+.2..++.+.1+	.+...	.1.	.+.	.	+.+.	......	..	.	+	.+..	+..+.	.+....	++.+....+.	++	+1
Rubu frut	32113.2	222322123234	.+143	222	1++	.	2223	112321	42	2	2	5413	3222+	331134	+322324132	32	21
Frag vesc	....	....	.....	...	...	.	....	11.+11	..	.	.	....	.....	1.....	....	..	..
Geum urba	....	+...........	.....	...	...	.	....	......	++	+	.	...+	.....	1.....	....	..	..
Crat mono	....	....	.....	...	...	.	....	+.....	.+	.	+	..+.	.+++.	+...++	+..+......	..	..
Sorb aucu	+....+.	...+......+.	.....	...	...	.	+...	......	..	.	+	....	++...	+..+.+	....	..	..
Cham angu	....	...1........	+..11	...	...	.	....	11.32.	..	.	.	....	.....	....2.	....	..	..
Circ lute	....	1..+..1.....	1	...	...	2	....	+11111	11	1	1	...+	++...	+.....	....	..	..
Hede heli	....+..	+...32...+.2	...1.	...	..+	.	....	+...+.	22	.	+	..22	123..	+2+.1.	.+.1......	.+	..
Urti dioi	....	......1.....	...+.	...	...	.	....	+.....	+.	1	.	....	.....	1.....	....	..	..
Betu pend	....	....	.....	...	...	.	....	++.++.	..	.	.	....	.....	..1...	....	..	.+
Cory avel	.+....+	.......+....	...+.	...	..+	.	....	+..+..	..	.	.	...+	..+..	......	+.........	++	..
Quer sp.	1111+1+	.1.....111+.	+111.	111	1+1	.	112+	+...1.	.+	.	+	....	.++.1	+.11++	111.211111	++	1+
Lysi nemo	...++..	++.+..1+....	....+	...	...	1	....	++++12	+.	1	.	..11	.++..	1	..+.......	..	..
Frax exce	+....+.	1+1+..++.+11	++.+.	...	+1.	2	+..1	111.+2	1+	1	+	..+1	.....	2.1+.+	1+++.....+	..	..
Sola dulc	....	....	.....	...	...	1	....	1+.1+.	1.	1	1	....	.....	......	....	..	..
Teuc scor	..1....	.11.......+.	+..11	...	.+.	.	....	1.+...	..	.	.	....	.....	1.++1.	....	..	..
Ajug rept	....	1.....1.....	.....	...	...	1	....	+1.+++	.+	1	.	....	.....	......	....	..	..
Gali apar	....	......1.....	.....	...	...	+	..+.	++...+	.+	1	.	+...	.+...	....1.	....	..	..
Vibu opul	....	.........+..	.....	...	...	2	....	......	.1	+	.	...1	.....	......	...1......	..	..
Loni peri	13.2212	.221+11+2212	.+12.	121	21+	1	2312	.11.+.	21	.	+	..11	21211	.112.2	21111...12	22	11
Arct minu	....	....	.....	...	...	.	....	1+++1+	..	.	.	....	.....	......	....	..	..
Hyac nons	+...1..	.1.1.+.1+...	.11..	...	1..	.	.1.1	+3+..1	+.	.	1	.+.+	.+...	..11+1	...++11++.	..	..
Junc effu	....	+1.+..1.....	.....	...	...	.	....	......	..	.	.	....	....+	......	.......+..	..	..
Luzu pilo	....	....	.....	...	.+.	.	+..+	......	..	.	.	....	..+..	+....+	....	..	..
Luzu sylv	...++..	.111...+1..1	..1+.	+22	.+1	.	2...	....+.	..	.	+	..++	.+11.	......	4++.+..1+1	13	+2
Care pend	....	++.+..2.....	.....	...	...	.	....	......	..	1	.	....	.....	......	...1......	..	..
Care remo	....	+.....+.....	.....	...	.+.	2	....	......	..	1	+	...+	.....	......	..+.......	..	..
Poa annu	....	....	.....	...	.+.	.	..+.	......	..	.	.	....	.....	..+.1.	+......+..	..	.1
Poa triv	....	+.....1.....	.....	...	...	1	....	+.+...	..	1	+	...+	+.++.	1.+...	....	..	..
Desc cesp	+...1.+	1+.1..2...1.	...+1	...	.+.	1	..+.	++.++.	+.	.	.	..++	.+1+.	+++..+	+.11......	..	..
Desc flex	..21.2.	.+.+........	21..+	...	++1	.	4...	......	..	.	.	....	...+.	...11.	1.....++..	.2	.+
Holc lana	..1....	.+..........	.....	...	...	.	....	.+....	..	.	.	....	.....	1...+.	.......+..	..	..
Holc moll	...31+1	1..211121.1+	.22..	+.+	.1.	.	.1..	......	..	.	2	....	.1.14	..2211	1.1...12.1	..	21
Agro capi	..2....	.1.......+..	...++	...	...	.	..+.	......	..	.	1	....	..+..	1...1.	.....+.+..	..	..
Mili effu	.+.....	....	.....	...	...	.	....	......	..	.	.	...1	.++..	++..+.	.+........	..	.+

Table 6.4. Details of species found in five or more quadrats. The columns headed by the symbols .+12345 show the number of quadrats in which the species occurs with the corresponding Braun-Blanquet score. For example, *Pteridium aquilinum* is absent from 11 quadrats, sparse in 3, plentiful in 6, has 5-25% cover in 33, and so on. The maximum in the + to 5 columns is shown in **bold**. *Frequency* is the percentage of quadrats in which the species occurs. *Cover* contains an estimate of cover averaged across all quadrats.

Species	.	+	1	2	3	4	5	Frequency, %	Cover, %
Pter aqui	11	3	6	**33**	11	7	3	85.14	21.81
Athy f-f	63	**6**	5	0	0	0	0	14.86	0.08
Dryo f-m	49	**14**	10	1	0	0	0	33.78	0.36
Dryo dila	20	**34**	18	2	0	0	0	72.97	0.69
Dryo cart	65	**8**	1	0	0	0	0	12.16	0.02
Anem nemo	50	**11**	10	1	1	1	0	32.43	1.70
Ranu repe	69	**3**	2	0	0	0	0	6.76	0.03
Card flex	67	**5**	2	0	0	0	0	9.46	0.03
Viol sp.	67	**4**	2	1	0	0	0	9.46	0.24
Moeh trin	68	**6**	0	0	0	0	0	8.11	0.01
Tili cord	68	**4**	2	0	0	0	0	8.11	0.03
Oxal acet	53	**18**	3	0	0	0	0	28.38	0.06
Acer pseu	48	**15**	9	2	0	0	0	35.14	0.55
Ilex aqui	47	**23**	3	1	0	0	0	36.49	0.27
Rubu frut	3	5	13	**29**	17	6	1	95.95	20.93
Frag vesc	68	1	**5**	0	0	0	0	8.11	0.07
Geum urba	68	**5**	1	0	0	0	0	8.11	0.02
Crat mono	62	**12**	0	0	0	0	0	16.22	0.02
Sorb aucu	63	**11**	0	0	0	0	0	14.86	0.01
Cham angu	65	1	**5**	2	1	0	0	12.16	0.98
Circ lute	55	6	**12**	1	0	0	0	25.68	0.37
Hede heli	49	**11**	4	8	2	0	0	33.78	2.70
Urti dioi	68	**3**	3	0	0	0	0	8.11	0.04
Betu pend	68	**5**	1	0	0	0	0	8.11	0.02
Cory avel	62	**12**	0	0	0	0	0	16.22	0.02
Quer sp.	23	17	**32**	2	0	0	0	68.92	0.86
Lysi nemo	51	**15**	7	1	0	0	0	31.08	0.32
Frax exce	35	**22**	14	3	0	0	0	52.70	0.83
Sola dulc	66	2	**6**	0	0	0	0	10.81	0.08
Teuc scor	60	6	**8**	0	0	0	0	18.92	0.12
Ajug rept	64	**5**	5	0	0	0	0	13.51	0.07
Gali apar	63	**8**	3	0	0	0	0	14.86	0.05
Vibu opul	68	2	**3**	1	0	0	0	8.11	0.25
Loni peri	15	6	**29**	22	2	0	0	79.73	5.87
Arct minu	68	**4**	2	0	0	0	0	8.11	0.03
Hyac nons	43	14	**16**	0	1	0	0	41.89	0.74
Junc effu	68	**4**	2	0	0	0	0	8.11	0.03
Luzu pilo	68	**6**	0	0	0	0	0	8.11	0.01
Luzu sylv	40	**16**	12	4	1	1	0	45.95	2.35
Care pend	68	**3**	2	1	0	0	0	8.11	0.23
Care remo	66	**6**	1	1	0	0	0	10.81	0.22
Poa annu	67	**5**	2	0	0	0	0	9.46	0.03
Poa triv	61	**9**	4	0	0	0	0	17.57	0.07
Desc cesp	44	**20**	9	1	0	0	0	40.54	0.35
Desc flex	54	**9**	6	4	0	1	0	27.03	1.75
Holc lana	68	**4**	2	0	0	0	0	8.11	0.03
Holc moll	40	4	**19**	9	1	1	0	45.95	3.44
Agro capi	62	**7**	4	1	0	0	0	16.22	0.27
Mili effu	65	**8**	1	0	0	0	0	12.16	0.02

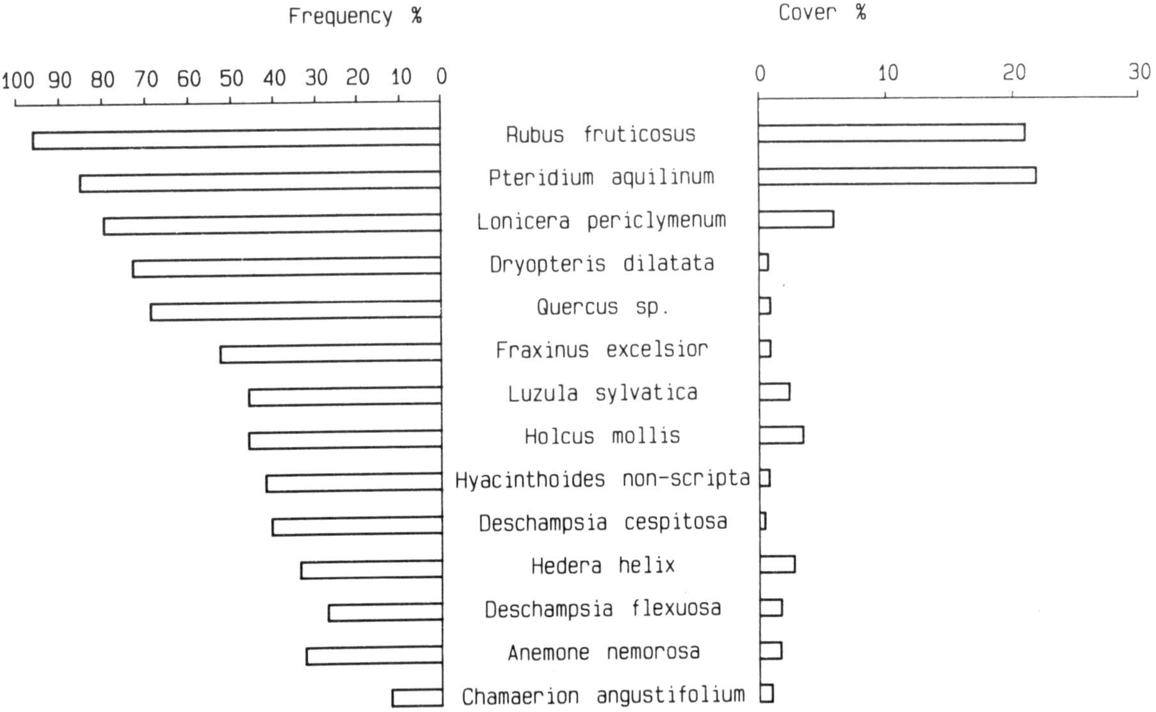

Figure 6.4. Frequency and cover of common field layer species. The fourteen species shown are those within the top ten of of either frequency or cover.

Abundance

Cover is a more satisfactory measure of abundance than frequency. Although for simplicity, the actual cover percentages were not recorded in the field, the Braun-Blanquet scores can be approximately converted back into cover by assuming typical cover values for each score. These values are included on table 6.1. For Braun-Blanquet scores of 2 and above, the mid-point of the cover range is used; for + and 1, low arbitrary values have been assigned. Having made the substitutions, the average across all quadrats was calculated; the results are given in table 6.4 alongside frequency. The errors introduced by this technique should tend to cancel out for species with high frequencies, and the results are believed to be reasonable estimates of true cover. The ten most abundant species are included in figure 6.4. *Rubus* and *Pteridium* are by far the most abundant, each with about 21% cover. Only another six species exceed 1% cover. Nearly three quarters of all species recorded in the quadrats each cover 0.05%, or less, of the woodland floor.

Distribution

Figure 6.4 emphasises that frequency and cover give very different impressions of abundance. Furthermore, it tells us something about the way plants are distributed around the wood. Consider, for example, rose-bay willow-herb *Chamerion angustifolium,* which has high cover relative to its frequency. This is because it generally occurs as dense patches rather than odd plants (figure 6.5). Its spatial distribution may be described as *clumped.* Others may be picked out in table 6.4 by observing which of Braun-Blanquet score (+ to 5) contains the highest number (shown in bold type). If it is not the + column, then the species is clumped. On the other hand, species with low cover relative to frequency, for example *Dryopteris dilatata,* are spread more evenly, either as scattered individuals or in numerous small clumps (figure 5.4). The highest total is invariably in the + column of table 6.4.

Figure 6.5. The widely spreading roots of *Chamerion angustifolium* are able to send up many new shoots, allowing dense patches to form quickly in woodland clearings and on quarry spoil heaps. (Photo: P. H. Gamble)

Theoretical studies on plant distribution patterns, and the way they interact with sampling strategies, demonstrate that a pattern may be described as clumped (or otherwise) only with reference to a particular scale (Greig-Smith 1957, page 52). If the populations which have been described above as having clumped distributions were to be re-sampled with a different quadrat size, they might then be found to have *random* or even *regular* distributions. Both assessments would be equally valid.

These findings verify, and to a limited extent quantify, the field observation that many woodland field layer plants are gregarious, rather than dispersed randomly or evenly. They are responding to different soils, to variations in shade, trampling by visitors and any number of other ecological factors. The information gathered for the present study falls far short of that needed to analyse ecological relationships conclusively. Nonetheless, one environmental parameter was measured in each quadrat which does seem to be an important factor for at least some species. This parameter is soil reaction.

Soil reaction

As described in more detail in section 2.3.5, soil samples for pH analysis were taken at the depth of most field layer plant roots. For each species in table 6.4, the *mean* pH of the quadrats in which it occurs was calculated. The *standard deviation* was also computed, which is a statistical measure of how the values are scattered around the mean (Chalmers & Parker 1986). The results appear in figure 6.6. The most abundant species such as *Pteridium, Rubus, Lonicera, Luzula sylvatica* and creeping soft-grass *Holcus mollis* are centred on acid soils of about pH 4.8. Two grasses appear to be restricted to more acidic soils, *Deschampsia flexuosa* and annual meadow-grass *Poa annua*. The affinity of the first species for acid conditions is well established (Clapham, Tutin & Warburg 1962), but this is certainly not the case for the other, which is a widespread weed of trampled footpaths. Prior

Figure 6.6. Relationship between plant distribution and soil reaction (pH). The diamond shows the mean, and the lines extend out to one standard deviation each side.

to seeking an ecological explanation for its unexpected behaviour, let us pause to review the nature of the data which form the basis of all these statistics. In the first place, there is a strong bias towards acidic soils. Secondly, some species such as *Poa annua* were found in rather few quadrats, whereas others were found in very many. It is very probable, therefore, that some infrequent species will show a spurious correlation with acid soils, and *Poa annua* would appear to be one of them.

We may be more confident in attributing to genuine ecological factors the association of certain species with more alkaline soils, with a pH of 6 or more. Lesser burdock *Arctium minus* and wild strawberry *Fragaria vesca* are both virtually confined to quadrats in the centre of compartment 9 (i.e. 9C) where the soil is unusually alkaline (perhaps due to base enrichment from Hallgates Filter Station, as described in section 3.8). The other species with an apparent preference for a high pH are creeping buttercup *Ranunculus repens*, bugle *Ajuga reptans* and *Solanum dulcamara*. These three commonly occur in the marshy areas which receive the minerals that have been leached out of soils elsewhere, and are consequently richer in bases. Without carrying out experiments, it is difficult to be certain whether these plants are attracted by soil alkalinity, increased moisture, a combination of the two, or some other factor. Another plant that was observed in the vicinity of the marshes was dog's mercury *Mercurialis perennis*. It is uncommon in Swithland Wood, and did not occur in sufficient quadrats to qualify for inclusion in figure 6.6 or table 6.4. In woods with calcareous soils, it is a familiar and often dominant herb that is not at all associated with marshes; on the contrary, it is highly susceptible to poisoning by ferrous ions which accumulate in waterlogged soils (Packham & Harding 1982). *Mercurialis* is less vigorous on acid soils, where it would face competition from *Pteridium* and *Rubus*. Perhaps in Swithland Wood, its need for nutrients that occur only in the marshes outweighs its dislike for damp soils.

6.3.2 Vegetation of the quadrats

Having considered the behaviour of species, let us now examine some characteristics of the vegetation in the quadrats.

Biomass

Some quadrats were found to be very sparsely vegetated, whereas others sustained a fairly luxuriant growth. No attempt was made to measure the actual biomass in the field layer. It is possible, however, to calculate from the quadrat data an approximate biomass index, by summing all the species cover values (estimated by the procedure given in section 6.3.1). This *total cover* percentage is shown in table 6.2. The variation is striking; from 5% to 144%, with a mean of 70%. The range of values reflects the very patchy nature of the field layer, and the common occurrence of substantial areas of bare ground.

Number of species

The number of species found in any one quadrat ranges from 6 to 33 with a mean of 13.95. The distribution is in fact skewed towards the species-poor quadrats, for more than half of them contain 12 species or less (figure 6.7). When the number of species is compared with the total cover in each quadrat (figure 6.8), it emerges that cover does not increase with more species, as might perhaps be expected. In fact, there is a slight but discernible trend in the opposite direction. This may be interpreted as the effect of competition. High total cover is usually attributable to one or two aggressive species such as *Pteridium*, which leave little room for other species. On the other hand, where no single species has achieved dominance, the less competitive plants are able to share the available resources.

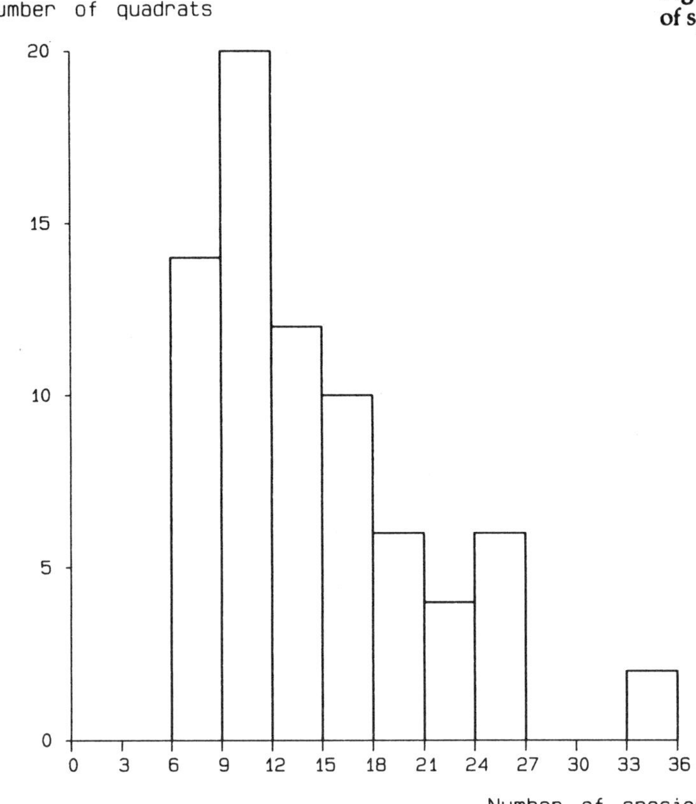

Figure 6.7. Distribution of the number of species found in each of 74 quadrats.

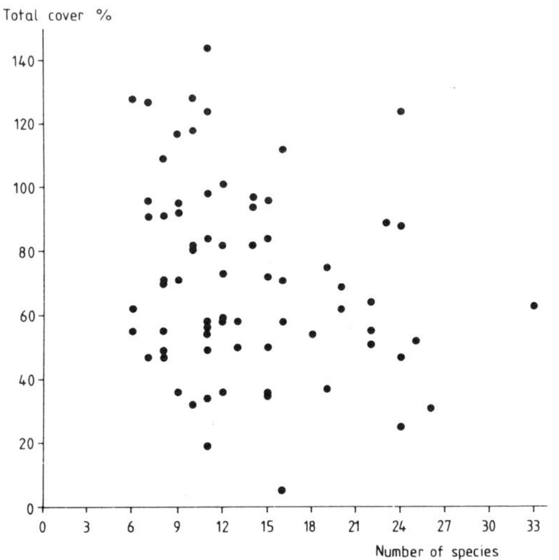

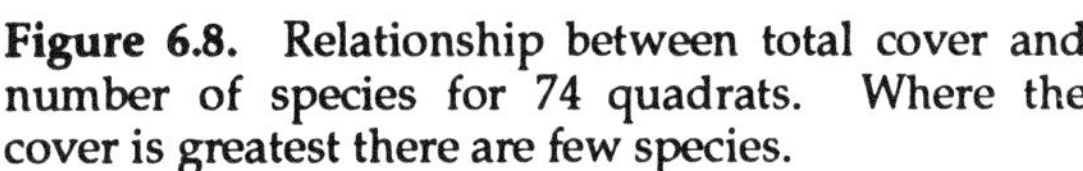

Figure 6.8. Relationship between total cover and number of species for 74 quadrats. Where the cover is greatest there are few species.

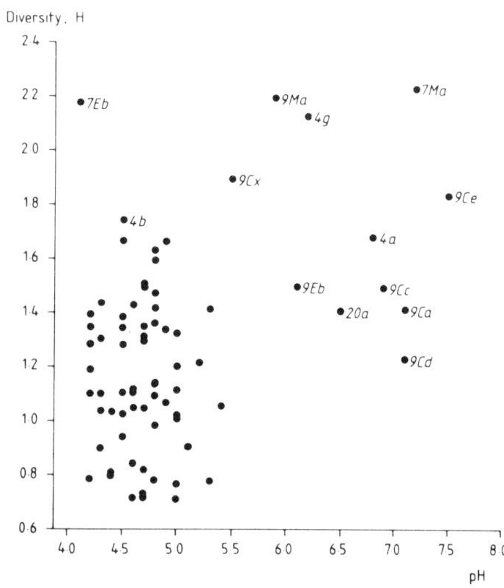

Figure 6.9. Relationship between soil reaction (pH) and Shannon's index of diversity (H). Of the 74 quadrats shown, space allows only those mentioned in the text to be identified (italics). Others may be identified with reference to table 6.2.

Diversity

In the preceding section, quadrats were characterised by counting the number of species. No account was taken of the relative abundance of each species. Thus, it is possible for two samples of essentially similar vegetation to differ significantly in number of species due to odd plants of 'rogue' species. Furthermore, two quadrats, each with identical species, could present a very different impression in the field; one with a more or less equal proportion of each species and the other dominated by just one or two. A fairer assessment of the numerical structure of plant communities, or *diversity*, should take into account the proportion of each species and not just the total number (Begon, Harper & Townsend 1986). Various indeces of diversity have been devised, but their individual merits and drawbacks cannot be discussed here (see Usher 1983). The index associated with C. E. Shannon is widely used, and is the one that will be adopted here.

If there are s species and the proportion of species i is P_i, then the Shannon diversity index, H, is defined as:

$$H = - \sum_{i=1}^{s} P_i \ln P_i$$

where $\ln$ denotes natural logarithm. In the present application, the proportion P_i is taken to be the estimated cover value of the species concerned divided by the total cover value for the quadrat. The results are included in table 6.2. The actual values, which range from 0.706 to 2.232, are difficult to interpret and are best regarded simply as an index; the higher the value, the more diverse the community. The frequency distribution of H (not illustrated) is not so skewed as that for the number of species (figure 6.7); in other words there are fewer quadrats with low diversity than we might expect on the basis of species richness. This implies that quadrats which contain few species at least have them in fair proportions.

Figure 6.9 demonstrates how diversity is influenced by soil reaction. There is a strong tendency for acid soils (say pH 5.4 or lower) to be less diverse than the more alkaline ones.

Most of the diverse quadrats are either from marshes (4a, 4g, 7Ma and 9Ma), or from elsewhere in compartment 9. One curious exception is quadrat 7Eb, which has the most acidic soil of all (pH 4.1), yet supports a plant community with a diversity index of 2.18.

6.3.3 Field layer associations

Examination of table 6.3 will show that certain groups of species tend to occur together, for example birch *Betula pendula*, *Fragaria vesca* and *Arctium minus*. This particular grouping is obvious because the quadrats concerned happen to be in adjacent columns of the table, but there are are many other associations which are more difficult to pick out by eye, for example remote sedge *Carex remota* and wood bitter-cress *Cardamine flexuosa*. We require a better method of detecting and presenting such associations.

Index of similarity

Ecologists often use an *index of similarity* as a means of quantifying how similar one quadrat is to another. Jaccard's index of similarity, IS_j, for example, is calculated as follows:

$$IS_j = \frac{c}{a + b + c} \times 100$$

where a is the number of species in quadrat *A* only; b is the number of species in quadrat *B* only, and c is the number of species common to both *A* and *B*. The factor 100 turns the ratio into a percentage. An analogous procedure may be used to compare the behaviour of two species in terms of the quadrats in which they occur. Then a becomes the number of quadrats containing species *A* only; b is the number of quadrats containing species *B* only; and c is the number of quadrats containing both species. This latter procedure was used to compare each species with every other species of table 6.3.

Jaccard's index does not take into account the abundance of species in a quadrat, but uses simply presence or absence. Experiments were carried out on the computer with other indeces of similarity, including those of Gleason (IS_g) and Spatz (IS_{sp}), which make full use of the cover estimates (Mueller-Dombois & Ellenberg 1974). As they did not yield results that were any clearer than those for Jaccard's index, I shall present neither the results nor the methods of calculating these more complicated indeces.

Constellation diagram

The results are most eloquently expressed as a *constellation diagram*, where species are represented as nodes, and associations between them as interconnecting lines. If stronger associations are shown by shorter lines, then species which occur together in the field should be close to each other in the diagram. Hence, recurring plant communities ought to appear as clusters of nodes. In practice, it is impossible to represent faithfully the degree of association (i.e. the index of similarity) by line shortness alone, because a certain minimum length is needed to fit all the nodes and lines onto the paper. This problem arises because the diagram is actually a two-dimensional approximation of a multi-dimensional concept. For this reason, the degree of association is more conveniently denoted by line thickness in combination with shortness. The thicker and shorter the line, the stronger the association. The process of laying out the constellation diagram is not one that is easily computerised, so this was done manually. After several iterations, figure 6.10 emerged.

Plant associations

For the purposes of discussion, the diagram has been apportioned into six regions, each centred around a cluster of species. They will be referred to as *plant associations A - F*. (N.B. the word *association* is not used here in the strict sense that some authors on plant sociology have defined for it, e.g. Tansley 1939.) The boundaries are somewhat arbitrary in places, and interpretations with a lesser or greater number of clusters might be equally valid. Some species, such as *Circaea lutetiana*, occupy an intermediate position between two clusters. Most associations, however, do seem to relate to groups of plants that are commonly found together in the field, i.e. *plant communities*.

Nine species are tightly packed together to form the core of association *A*. These are *Pteridium, Rubus, Lonicera*, bluebell *Hyacinthoides non-scripta, Luzula sylvatica, Holcus mollis, Dryopteris dilatata*, and seedlings of *Quercus* and *Fraxinus*. These are at once recognised as the constituents of the most widespread plant community of Swithland Wood, which occurs on moderately acid, fairly deep and well-drained soils. Holly *Ilex aquifoilum*, male fern *Dryopteris filix-mas, Deschampsia flexuosa*, and sycamore *Acer pseudoplatanus* seedlings are more loosely associated with these core species. Although they are associated with each other, we should not expect all, or even most, of these species to occur in any one quadrat; indeed it is notable that the poorest quadrats contain only six or seven species drawn mainly from the above list.

A. pseudoplatanus links association *A* to association *B*, which also contains wood sorrel *Oxalis acetosella*, ivy *Hedera helix*, and hawthorn *Crataegus monogyna*. Several of these species suggest recent disturbance, but *Oxalis* is generally recognised as an indicator of just the opposite (see page 80). If cluster *B* has a genuine ecological significance, its meaning is not clear.

Association C is ill-defined, having several links to both *A* and *D*. However, the species here, namely tufted hair-grass *Deschampsia cespitosa, Fraxinus, Anemone*, yellow pimpernel *Lysimachia nemorum* and *Circaea*, are frequently found in deeper shade and on damper soil. The last species has its headquarters in compartment 9. Other species with a strong affinity for this part of the wood are contained within association *D*. *Ajuga* and *Solanum* find suitably wet places in the disused gulleys here (see section 3.8), while *Arctium, Chamerion* and *Fragaria* occupy the drier, more open parts of this disturbed area. The remaining plants in this association are widespread 'weedy' species. *Urtica dioica* and cleavers *Galium aparine* prefer moist, nutrient-enriched sites, whereas rough meadow-grass *Poa trivialis* and *Ranunculus repens* inhabit the edges of tracks.

Association *E*, linked to *D* by *Poa trivialis*, contains plants characteristic of the woodland marsh communities. These are soft rush *Juncus effusus*, pendulous sedge *Carex pendula, C. remota, Cardamine flexuosa*, wood avens *Geum urbanum* and *Viburnum opulus*. They occur not only in the extensive marshes (7M, 9M etc.), but in ditches and along the edges of muddy rides throughout the low-lying parts of the wood.

Finally, association *F* comprises species which, according to the diagram, are not very strongly correlated with one other; wood sage *Teucrium scorodonia, Deschampsia flexuosa*, common bent-grass *Agrostis capillaris*, and Yorkshire fog *Holcus lanatus*. Field experience, however, confirms that they do indeed form an easily recognised plant community, which develops on the thin, acid soils around outcrops and old spoil heaps. Another species which frequents spoil heaps is *Chamerion* which, although included in cluster D, is associated with both *Agrostis* and *Teucrium* (figure 6.5).

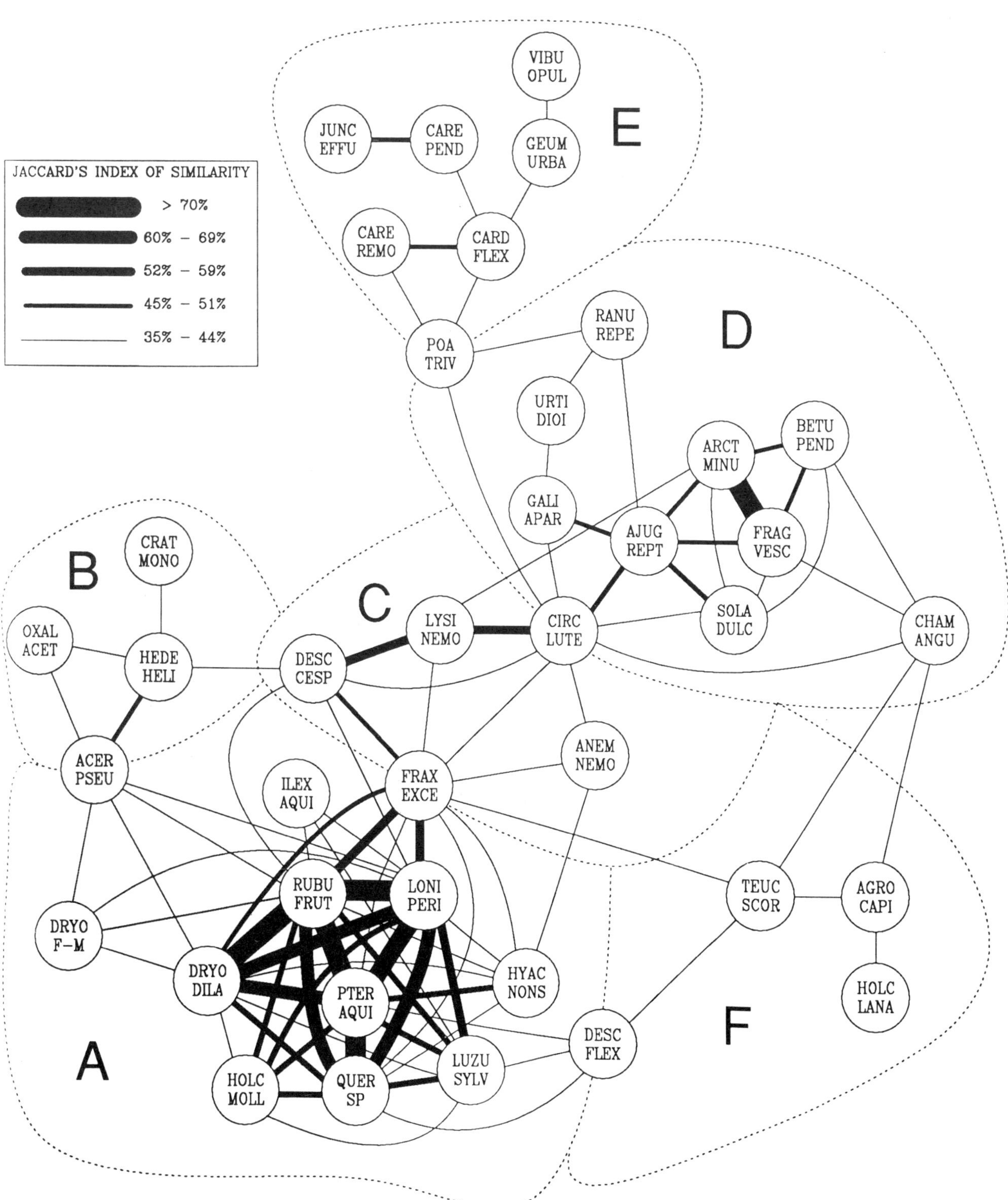

Figure 6.10. Field Layer Associations. Constellation diagram showing associations between field layer species. Line thickness represents the value of Jaccard's index of similarity. As far as possible, the higher the index, the shorter the line. In a few cases, the similarity threshold for the thinnest line has been reduced to 30% in order to capture clusters or species which would otherwise have been 'floating'. Dashed lines draw attention to the six associations A-F referred to in the text. The abbreviated species names may be interpreted with the aid of table 5.10.

6.4 Discussion and Conclusions

6.4.1 Limitations of the survey

The previous chapter showed Swithland Wood to be exceptionally rich in plant species, yet the sample areas judged to be typical of each 100 m grid square are, in general, surprisingly poor. Most quadrats contain between six and twelve species, and tend to be dominated by just one or two. The reason is that a large proportion of the wood's flora is dispersed in such a way that it is unlikely to be picked up by 'representative' quadrats. Many plants are more or less confined to special habitats such as ditches, rides, open glades and disturbed ground. These habitats are small in extent, compared to a compartment or grid square, and must therefore be regarded as atypical. A sampling strategy devised to assess large areas can hardly be expected to resolve this level of detail. Nonetheless, there are differences in field layer vegetation on a scale large enough to be clearly shown in the quadrats.

6.4.2 *Rubus-Pteridium-Lonicera* community

Virtually all areas of the wood contain substantial quantities of association *A* species. These plants are poorly represented only in the marshy quadrats (4a, 4g, 7Ma and 9Ma) where association *E* species take over. Association *B, C, D* and *F* species occur in quadrats alongside those from association *A*. By far the commonest plant community in Swithland Wood is dominated by association *A* species, with just a few extra plants. The *Rubus-Pteridium-Lonicera* community, as we shall call it, covers compartments 6, 7 (marsh excepted), 81 and 82 as well as significant portions of 3, 4, 5, 10, 11, 20 and 80.

Field observation suggests that there are significant variations within this community. Given optimum conditions *Rubus, Pteridium* and sometimes *Luzula sylvatica* can each dominate areas of the woodland floor, squeezing out the less competitive species (figures 6.11, 6.12, 6.16). In certain well-defined areas the density of *Luzula* is very high indeed, growing in tightly packed tufts of stiff leaves which form a persistent and impenetrable litter. This growth habit not only holds *Rubus* and *Pteridium* at bay, but forcefully resists attempts by ecologists to obtain soil samples! Although the *Luzula* dominated community occurs in several places (such as the western edge of compartment 4), it is best illustrated at the south-western edge of compartment 80 (e.g. quadrat 80a). There is an abrupt change to the the more widespread mixture of *Rubus, Pteridium* and *Lonicera* further up the slope, perhaps reflecting a soil change.

6.4.3 Marshes

The marshes which fringe the streams, with their very different soils, naturally give rise to a kind of vegetation which is dissimilar in most respects to that of the surrounding woodland. The marsh flora is different for two main reasons. The most obvious is that certain plants seem to require marshy, base-enriched soil. The dominant plants of the drier woodland (association *A*) are unable to grow properly in waterlogged ground, and are often absent altogether. A second factor, then, is a lack of competition from the aggressive plants of dry, acidic soils. In the marshes, both the number of species and the diversity (Shannon index) are significantly higher than elsewhere in the wood. Evidently, many species (including those of associations *C* and *E*) favour or tolerate these conditions, but none is capable of exploiting them at the expense of other species. A third factor may account for the presence of at least one species in the marshes. Is it not the reluctance of the visiting public to venture into the marshes that explains the survival of primrose *Primula vulgaris* there, which has been virtually exterminated elsewhere by picking and uprooting?

Figure 6.11. Field layer dominated by bramble. Bracken is also present, but bramble can tolerate deeper shade, such as that cast here by lime trees. (Compartment 10, SK535129, December 1982.)

Figure 6.12. Field layer dominated by bracken. Also present are bramble, honeysuckle, and *Luzula sylvatica*. (Compartment 80, SK541120, November 1984.)

Figure 6.13. *Caltha palustris*, one of the more striking flowers in the woodland marshes. (Photo: P. H. Gamble)

Although not attaining any significant cover, the woodland marshes are noted for the presence of marsh marigold *Caltha palustris* (figure 6.13) and marsh valerian *Valeriana dioica*.

6.4.4 Compartment 9

The vegetation of compartment 9, notably the central part 9C, stands out from the rest of the wood. The species richness found during the flora survey (chapter 5) is also expressed here in the field layer quadrats. The vegetation is inherently more diverse - the long species list is not simply the consequence of a mixture of habitats within the compartment. The species of associations C and D are particularly common. *Anemone nemorosa*, although fairly widespread in Swithland Wood, is much better developed here than elsewhere, and from time to time puts on a spectacular show (figure 5.2). Other plants that do well here are common violet *Viola riviniana*, lady-fern *Athyrium filix-femina*, figwort *Scrophularia nodosa*, elder *Sambucus nigra*, creeping thistle *Cirsium arvense* and skull-cap *Scutellaria galericulata*. Some of these reflect the moist conditions, though prior to the diversion of the stream in the 1920s this part of the wood must have been wetter.

Figure 6.14. Ivy with seedlings and saplings of sycamore, growing on disturbed ground near a quarry. (Compartment 5, SK53961222, March 1990.)

6.4.5 *Hedera* association

Hedera helix is usually the most conspicuous of the association *B* species. The others are *Crataegus, Acer pseudoplatanus* and *Oxalis*. These will be called the *Hedera* association. Rackham (1980), in his extensive study of East Anglian woods, finds *Hedera* to be highly characteristic of secondary woods, or parts of primary woods that have been disturbed, by re-planting for example. *Crataegus* and *A. pseudoplatanus* are also common in such woods, though by no means confined to them. As the earthworks testify, much of Swithland Wood is secondary, but this field layer association seems to pick out areas of relatively recent disturbance. We shall see in chapter 7 that compartments 10 and 11 in particular show, in their canopy structure, signs of interference. The other quadrats with the *Hedera* association are 80d, 9Ea, 9Eb. All are on, or very near, disturbed parts of the wood; the first two beside quarries (figure 6.14) and the third by the course of the water main.

The fourth member of the association, *Oxalis*, is certainly not generally associated with disturbance. In eastern England it is regarded as an ancient woodland indicator (see page 81). Within a wood, however, it appears that this plant cannot be relied upon to identify the ancient parts.

6.4.6 *Teucrium* community

Association *F* plants form a recognisable community in which *Teucrium scorodonia* is probably the most prominent species, the other three being grasses. The best examples are seen in quadrats 3c and 4b which represent the vegetation of a rocky ridge. Around outcrops, the *Teucrium* community may be regarded as transitional between the exposed rock and the *Rubus-Pteridium-Lonicera* community that typically occupies the slopes below.

Figure 6.15. Sparse vegetation on a spoil heap; *Deschampsia flexuosa, Rumex acetosella,* and the moss *Dicranum scoparium.* (Compartment 5, SK53871214, May 1989.)

Figure 6.16. The southern extremity of compartment 80, where the field layer is a dense sward of *Luzula sylvatica.* The canopy here is *Tilia cordata.* Another example of this community was sampled in quadrat 81s. (SK540118, October 1989. Photo: P. H. Gamble)

A succession of vegetation types is seen on the the slate spoil heaps, of which the *Teucrium* community is one possible stage. The most recently disturbed heaps become colonised by sheep's sorrel *Rumex acetosella*, early hair-grass *Aira praecox* and the moss *Dicranum scoparium* (figure 6.15). Older heaps develop the *Teucrium* community into which *Rubus* intrudes. Quadrats 20a and 20e are examples. Eventually, *Teucrium* and its associated grasses are shaded out by the developing canopy of *Fraxinus* and *Betula*, leaving a dense tangle of *Rubus* below.

6.4.7 Other communities

Finally, there are some other field layer communities or associations which were observed in the field, but not picked out by the sampling procedure. They have not been studied in detail and only a brief mention of each can be given.

The eastern edge of compartment 3 is notable for its fine display of the wood melick *Melica uniflora*, which occurs nowhere else in the wood with such abundance. This is also the only locality where the writer has found yellow archangel *Lamiastrum galeobdolon*. The reasons for the distribution of these two may be historical - they are both ancient woodland indicators - although the latter plant seems to prefer the moist conditions at the north-east corner of compartment 3.

Paths in the drier parts of the wood have a very noticeable zonation, attributable to the degree of trampling. Between the bare, compacted soil in the centre of paths and the *Rubus-Pteridium-Lonicera* community that surrounds them, are two zones each occupied by a species of grass. The narrow inner strip of *Poa annua* gives way, fairly abruptly, to a wider zone dominated by *Holcus mollis*. The more heavily used rides in the damper parts of the wood, particularly those frequented by horse-riders, develop a marginal vegetation similar to that of the marshes; with *Deschampsia cespitosa, Carex remota, C. pendula, Ajuga reptans, Ranunculus repens* and wild angelica *Angelica sylvestris*.

Other disturbed areas (where the soil is not necessarily compacted) provide opportunities for weedy species to establish themselves, especially where the canopy casts only a light shade. The species involved are various and not constant from one place to another, so it is difficult to characterise this type of vegetation floristically. Typical species include knotgrass *Polygonum aviculare, Urtica dioica, Cirsium arvense*, sow-thistle *Sonchus* spp., ivy-leaved speedwell *Veronica hederifolia* ssp. *hederifolia*, great plantain *Plantago major, Poa annua* and *Poa trivialis*.

In 1985, a small part of compartment 9 (near the car-park entrance) was dug up in order to connect a water main into the existing system (figure 3.19). The trench for the new main extended eastwards to Cropston Reservoir. After the trench was filled, several of the usual weeds appeared, together with four unexpected species, three of which were new records for the site. The location is not particularly wet, but the plants concerned: short-leaved water-crowfoot *Ranunculus trichophyllus*, celery-leaved crowfoot *R. sceleratus*, water chickweed *Myosoton aquaticum* and orange fox-tail *Alopecurus aequalis*; are all species of wet places. The last named species gave a clue to the origin of this curious collection. *A. aequalis* is characteristic of reservoir margins, and occurs with the other three species at Cropston Reservoir. Evidently, these plants had made their way from one end of the trench to the other, either on the wheels of the machinery or the boots of the workmen! This association (if it can be described as such) cannot be expected to persist for more than a year or two, as other plants better suited to woodland conditions reassert themselves.

Chapter 7

Vegetation: Shrub and Canopy Layers

7.1 Scope

Whereas the botanical richness of Swithland Wood is concentrated in its field layer, the general character of the site is determined by its shrub and canopy layers; in particular the size, growth-form and density of the various woody species. These are the aspects that will be investigated in the present chapter. In chapter 4, a distinction was drawn between the shrub and canopy layers, and in Swithland Wood they may generally be separated without difficulty. However, a survey technique has been adopted which does not demand formal definitions of shrub and canopy layers. The two were surveyed together, and it will be convenient to deal with both layers in a single chapter. In the discussions that follow, the word *tree* is used in a broad sense to include standard trees, coppiced trees, and hazel, a species whose 'self-coppicing' habit rarely allows it to assume the growth-form of a standard tree. Tall, single-stemmed trees of the canopy layer are referred to as *canopy trees* where the intention is to exclude those of coppice form. Canopy tree species such as oak are not, of course, confined to the canopy, nor shrub species to the shrub layer. All woody plants begin their lives as seedlings in the field layer. Successful seedlings make their way into the shrub layer as saplings, some of which grow on to become canopy trees. The methods for assessing seedlings, saplings and small shrubs have been described in the previous chapter, but it is more appropriate to analyse the results here, because one of the topics to be explored is the age structure of the tree populations. A full discussion on the objectives and the selection of the various techniques has been included in chapter 4.

The basic unit of study is the compartment, but the survey has recognised the existence of significant areas of atypical vegetation within compartments. In particular, the areas of alderwood (dominated by *Alnus glutinosa)* in compartments 7 and 4 were deliberately excluded from the surveys of those compartments. Unfortunately, they were too small to be surveyed in their own right by a comparable method. Compartment 5 could not be surveyed because of its discontinuous tree cover, due to the outcrops, quarry, and spoil heaps. The study, being principally concerned with semi-natural vegetation, did not extend to the plantation (cmpt 22).

7.2 Saplings and Small Shrubs

These are defined as woody plants greater than one metre in height, but with the largest stem (if more than one) less than 15 cm in girth.

7.2.1 Method

Data on saplings and small shrubs were collected during the field layer survey; see section 6.2.3. Of the 74 quadrats that comprise the field layer survey, six were derived from a pilot study in which saplings were not recorded. Hence, these plants were counted in each of 68 quadrats (each 10 m square) throughout the wood. For young regrowth and for suckering species such as *Prunus spinosa* and *Viburnum opulus*, the number of clonal groups was counted rather than the number of stems.

7.2.2 Results and analysis

Table 7.1 summarises the results, which are presented in order of frequency. Seventeen species were found. *Corylus* is the most widespread, being found in about half of the quadrats, followed by *Acer pseudoplatanus* with 27.9% frequency. Another five occur in 10% to 20% of quadrats; *Fraxinus*, rowan *Sorbus aucuparia, Ilex, Betula pendula* and *Quercus petraea*. In terms of numerical abundance, the ranking is somewhat different, with *A. pseudoplatanus* by far the most numerous (36.9% of the total), then *Fraxinus, Corylus* and *Ilex*.

7.2.3 Discussion

Most species are represented by too few individuals to exhibit clear distribution patterns, but those with 25 or more individuals are shown in figure 7.2. Various patterns emerge from a study of this figure and table 7.1. Large numbers of *A. pseudoplatanus* saplings occur in relatively few quadrats. These are concentrated in compartments 10 and 11. Similarly, *Ilex* occurs as 30 saplings in quadrat 4c, with the remaining 16 spread among nine other quadrats. This clumped type of distribution is typical of saplings, and is particularly marked in these two species. It will be noted that each species ranks higher in abundance than it does in frequency. These saplings spring up in well defined areas where good conditions for germination and development have followed abundant seed production (Packham & Harding 1982). *A. pseudoplatanus* has large fruits which do not disperse far in woodland, but where light breaks through a gap in the canopy close to a mature tree, then a thicket of saplings quickly develops, shading out virtually all competition (figure 7.1). *Ilex* berries, on the other hand, are widely dispersed by birds. Perhaps it is beneath the favourite perches of these birds that the small but dense areas of young hollies form, such as the one in quadrat 4c. *Fraxinus* saplings seem to be correlated with two distinct types of habitat. Firstly, they occur on the moist ground in the central part of compartment 9 and the adjacent marsh (7Ma, 9Ma), and secondly, on slate spoil (20a).

Sambucus nigra is confined to compartment 9 which, as we have seen from the field layer study, differs in many respects from the rest of the wood. *Corylus* exhibits another kind of pattern; being nowhere very abundant but fairly evenly distributed throughout. It ranks top in frequency but only a poor third in abundance.

The frequency and distribution of saplings make an interesting comparison with those of their parent trees. *Quercus petraea* for example, ranks only fifth as a sapling, yet it is the most numerous and widespread of the canopy trees. Small-leaved lime *Tilia cordata* is a locally important component of the canopy, yet not a single sapling was found. These observations will be considered further in sections 7.5 and 7.6.

Table 7.1. Frequency and abundance of saplings (including small shrubs). *Frequency* is the percentage of the 68 quadrats, each 10 m square, in which at least one sapling was found. *Abundance* is calculated on the basis of the total number of saplings. A * indicates that the species normally occupies the shrub layer.

Species	Shrub	Frequency (%)	Abundance (%)
Corylus avellana	*	51.5	14.1
Acer pseudoplatanus		27.9	36.9
Fraxinus excelsior		19.1	20.0
Sorbus aucuparia		17.6	2.8
Ilex aquifolium		14.7	7.9
Betula pendula		14.7	4.3
Quercus petraea		13.2	4.8
Sambucus nigra	*	7.3	4.3
Quercus robur		7.3	1.2
Viburnum opulus	*	7.3	1.0
Salix caprea	*	4.4	1.0
Rosa canina	*	2.9	0.3
Alnus glutinosa		2.9	0.3
Quercus hybrids		2.9	0.3
Prunus spinosa	*	1.5	0.2
Crataegus monogyna	*	1.5	0.2
Rhododendron ponticum	*	1.5	0.2

Figure 7.1. A thicket of sycamore saplings, growing under a canopy of small-leaved lime. (Compartment 10, SK53781291, December 1983.)

7. Shrub and Canopy Layers

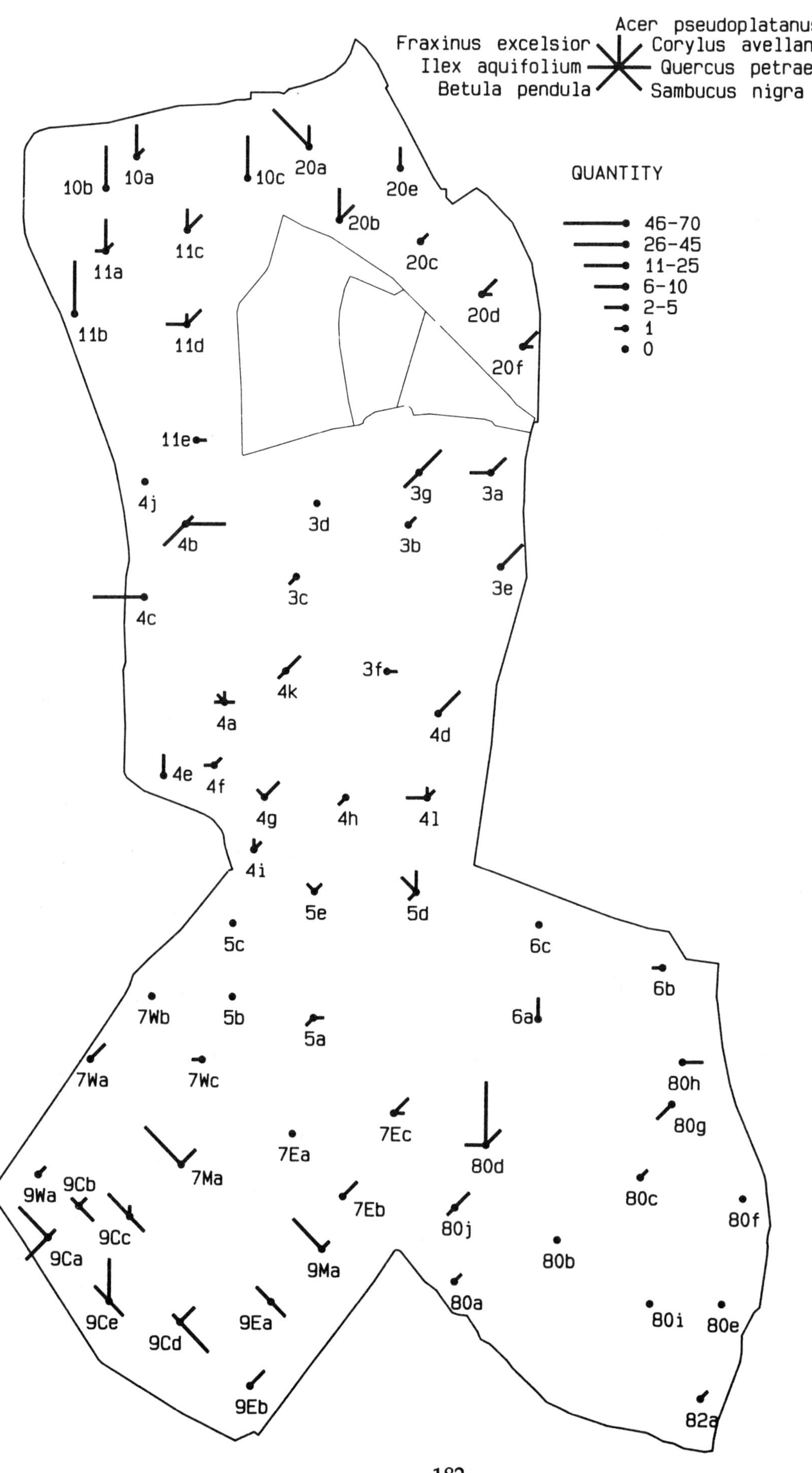

7.3 Girth-Age Relationship

It is common knowledge that a tree's age can be estimated from the diameter of its trunk. The widths of the annual growth rings vary somewhat from year to year according to local environmental conditions (Fletcher 1974, page 80), but over many years the annual increment in trunk diameter is constant to a surprising degree (Mitchell 1974, page 25). In practice, it is easier to work with girths since they are more easily obtained with a tape measure. Girths are conventionally measured at 1.3 metres up the trunk ('breast height'), in order to avoid any buttresses near the roots. The rule-of-thumb, according to Mitchell, is that a typical woodland tree, in average conditions, puts on half an inch (1.27 cm) of

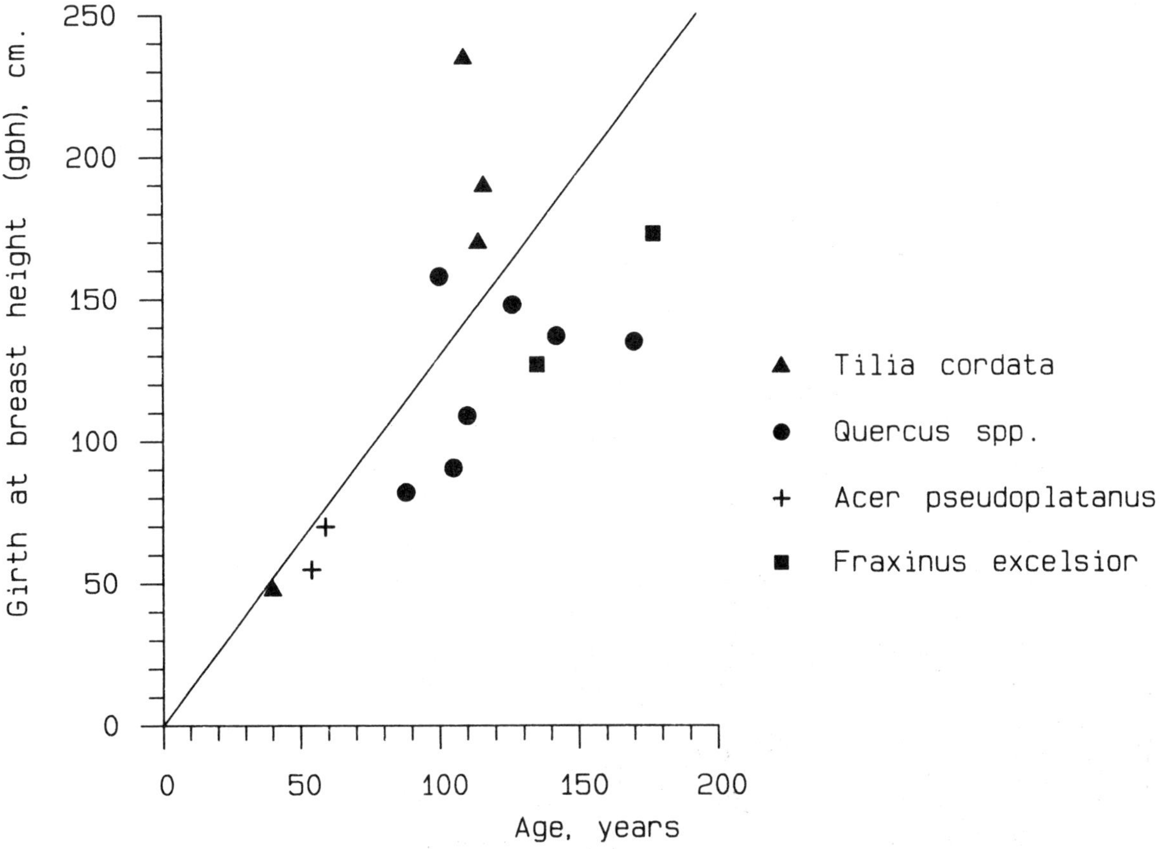

Figure 7.3. Girth-age relationship. The line represents a growth rate of half an inch (1.27 cm) per year.

< **Figure 7.2.** Quantity of each of the seven commonest sapling species in the field layer quadrats. All quadrats are 10 x 10 m. The line length represents the quantity, and the angle relative to 12 o'clock distinguishes the various species. For example, quadrat 20a (top) contains between two and five sycamore *Acer pseudoplatanus* saplings and between 26 and 45 of ash *Fraxinus excelsior*.

girth per year. One of the reasons for recording girth during the survey was to try to relate the stand structure to its history. Rather than rely on this approximation, it was clearly preferable to establish the local relationship between age and girth. For this purpose annual growth rings were counted whenever they were exposed by felling. Felling trees has not been part of regular management in Swithland Wood, so the number of ring counts is small. Furthermore, ring counts on a stump were only useful if the felled trunk was still lying around to be measured at what would have been breast height, which was very often not the case. The results are shown in figure 7.3. Statistically, there are too few measurements to be very helpful, but they have been included for completeness. The line corresponding to Mitchell's approximation is also shown. The figure demonstrates that growth rates are very variable. Considering the range of environmental conditions within the site, perhaps it was a little simplistic to expect a straight line to emerge! It appears that *Tilia cordata* grows faster than *Quercus*. The largest tree in the wood, a lime with a girth of 432 cm (figure 7.4), must be between 200 and 300 years old. We cannot be more precise than this, on the basis of the available information. The largest oaks, of about three metres in girth, would be roughly 300 years old; somewhat older than Mitchell's rule would lead us to believe.

Figure 7.4. The biggest tree in the wood, a small-leaved lime with a girth at breast height of 432 cm (measured in December 1983), and a height of 32 metres. The trunk bifurcates fairly low down, and it is possible that this is an ancient coppice stool with two very old stems that have coalesced at the base. (Compartment 3, SK54031255, March 1984.)

7.4 Point Centred Quarter Survey

7.4.1 Method

The recording procedure is a version of the *Point Centred Quarter* (PCQ) method of Cottam & Curtis (1956). The method does not use plots or quadrats, but establishes a regular grid of sampling points in the stand to be described. For each of the four quadrants around every point, the distance from the point to the nearest tree, its species, the number of stems and their girths are recorded (figure 7.5). The actual shape of the whole grid of points is immaterial. Neither does the distance between points matter, so long as it is not so short that a particular tree is likely to be recorded twice. Thus, the method is adaptable for any shape of stand, and for any size above about one hectare. It is efficient in terms of the information gathered for the effort required. Calculations provide an estimate of the frequency and density of each species, along with an index of its biomass. The technique has been popular in North America (e.g. Habek 1968, Capelnor 1968), but less so in Britain (Cameron 1980).

In practice, a grid of 30 x 30 m was found to be suitable for most compartments. The cardinal points of the compass established the orientation of the grid. The aim was to get 25 points, yielding data on 100 trees, in each compartment. Compartments 20 and 82 were surveyed with a grid of 25 m, but in the latter case only 17 points would fit within the compartment boundary. With the grid reduced to 20 m, 25 sampling points were squeezed into compartment 81. Large compartments, such as 4, could have been surveyed with a larger grid so that samples would have been more equitably spread throughout the compartment. However, to have increased the grid size beyond 30 m (the length of a tape) would have greatly extended the time taken to locate each sampling point, and pushed the fieldwork into a fourth year. The procedure actually adopted in large compartments was to survey a 'typical' part of it with a 30 m grid. The shaded areas on figure 7.6 show the compartments (or stands within compartments) that were surveyed.

Point-to-tree distances were measured to the centres of tree-trunks or, for trees with multiple stems, to the centre of the stool. They were rounded to the nearest half metre. Girths at breast height, *gbh*, were measured to the nearest centimetre. Some oak and lime trees were found to have prominent bosses at this level, so then girth measurements were taken a little higher or lower. A few centimetres were deducted from girth measurements that included stout stems of ivy. For a plant to qualify for inclusion in this survey it must have had at least one living stem of 15 cm gbh or more, or else at least two living stems of 12 cm gbh or more. In counting the number of stems, those smaller than 10 cm gbh, and dead stems, were ignored. Occasionally, there was some doubt as to whether or not stems belonged to the same individual tree. These problems were resolved by checking for such genetic traits as leaf characters, branching angle, bark texture and so on. In Swithland Wood these characters are often noticeably different from one tree to the next.

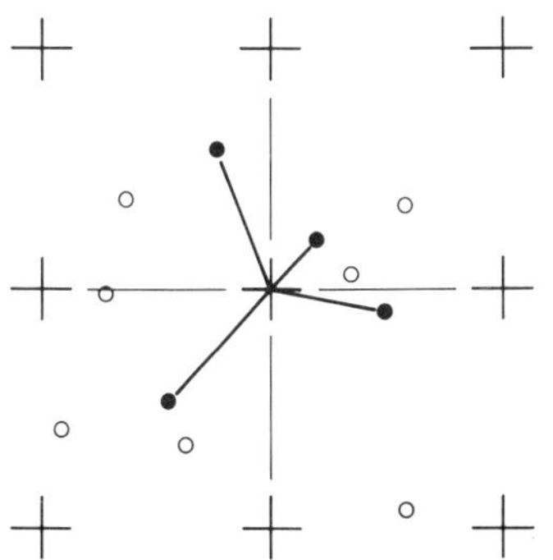

Figure 7.5. Point Centred Quarter method for estimating stand structure and species composition. The nine crosses represent part of the grid of sampling points. The circles denote trees in an imaginary piece of woodland. The solid circles and thick lines show, respectively, which trees and distances are recorded from the sampling point in the centre of the figure. The density of trees per unit area is is given by the reciprocal of the square of the mean distance.

The survey was carried out in the late summer/autumn of 1983, 1984 and 1985.

7.4.2 Results and analysis

The raw field data (details of 2347 stems) are too voluminous to be included in this report, but a paper copy has been lodged with the biological records section of Leicestershire Museums. Summaries of each compartment are contained in tables 7.2 to 7.12 (page 205). The following paragraphs explain the terms used on these tables and how the various parameters have been calculated.

The density of trees, i.e. the number per hectare, is calculated from the point to tree distances as follows:

$$\text{Density} = \frac{10000}{(\text{mean distance})^2}$$

Frequency here is the number of individuals of the species concerned. It should be noted that this use of the word is not the same as its use in the field layer and sapling studies. The reason for the different interpretation is that those studies were based on quadrats, whereas the present technique is plotless. Frequency has been quoted separately for standard or single-stemmed trees (std) and coppiced or multi-stemmed trees (cop). *Total frequency* is also given in the tables, along with *relative frequency* expressed as a percentage.

The *basal area* of a tree is its cross-sectional area at breast height. It may be calculated from the girth by assuming that the section is circular. If the tree has multiple stems, the basal areas of all stems are totalled.

$$\text{Cross-sectional area} = \frac{\text{girth}^2}{4\pi}$$

Clearly, the larger the basal area of a tree, the greater will be its contribution to the canopy. Cottam and Curtis (1956) used the term *relative dominance* for the proportion of the total basal area contributed by each species.

$$\text{Relative dominance of species } i = \frac{\text{Cross-sectional area of species } i \times 100}{\text{Total cross-sectional area}}$$

Relative dominance is comparable with *cover* used in the field layer study, in that both may be regarded as an approximate index of biomass (Goldsmith, Harrison & Morton 1986). The relative dominance of the species within each compartment is shown graphically in figure 7.6.

Mean basal area describes the average size of a tree in a given compartment:

$$\text{Mean basal area} = \frac{\text{total basal area of the sample}}{\text{Number of trees in sample}}$$

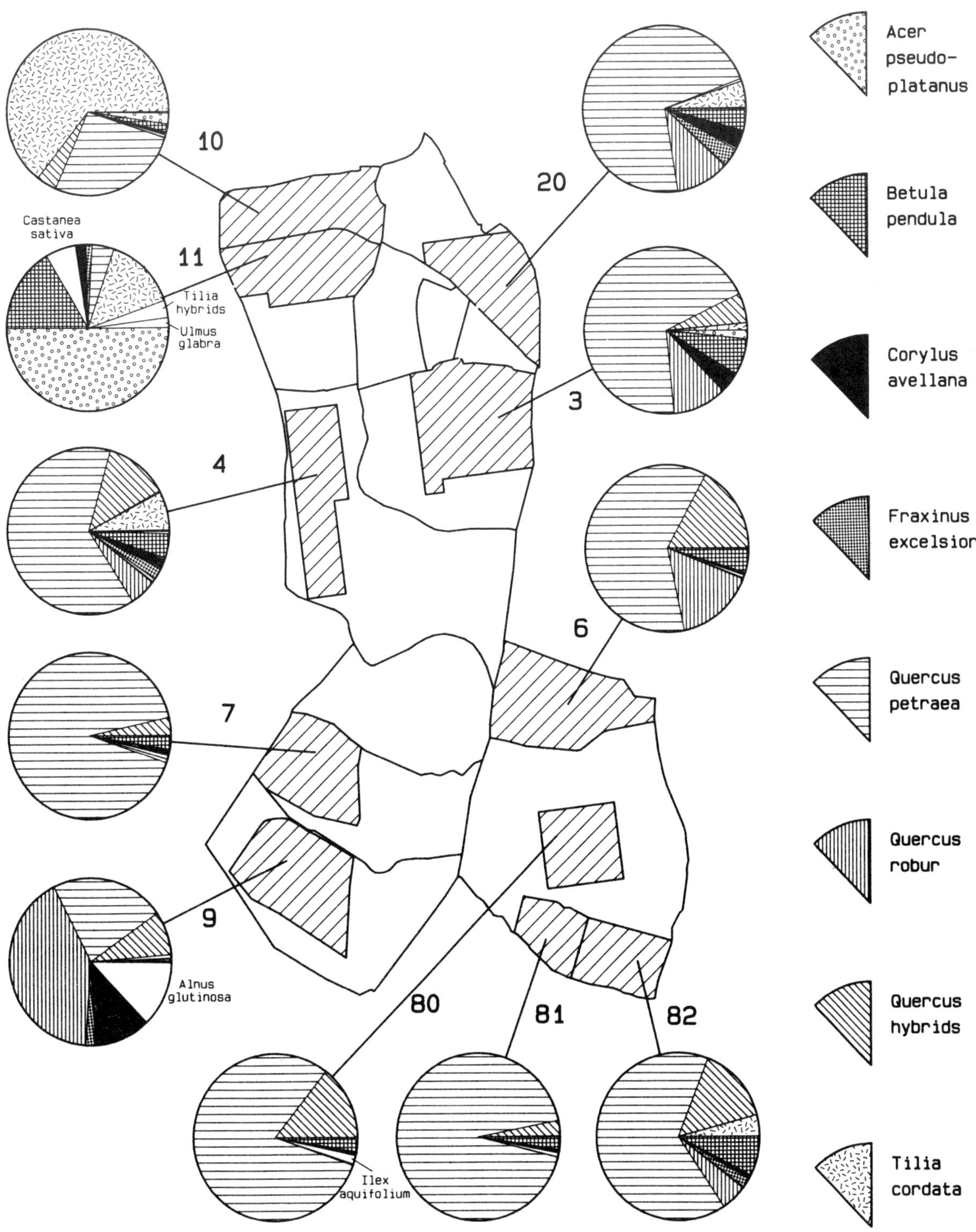

Figure 7.6. Locations and results of the Point Centred Quarter surveys. The areas surveyed are shaded on the map. The pie charts express the relative basal area of each species. The figures are compartment numbers. The principal species have been denoted by shading and some less important ones are named alongside the pie charts. No attempt has been made to identify the least important species on this diagram; reference should be made to tables 7.2 to 7.12.

To understand *relative basal area*, as this term is used here, it is helpful to imagine a surface at 1.3 m (breast height) above the ground. Relative basal area is the percentage of this surface occupied by the stems of trees and shrubs. It is an index of the total biomass of woody plants per unit area, or how thickly wooded a particular compartment is. It is analogous to *total cover* used in the field layer study. The calculation is as follows:

```
Relative basal area = Density x Mean basal area x 100
```

Girth distributions for the more frequent species are shown as histograms in figure 7.8. These plots have been compiled from both standard trees and the largest stems of coppiced trees.

7.4.3 Discussion

The PCQ survey has gathered a great deal of data on the canopy and shrub layers. Before analysing the results at the compartment level, we will first discuss some more general aspects, including some of the parameters to be used in the compartment descriptions.

Density

In calculating density from distance measurements, it is necessary to assume that there is no correlation between the regular grid of sampling points and any periodicity that may exist in the stand, such as might be expected in a plantation. Trees did not appear to be regularly spaced, but this assumption has not been formally tested. Since sampling was non-random, confidence limits cannot be quoted for the calculated estimates. However, regular sampling need not be less accurate than random sampling; indeed it has often been found to be more accurate (Prince 1986). In their study sites, using random point locations, Cottam and Curtis (1956) found that 40 distance measurements gave a standard error of 10%, a value generally considered to be satisfactory for ecological work. The present survey, being based on substantially more measurements than this, should be at least as accurate with regard to density.

The values of density range widely, from 198 trees/hectare in compartment 4, to 578 in compartment 11. In compartments such as 11, where trees are packed closely together, the mean basal area is small. This is perhaps not surprising, but the statistical correlation between the two parameters is remarkably strong (figure 7.7). The regression equation which best fits the data tells us that the product of density and mean basal area is approximately constant for all compartments. This product is, in fact, relative basal area (quoted on tables 7.2 - 7.12) which ranges from 0.29% (cmpt 9) to 0.45% (cmpt 81). It appears that the biomass of woody growth per unit area that is supported by each compartment is roughly equal, whether it is made up of many small trees or fewer large ones.

This result was not expected. Some compartments, such as 10 and those with many shrubs, give the impression of being much more thickly wooded than others, such as 80. In fact, compartment 10 is only 25% greater than compartment 80 in terms of relative basal area. Furthermore, compartment 11, whose age structure testifies to a recent felling (see below), yields a similar figure to the more mature compartments. Recent management of Swithland Wood has not entailed thinning. It looks as though a natural processes of self-thinning is responsible.

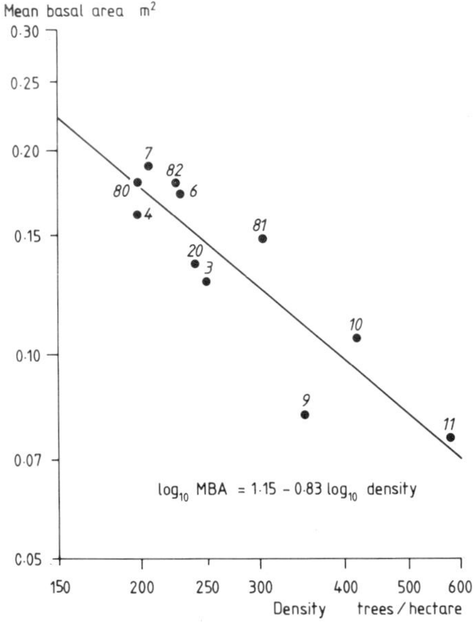

Figure 7.7. Tree density against mean basal area (both on logarithmic scales). The linear regression line and its equation are shown. The coefficient of determination, r^2, is 0.8. The compartment number is shown beside each point.

Frequency

Which are the commonest tree species in Swithland Wood, and how common are they? To answer to this simple question, we need to perform more calculations on the results, to allow for the different sizes of the compartments. Assuming that the PCQ stands are truly representative of their respective compartments, the number of trees per compartment is found by multiplying the total density by the compartment area and then by the relative frequency for the species concerned. Having done this for each compartment, a grand total for all compartments can be computed. The results are shown in figure 7.9. They require some qualification. Firstly, they are strongly influenced by the minimum girth requirement: *A. pseudoplatanus*, for example, would decline significantly in frequency if the minimum girth were raised from 15 cm to (for the sake of argument) 25 cm, because its population is dominated by small trees. Secondly, the species that predominate in the marshes, notably *Alnus*, are under-represented because these areas were not sampled. To a lesser extent the same applies to the vegetation of outcrops, in which *Betula* is important, if somewhat low in density. Bearing in mind that these areas are small in proportion to the whole wood, the results shown in figure 7.9 may be taken as a reasonable assessment of tree frequencies in Swithland Wood.

Frequency follows a familiar ecological pattern, with a few species being found often, and rather more occurring infrequently (Begon, Harper & Townsend 1986, page 596). Of the 24 species recorded, seven of them account for 90% of trees. These are, in order of importance, *Quercus petraea, Corylus, A. pseudoplatanus, Betula, Tilia,* pedunculate oak *Quercus robur* and intermediate oaks (presumed hybrids). Inevitably, some of the other species are represented in the samples by so few individuals that little can be said about their populations. Thus, trees such as wild cherry *Prunus avium* and sweet chestnut *Castanea sativa* do not warrant inclusion in the girth distribution histograms.

Dominance

A similar procedure may be used to estimate the dominance of each species, by taking into account basal areas. For each compartment, the density figure is used to calculate what proportion of all its trees was sampled. Then, by dividing the total basal area of the sample by this proportion, the total basal area of the compartment is obtained. This total is apportioned among the various species. Finally, for each species, the contributions from all compartments are summed.

7. Shrub and Canopy Layers

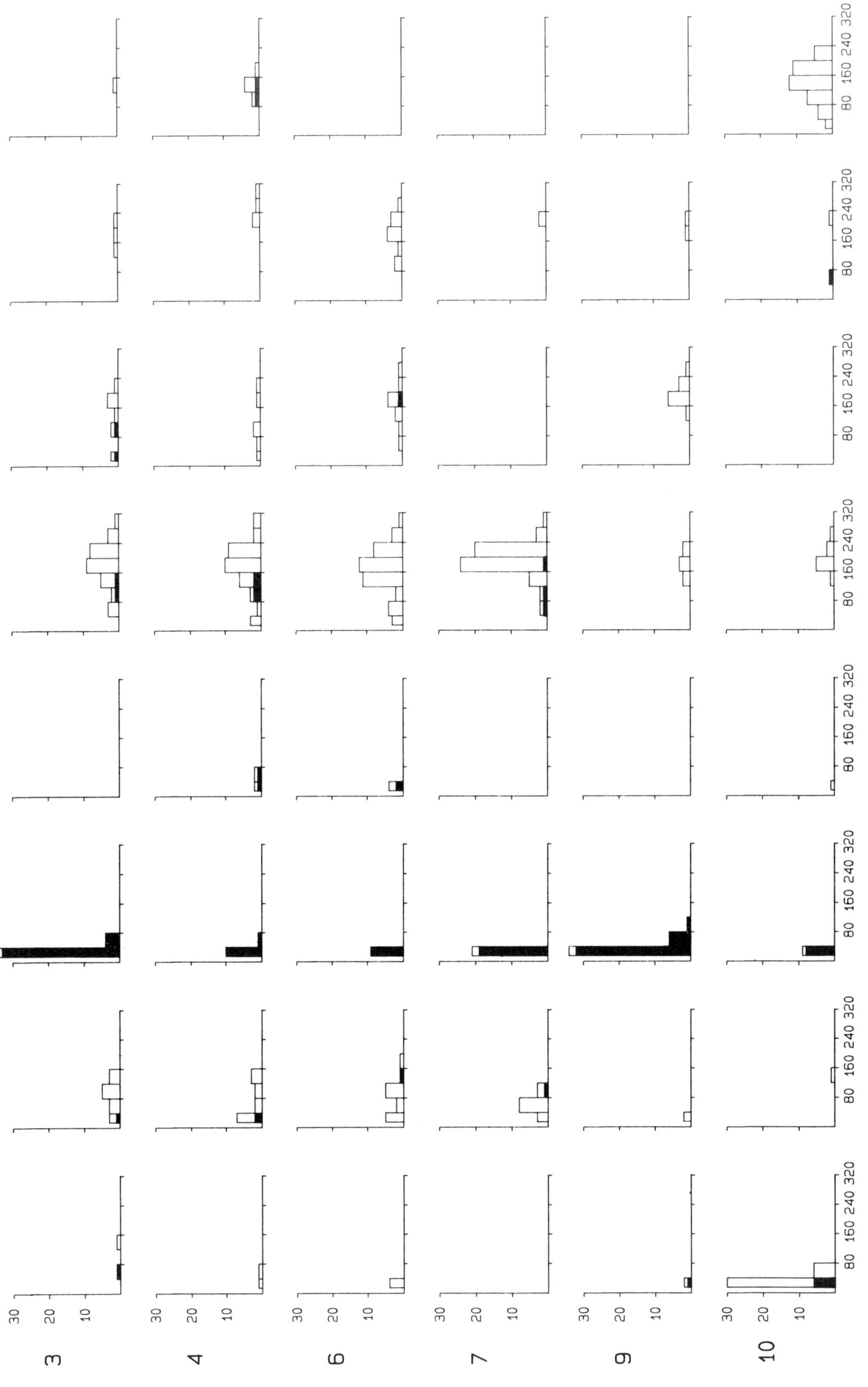

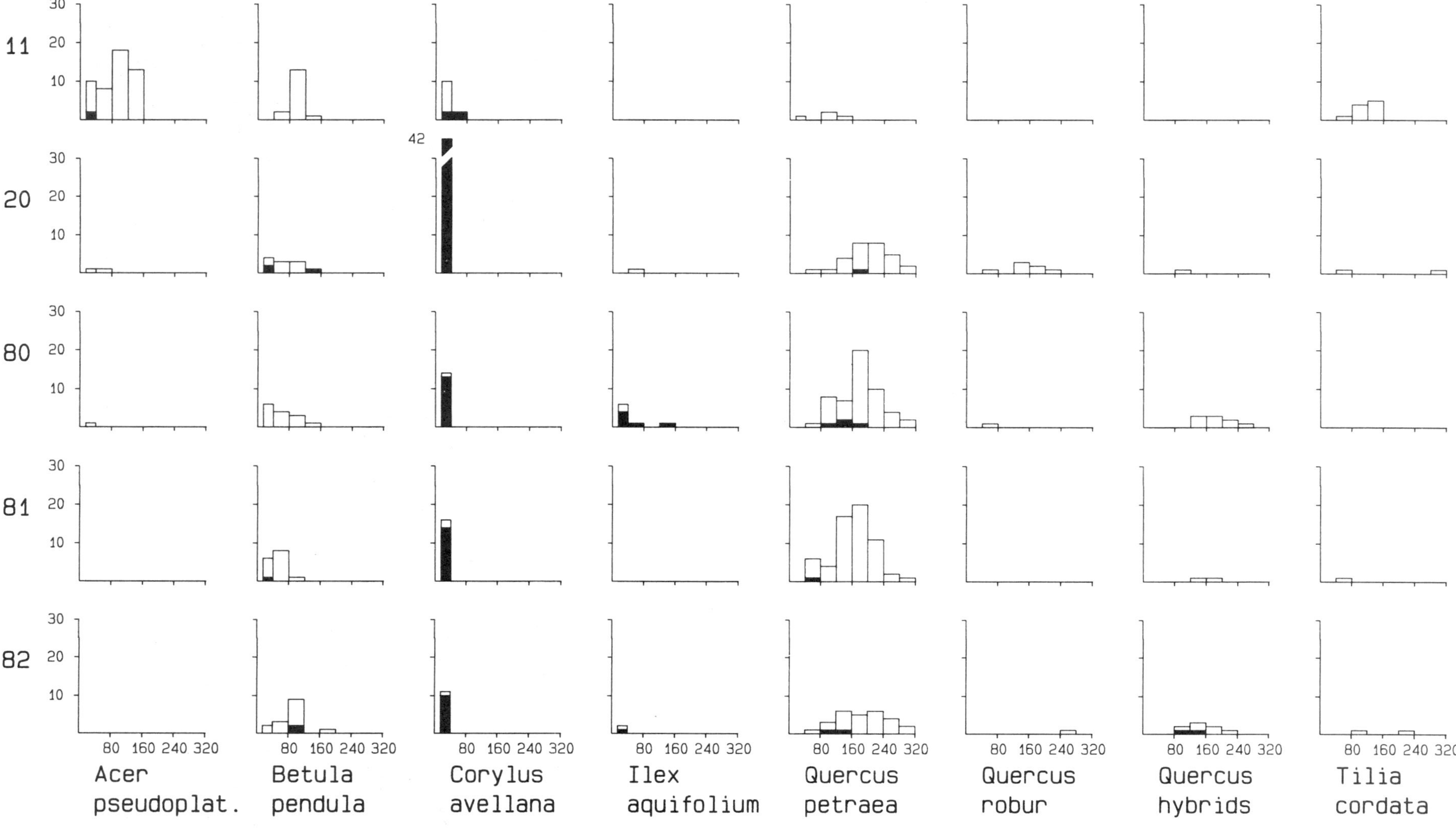

Figure 7.8. Girth distributions of the eight principal species in the eleven compartments. Each histogram shows girth of the largest stem in centimetres (horizontal axis) against the number of trees recorded (vertical axis). The width of each girth class is 40 cm, except the first which is 15 to 40 cm. Solid areas represent the largest stems of multi-stemmed trees.

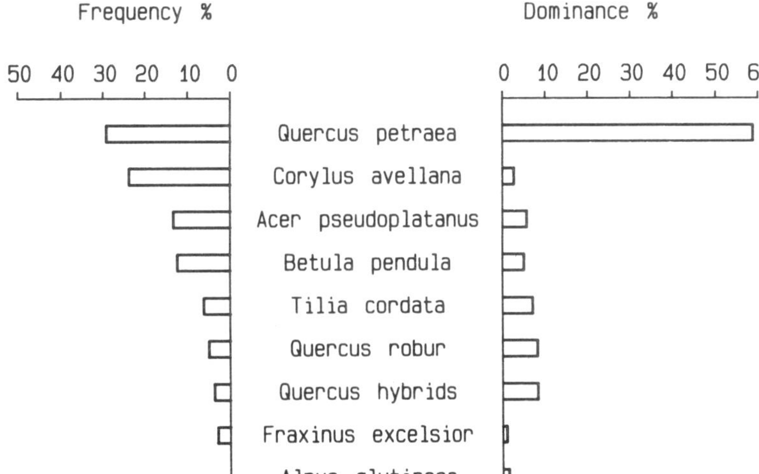

Figure 7.9. Frequency and dominance of common trees and shrubs. The species shown are those within the top eight of either frequency or dominance.

The results are also shown on figure 7.9. The pattern is strikingly different from the frequency results. *Quercus petraea* is far more dominant than any other species, accounting for 58.7% of basal area. In second place are oak intermediates (8.2%), closely followed by *Quercus robur* (8.1%). Hence, three quarters of Swithland Wood's canopy is oak of various sorts. Foremost among the remaining species are: *Tilia* (7.0%), *A. pseudoplatanus* (5.7%), *Betula* (5.0%), *Corylus* (2.7%) and *Alnus* (1.4%). The latter species has been underestimated, as previously explained.

Canopy species prevail in the above list, with only one shrubby species, *Corylus*, represented. *Ilex*, with 0.43% dominance and *Crataegus* with 0.26% are the only other shrub layer species which score greater than 0.1%. These figures emphasise the very poorly developed shrub layer throughout much of the wood (figure 7.10).

Figure 7.10. Compartment 80 is typical of much of Swithland Wood in having no shrub layer (SK54191194, March 1990.)

Species composition of compartments

The species composition of the compartments (using basal areas) is shown on figure 7.6. There are some striking similarities and some equally conspicuous differences. Five compartments (3, 4, 6, 20, 82) share the following characteristics: three kinds of oak make up 81-94% of basal area with *Q. petraea* predominant; the remaining species are *Betula, Corylus* and usually *Ilex* and *Tilia*. In three other compartments (7, 80, 81), oak contributes about 95%, but *Q. robur* is all but absent (0.2% in cmpt. 80). The remaining cover is mainly *Betula*. Compartments 9, 10 and 11 are very different from both each other and from those mentioned above. In each case *Q. petraea* is not the most important species. The principal tree in compartment 9 is *Q. robur* (42%). The total for all kinds of oak is 73%. It contains a lot of *Alnus* growing alongside the former course of the stream, and the greatest proportion of *Corylus* (11%) of any compartment. *Tilia* (64%) prevails in compartment 10, the bulk of the remainder being *Q. petraea* (27%). A little *A. pseudoplatanus* (2%) gets into compartment 10, but this species is most abundant in compartment 11. Here, it forms 50% and grows alongside *Betula* (17%) and *Tilia* (15%). Oak is notably scarce (4%). The sample happened to include the two large specimens of *Castanea sativa*, so the 6% assigned to this species is an over-estimate for the compartment. Wych elm *Ulmus glabra*, an uncommon species in the wood, accounts for 2% of the basal area in compartment 11.

Structure of compartments

The girth measurements and stem counts allow the structure of the compartments to be investigated, that is to say the relative proportion of trees of various forms and sizes. Figure 7.8 shows the structure of each compartment, as far as the eight main species are concerned. The figure distinguishes multi-stemmed from single stemmed trees by shading. It will be seen at once that nearly all the multi-stemmed trees are *Corylus* bushes, and that relatively few specimens of *Corylus* were recorded as having a single stem. It was observed in the field that the largest stem is nearly always rotten; evidently once a stem attains a girth of about 40 cm it dies and makes way for the younger shoots, which invariably spring from the stool. The height of a hazel bush is generally between 6 and 10 m. The 'self-coppicing' habit frustrates attempts to identify those that have been deliberately cut.

Looking at the overall proportion of multi-stemmed to single-stemmed trees in each compartment, it appears that this is directly related to the quantity of *Corylus*. Hence, compartment 9 is the only one with more multi-stemmed than single-stemmed trees (60:40). The scarcity of multi-stemmed *Quercus* and *Tilia* is remarkable in view of the wood's history of coppicing (but see section 7.5).

Betula is too short-lived to attain any great girth, 160 cm being the normal limit, yet it rapidly grows up to 25 m tall alongside the other canopy species. Although numerous birches were either felled or wind-thrown during the survey, the writer was never successful in obtaining a reliable ring-count, so its typical lifespan in Swithland Wood is unknown. The population is deficient in young trees, but less so than some other species. In contrast, *A. pseudoplatanus* is very well represented in the lower girth classes (notably in compartment 10) but there are few large trees. *Ilex* does not grow large enough to reach the canopy, but usually forms short trees with numerous low branches. It normally attains 10 m in height, alongside *Corylus* and other shrubs. A few specimens, however, have grown into respectable trees that tower above the shrub layer, up to 18 m tall (figure 7.11). Of the three kinds of oak shown, *Q. petraea* shows the clearest trends since it is the most numerous, but there is nothing to suggest that *Q. robur* nor the hybrids behave any differently. A wide range of girths is found, up to about 320 cm. The size distribution of oak peaks in the girth class 160-200 cm: middle-aged trees predominate here. These would be roughly 140 years old according to figure 7.3. A typical height for mature oaks is 25 m,

Figure 7.11. A large holly tree (behind a birch), 16 m tall. (Compartment 4, SK53991234, February 1991.)

maximum 30 m. Young trees are uncommon: very few compartments were able to contribute trees of the smallest girth class (15-40 cm) to the sample.

In compartment 10, the girth distribution is very similar to most other compartments, but here, the dominant canopy species is *Tilia* rather than *Quercus*. A detailed discussion of the lime population beyond compartment 10 will be included in the following section, where extra data arising from a special study are presented. Three ring counts from felled limes here gave the year of establishment as 1868, 1870 and 1874 respectively. These dates are remarkably close to one another considering the spread of their girths: 190, 170 and 235 cm. With only three non-random samples available, no definite conclusions may be reached, but these observations do remind us to exercise caution when using girth as an index of age. It looks as though the limes were established at the same time, say 1871, and the spread of girths is due to different growth rates.

In a wood that has been managed for timber, as Swithland Wood certainly has, we might expect to find peaks in the girth distributions corresponding to phases of planting, and troughs corresponding to fellings. In particular, the historical record leads us to expect a peak corresponding to the planting in 1909 of more than 12,000 trees (see section 3.6.4).

This quantity of trees, even allowing for thinning, should be very conspicuous in the wood today, which is manifestly not the case. Only compartment 7 exhibits a clear peak (in *Q. petraea*), which probably relates to an unrecorded planting about 140 years ago. Evidence of felling is found in compartment 11, which lacks trees over 160 cm in girth. An aerial photograph taken in 1969 (ref. 26) clearly shows that trees were smaller here than elsewhere in the study area. Generally, though, the effects of management are not obvious. In part, this is due to the variation in growth rates of individual trees, as we have seen in lime. Girth distribution provides, at best, a blurred representation of age distribution (Buchholz & Pickering 1978, Stewart 1986). Other factors, related to felling and planting practices, will be discussed in chapter 8.

7.5 Small-leaved Lime in Swithland Wood

Woods with a large population of small-leaved lime are by no means widespread in the east Midlands, particularly so in Leicestershire (Rackham 1980, Primavesi & Evans 1988). Moreover, the magnificent high forest stand of lime in compartment 10 of Swithland Wood must be regarded as most unusual in a national context (Peterken, *pers. comm.*).

Lime is exceptionally interesting with regard to its historical ecology (Rackham 1976). Studies in various parts of Britain and Europe have demonstrated the fidelity of this species as an ancient woodland indicator (Greig 1982). It is regarded as a relict species, persisting in places where it has evaded clearance, but not spreading to new sites (Pigott 1969, Turner 1962). Yet, in Swithland Wood, lime commonly grows on ridge-and-furrow - incontrovertible evidence of secondary woodland! In an attempt to reconcile the occurrence of lime with ridge-and-furrow, a special study of the lime population was made. This work concentrated on details of spatial distribution, particularly the relationship to earthworks, and the size and form of the trees. (This study was submitted as a dissertation; see Woodward 1988.)

7.5.1 Method

The PCQ survey of compartment 10 was considered to describe the lime population there adequately. Elsewhere, lime is poorly represented in the PCQ samples, so a search was made for every individual tree or sapling. They were marked on a 1:2500 map, and a record was made of the number of stems and the girth at breast height of the largest stem. This was carried out in the winters of 1986/7 and 1987/8. Seedlings were also noted but not mapped.

7.5.2 Results

Lime was found in every woodland compartment except number 7. Some 402 individuals were mapped. Along with the estimated 378 trees in compartment 10, this gives a total for the wood of about 780 lime trees. The resulting map, figure 7.12, clearly shows a clumped distribution: this tree is strongly gregarious. Indeed, trees were often so close together, it was sometimes difficult to decide whether they were actually all one individual, connected below ground.

From previous fieldwork, it was known that a few lime trees in compartments 10 and 11 were not pure *Tilia cordata*, judging by the size of the leaves, and the tufts of pale coloured (not rusty brown) hairs in their vein axils. During the flora survey, they were identified as common lime *T.* x *europaea*, the hybrid that is often planted along town streets. The number of trees concerned, about five, is so insignificant that no precautions were taken to avoid them in the present survey.

7. Shrub and Canopy Layers

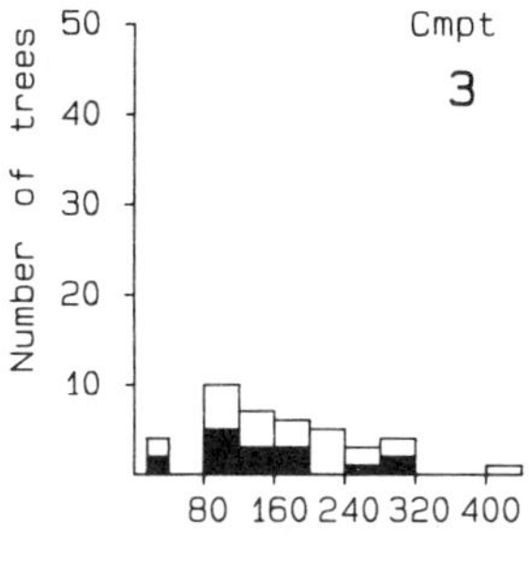

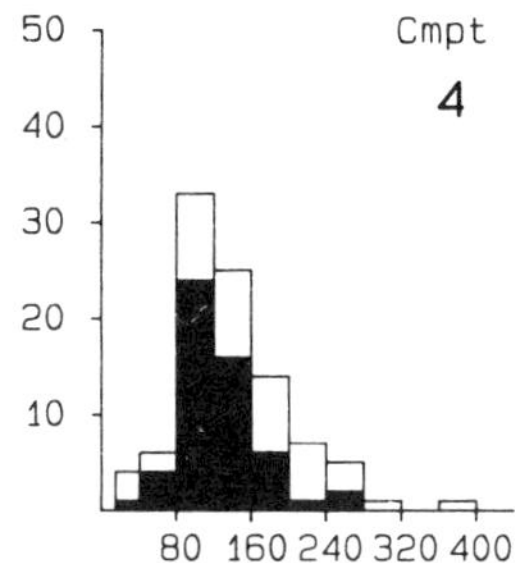

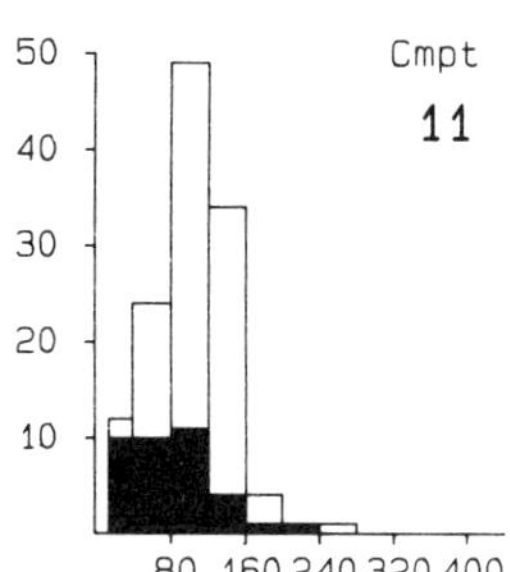

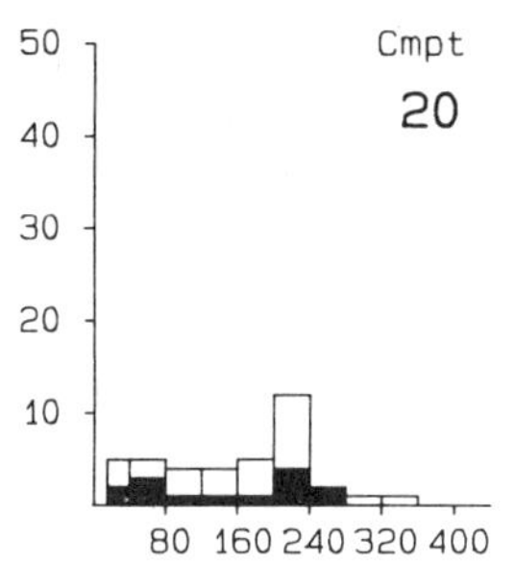

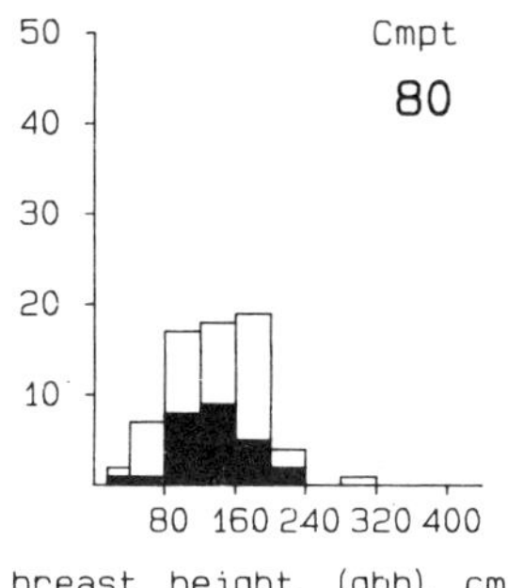

Figure 7.13. Girth distribution of all small-leaved limes in compartments where they are numerous. A sample of the population in compartment 10 is included on figure 7.8. The width of each girth class is 40 cm, except the first, which is 15 to 40 cm. Solid areas represent the largest stems of multi-stemmed trees.

The numbers of coppiced and standard trees outside compartment 10, are 240 and 158 respectively, to which should be added four saplings planted in 1986. Their overall girth distribution (not illustrated) has a single mode in the girth class 80 - 120 cm, tailing off towards a massive tree with a girth of 432 cm (figure 7.4). The sharp decrease in numbers towards the smaller trees accords with the findings of the PCQ survey: only 7.3% of individuals have their largest stem smaller than 40 cm in girth. Figure 7.13 gives the girth distribution for those compartments with sufficient trees for histograms to be meaningful. Compartment 4 and, to large extent, compartment 80 conform to the overall pattern. We have already noted the lack of large trees in compartment 11. Limes are not particularly numerous in compartments 3 and 20, but they are spread fairly evenly across the range of sizes.

It was mentioned in section 7.2.3 that lime saplings are conspicuous by their absence in the field layer quadrats. A thorough search of the whole wood located only seven examples, four of which are known to have been planted. Seedlings too were difficult to find. Their appearance is quite characteristic although, to the uninitiated, they would not be recognised as lime at all (figure 7.14). In compartment 10, some were found after a few minutes searching in June of 1984, 1985 and 1986. Less than five were found in compartments 3 and 11, but several searches in the south of compartment 80 and elsewhere failed to locate a single seedling. Attempts to re-find seedlings at the end of July invariably failed completely.

7.5.3 Discussion

Comparison of figures 7.12 and 2.10 reveals the extent to which lime trees grow over ridge-and-furrow. A statistical test has shown that the tree is not significantly commoner

< **Figure 7.12.** Distribution of small-leaved lime. Each spot represents an individual tree, so far as is possible at this scale. Crosses denote saplings known to have been planted. The compartments and their numbers are also shown.

Figure 7.14. Small-leaved lime seedlings. Unlike seedlings such as those of oak, in which the cotyledons remain in the seed-coat, lime seedlings withdraw them so that they may photosynthesise (Busgen & Munch 1929). The cotyledons bear no resemblance to the later leaves, which assume the familiar heart shape.

on unploughed (and therefore possibly primary) parts of the wood. However, it is strongly correlated with parts of the wood within 20 metres of outcrops, quarries and boundary features (Woodward 1988). Obviously, ploughing could never have taken place where the rock reaches the surface. The boundaries concerned are respected by the ridge-and-furrow, strongly suggesting that they are contemporary with the arable cultivation. In formerly wooded districts, it was common practice to create a field boundary by improvising a hedge out of the existing vegetation (Hoskins 1972, Pollard 1973), which would explain the persistence of lime there. It appears that outcrops (some of which later became quarries) and boundaries served as refuges where relicts of woodland vegetation survived.

Supporting evidence for lime's relict status is found in the age structure of the population and the form of the trees. The girth distribution histograms highlight the deficiency in young trees. Seedlings are scarce and apparently short-lived, whereas saplings (other than planted ones) are all but absent. For many years, lime has failed to regenerate from seed in Swithland Wood.

Vegetative reproduction is quite another matter. Lime's capacity for regrowth is amply demonstrated by the vigorous coppice stools. Nearly all of the young lime stems in the wood spring from coppice stools, although this is not reflected in the girth histograms because only the largest stems are shown. Some of the stools are impressively large (figure 7.15). Parts of the study area boundary (compartments 3, 4, 20 and 6) are occupied by 'layered' lime trees, apparently trained along the woodbank there. One massive individual measures 20 metres from end to end. Presumably, this boundary used to be a lime hedge. C. D. Pigott tells me that he has found similar boundaries in Lancashire (*pers. comm.*). During the blizzard of 8 December 1990, many lime tree branches were buckled over by the weight of snow. The instinctive reaction of wood owners to this kind of damage is, it seems, to send in men with chain-saws to 'tidy up'. In fact, the population of lime trees might, if left alone, have gained from such damage. Where branches come into contact with the ground, they are able to take root and give rise to new trees. There are several examples in Swithland Wood of natural layering (figure 7.16). The bizarre tree in compartment 11 (at SK53631284), which is rooted in no less than five different places, seems to have received some human encouragement. Coppicing and layering are management techniques that exploit the remarkable capacity of this tree to make the most of any physical injury.

< **Figure 7.15.** A large coppiced small-leaved lime, uncut for very many years. The largest of five stems is 224 cm in girth (measured December 1983) and the stool is about two metres in diameter. (Compartment 20, SK53891290, December 1986.)

Figure 7.16 (below). Layering in small-leaved lime. One of the stems has been partially split at the base, apparently by a lightening strike. The fallen stem has touched the ground 5.3 metres away, where it has taken root and given rise to a new tree. (Compartment 3, SK54011249, December 1986.)

These observations corroborate the findings in other areas (Pigott 1969, Pigott & Huntley 1978). The climate has cooled since lime spread across lowland Britain about 7000 years ago, sufficiently for the viability of seed to be significantly affected. Now, summer temperatures are generally too low for regular regeneration from seed. The few seedlings that do germinate are eagerly consumed by rodents, especially bank voles (Pigott 1985). Thus, seedling establishment might be expected to occur only when a warm summer is followed by one or two poor rodent years. Even if conditions were favourable just once per century, this could still be often enough for such a long-lived tree as lime to initiate the next generation, bearing mind that only a single successful seedling is needed per parent tree to maintain a population. The inability to spread any appreciable distance, coupled with its tenacity at a given site, explains why lime is such a reliable ancient woodland indicator. In Swithland Wood, most of the clusters of lime trees can be explained by vegetative spread from refuge sites; outcrops and former hedges. In addition, limited regeneration from seed appears to have occurred from time to time, judging from the isolated clusters on ridge-and-furrow. During the period of coppice management, limes in the body of the wood could not have set seed, but biologically mature trees may have been present in the hedges and perhaps around the outcrops.

The lime population in compartment 10 differs in several respects from the rest of the wood. Firstly, the cover is dense; secondly, the distribution is even rather than clumped; and thirdly, the trees are all standards except for a few old coppice stools along its northern margin. The overall impression is that of a plantation. Further discussion on the status of this stand will be presented in chapter 8 (page 215).

7.6 Conclusion

7.6.1 Regeneration

Having considered the regeneration of lime, we can now turn to other species, drawing together the data on seedlings, saplings (from chapter 6) and trees. Generally, the information available on seedlings and saplings is inadequate for analysis by compartment, so the results have been pooled for the whole wood. For this discussion, all three kinds of oak are aggregated, because seedlings were not identified to species. If we assume that all seedlings, of whatever kind, are similar in size, then the total cover of tree species recorded in the field layer is roughly proportional to the total number of seedlings.

Oak

On this basis, oak holds first place in terms of both seedling and tree numbers. Yet the girth histograms show that young trees are scarce; certainly too few to maintain the present dominance of oak in the canopy. As one comes down in girth from 160 cm there are progressively fewer trees. Have smaller trees been removed or did they never become established in the first place? Thinning on this scale seems unlikely since the lapse of commercial management in the 1920s. On the other hand, it is now very commonly observed that British oakwoods fail to regenerate naturally. This phenomenon was first noticed in the latter half of the nineteenth century, and has attracted the attention of woodland ecologists from the early 1900s (Rackham 1980). Watt (1919) attempted to explain the regeneration 'problem' in terms of the numerous hazards faced by acorns and seedlings; predation, shade, mildew and so on. He drew attention to factors whose impact on oak regeneration had increased in recent historic times, notably the rearing of game in woods. Not only do pheasants eat acorns, but so do the rodents whose populations benefit from the efforts of gamekeepers to keep down predators.

Figure 7.17. A small patch of woodland, south of the Wood Meadows, with numerous oak saplings. Generally, these are uncommon in Swithland Wood. (Compartment 3, SK53821266, March 1990.)

Later, Shaw (1974) concluded that the problem was not with regeneration as such, but with ecologists' perceptions of what the age structure of a healthy oakwood ought to be. The presumption that a naturally regenerating population should necessarily contain all ages of tree is, he argued, erroneous. Oak is not among the few British tree species that can grow up under their own shade; oaklings are suppressed not only by the shade itself but also by hungry caterpillars which fall from the canopy. Only when the canopy is opened up do opportunities arise for recruitment. In a truly natural wood, senescent oaks would collapse from time to time and initiate a local flush of saplings. Various areas of a large wood would be in different stages of regeneration, although locally the trees would tend to be even-aged (Jones 1945). The situation in British woods that are managed for oak timber is that large sections are deliberately manipulated to be even-aged, but not allowed to become senescent. Thus, opportunities for oak saplings are confined to the wood boundaries and edges of rides. In Swithland Wood there exist areas where numerous saplings have survived (figure 7.17), but these areas are tiny in relation to the area dominated by oak trees.

A closer look at the findings of the Swithland Wood survey shows that seedling mortality can only be part of the story. Some 37 oak saplings were found in a sample area of 6800 m^2, which is equivalent to about 3000 saplings in the whole wood. A similar calculation for the smallest girth class of the PCQ survey, i.e. 15 - 40 cm, gives an estimate of less than 200 trees. It is acknowledged that these extrapolations are based on somewhat limited data, but field experience concurs that there are many more oaks between (say) 5 and 15 cm girth than there are between 15 and 40 cm. Assuming that conditions have not altered in the last ten years or so, very few saplings alive now may be expected to attain a girth of 15 cm. Evidently, sapling mortality is a significant factor also.

Further detailed study would be needed to quantify the relative significance of seedling and sapling mortality, and to establish the actual causes. For the present study, we can do no more than conjecture as to the probable causes, in the knowledge of Swithland Wood's management history. The principal factor is almost certainly increasing shade. Following the conversion from coppice to high forest in the nineteenth century, the canopy has steadily closed in, and made recruitment progressively more difficult. Areas that were opened up by felling or thinning have been invaded by bracken and bramble. Trampling by visitors must surely account for some losses of young oaks, but this hazard would not have been significant while the wood was still under estate control. On the other hand, the influence of gamekeepers would have been greater then than at present.

Although over-mature by forestry standards, the oaks in Swithland Wood show little sign of collapsing of old age. Until this happens, oak regeneration will remain confined to very few small, open areas. When eventually the canopy does begin to break up, any saplings that were previously held back by the shade will be released, and will seize the opportunity to fill the gaps. There can be little doubt, however, that oak will be defeated in many places by aggressive species such as bracken and sycamore.

Other species

Sycamore contributes more saplings and young trees than any other species. In the vicinity of the parent trees in compartments 10 and 11, saplings form vigorous thickets, even in the deep shade of a sycamore or small-leaved lime canopy. Among native trees, lime is generally able to hold its own, but in this corner of the wood it is clearly under threat from the alien sycamore. In view of its failure to regenerate from seed, lime may lose out in the long term, unless measures are taken to control sycamore. Although by no means without some wildlife value (particularly for insects), a stand of sycamore would be a poor substitute indeed for the magnificent high forest of lime and oak for which Swithland Wood is renowned. Hazel seedlings are surprisingly difficult to find, considering how widespread and common are the shrubs. Most of the plants which have been recorded as saplings are, in fact, small shrubs that have re-grown from older stools. Like lime, hazel now regenerates vegetatively rather than from seed. Two factors are probably responsible. Firstly, the shrubs are generally well shaded by canopy species, so fruiting is limited to the wood margins and glades. Secondly, any nuts that do form are assiduously collected by grey squirrels. This might actually help with seed dispersal (as with jays and acorns) were it not for the squirrels' habit of taking nuts before they ripen. Woodpigeons may also play a part in the annihilation of the hazel-nut crop (Rackham 1980). Casual observation leads me to believe that populations of both these animals in Swithland Wood are very high indeed. Dispersal is evidently not a problem for the ash tree, for its seedlings were found in more than half of the field layer quadrats. The mature trees are very much less widespread. The curious distribution of the saplings, i.e. on quarry spoil and in the marshy valleys must be controlled by some environmental factor of the habitat, perhaps the availability of bases in the soil.

7.6.2 Variation and classification

This work has highlighted similarities and differences between compartments. It does not show the small-scale variation which undoubtedly exists within compartments - the PCQ technique is unsuitable for resolving this level of detail. Indeed, as discussed more fully in chapter 4, that technique was chosen partly *because* it summarises the vegetation over a relatively large area. Had finer detail been required, it might have been more appropriate to classify areas of the wood into 'vegetation types', and draw their boundaries on a map. Mapping of vegetation types was not attempted for this project, partly because a map had already been published (Peterken 1981, page 219). Figure 7.18 is an amended version of Peterken's map.

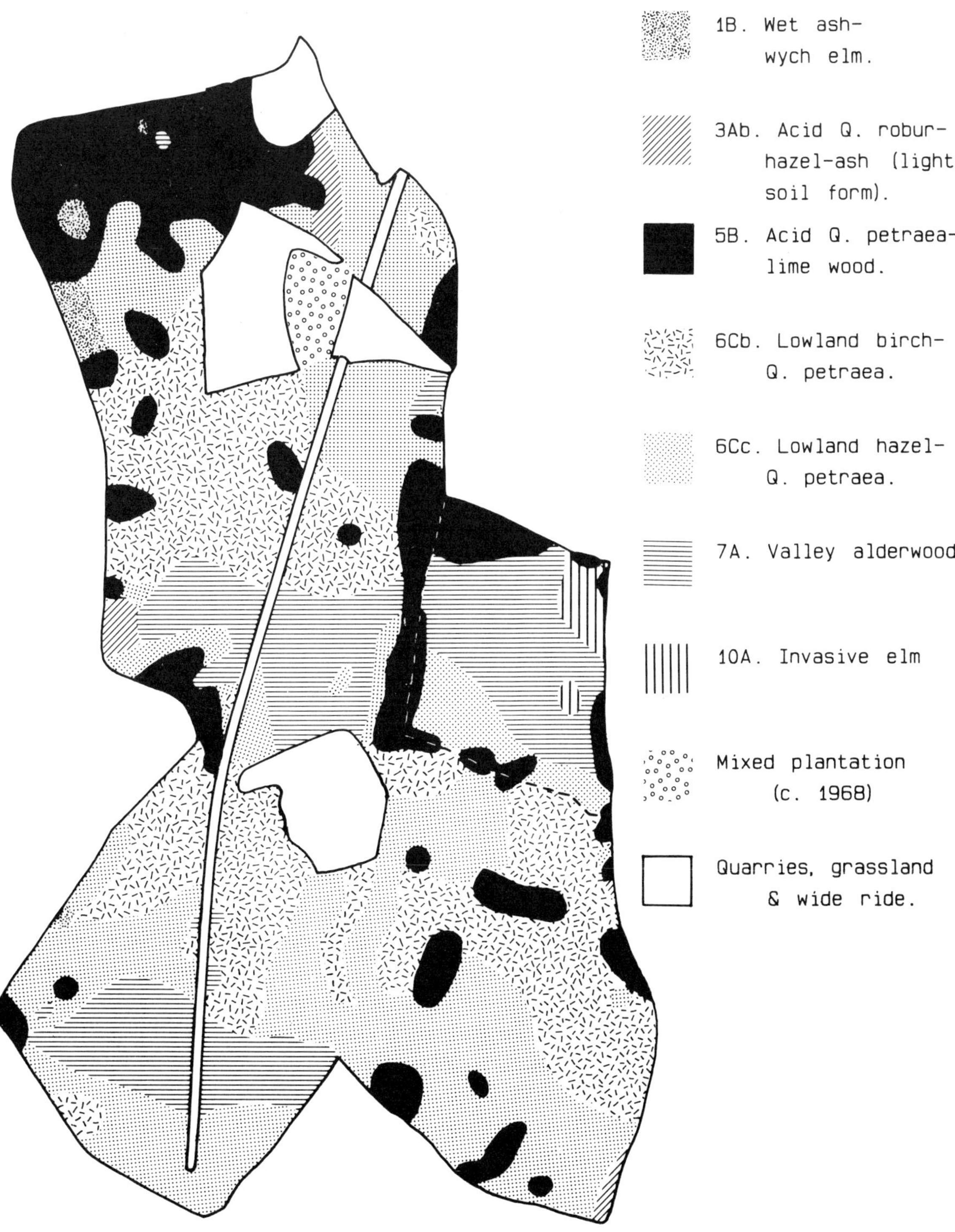

Figure 7.18. Peterken's map of 'stand types', incorporating amendments arising from the accurate plotting of lime trees by the present author. (Reproduced by permission of Chapman and Hall.)

Peterken recognised seven *stand types*, whose distribution within the wood proved to be unusually complex. His scheme is aimed at semi-natural woodland, so the plantation (cmpt 22) is not assigned a type number. For the same reason, the sycamore thickets are not recognised as a type (sycamore is an alien species). Generally, stand types are recognisable in Swithland Wood by the presence or absence of one or two tree species. For example, alder is sufficient to distinguish stand type 7A from any other; the presence of hazel separates 6Cc from 6Cb, and so on. Readers are referred to Peterken's book for further information on the rationale and details of this particular scheme. In a varied wood such as Swithland, it is especially difficult to decide where to draw the boundaries: does the odd lime tree within *Quercus petraea* woodland really mean that we have a small patch of 5B? If so, should we join it up with a nearby patch of 5B? Although boundaries are inevitably subjective to some extent, a map such as this gives a good overall impression of the variety within the the wood. It is clear, for example, that the Lowland birch-*Q. petraea* wood (6Cb) tends to occur on the outcrops and elevated sections of the wood (cf. figures 2.3 & 2.5); whereas Valley alderwood (7A) is confined to the low ground in between.

Table 7.2. Density and species composition of compartment 3.

Number of trees measured: 100 | Date surveyed: 22 Sep 1984

Density: 249 trees/hectare | Total basal area: 12.84 m^2

Relative basal area: 0.32%

Species	Frequency std	cop	tot	Relative frequency (total) %	Basal area m^2	Relative dominance %
Acer pseudoplatanus	1	1	2	2	0.22	1.7
Betula pendula	13	1	14	14	0.90	7.0
Corylus avellana	1	37	38	38	0.52	4.1
Fagus sylvatica	0	1	1	1	0.004	0.03
Quercus robur	7	2	9	9	1.38	10.7
Quercus petraea	29	2	31	31	8.90	69.3
Quercus hybrids	3	0	3	3	0.73	5.7
Salix capraea	0	1	1	1	0.006	0.05
Tilia cordata	1	0	1	1	0.18	1.4

Table 7.3. Density and species composition of compartment 4.

Number of trees measured: 100 | Date surveyed: 13 Oct 1984

Density: 198 trees/hectare | Total basal area: 16.12 m^2

Relative basal area: 0.32%

Species	Frequency std	cop	tot	Relative frequency (total) %	Basal area m^2	Relative dominance %
Acer pseudoplatanus	2	0	2	2	0.04	0.3
Alnus glutinosa	0	1	1	1	0.08	0.5
Betula pendula	12	2	14	14	0.75	4.7
Betula pubescens	1	0	1	1	0.05	0.3
Corylus avellana	0	11	11	11	0.26	1.6
Crataegus monogyna	1	1	2	2	0.05	0.3
Fraxinus excelsior	4	0	4	4	0.36	2.3
Ilex aquifolium	2	2	4	4	0.10	0.6
Populus tremula	6	0	6	6	0.03	0.2
Quercus robur	6	0	6	6	0.83	5.2
Quercus petraea	32	4	36	36	10.23	63.5
Quercus hybrids	4	0	4	4	2.04	12.7
Sorbus aucuparia	1	1	2	2	0.06	0.3
Tilia cordata	5	2	7	7	1.23	7.6

Table 7.4. Density and species composition of compartment 6.

Number of trees measured: 100 — Date surveyed: 2 Nov 1985

Density: 229 trees/hectare — Total basal area: 17.21 m^2

Relative basal area: 0.39%

Species	Frequency std	cop	tot	Relative frequency (total) %	Basal area m^2	Relative dominance %
Acer pseudoplatanus	4	0	4	4	0.01	0.1
Betula pendula	13	1	14	14	0.81	4.7
Betula pubescens	1	0	1	1	0.01	0.1
Corylus avellana	0	9	9	9	0.07	0.4
Crataegus monogyna	2	0	2	2	0.11	0.6
Ilex aquifolium	2	2	4	4	0.02	0.1
Populus tremula	1	0	1	1	0.02	0.1
Quercus robur	9	1	10	10	2.69	15.6
Quercus petraea	44	0	44	44	10.52	61.2
Quercus hybrids	11	0	11	11	2.94	17.1

Table 7.5. Density and species composition of compartment 7.

Number of trees measured: 100 — Date surveyed: 16 Oct 1983

Density: 206 trees/hectare — Total basal area: 18.99 m^2

Relative basal area: 0.39%

Species	Frequency std	cop	tot	Relative frequency (total) %	Basal area m^2	Relative dominance %
Betula pendula	13	1	14	14	0.52	2.7
Betula pubescens	1	0	1	1	0.01	0.03
Corylus avellana	2	19	21	21	0.23	1.2
Crataegus monogyna	0	2	2	2	0.16	0.9
Crataegus hybrids	2	1	3	3	0.10	0.5
Quercus petraea	54	3	57	57	17.32	91.2
Quercus hybrids	2	0	2	2	0.65	3.4

Table 7.6. Density and species composition of compartment 9.

Number of trees measured: 100 Date surveyed: 28 Sep 1985

Density: 350 trees/hectare

Total basal area: 8.16 m^2
Relative basal area: 0.29%

Species	Frequency std	cop	tot	Relative frequency (total) %	Basal area m^2	Relative dominance %
Acer pseudoplatanus	1	1	2	2	0.02	0.2
Alnus glutinosa	6	6	12	12	1.04	12.7
Betula pendula	2	0	2	2	0.01	0.1
Betula pubescens	1	0	1	1	0.02	0.2
Corylus avellana	2	39	41	41	0.88	10.8
Fraxinus excelsior	4	7	11	11	0.17	2.0
Quercus robur	11	0	11	11	3.38	41.5
Quercus petraea	7	0	7	7	1.86	22.8
Quercus hybrids	2	0	2	2	0.69	8.4
Salix capraea	2	1	3	3	0.05	0.7
Salix cinerea	0	2	2	2	0.01	0.1
Sambucus nigra	1	4	5	5	0.03	0.4
Sorbus aucuparia	1	0	1	1	0.003	0.04

Table 7.7. Density and species composition of compartment 10.

Number of trees measured: 104 Date surveyed: 25 Sep 1983

Density: 418 trees/hectare

Total basal area: 10.99 m^2
Relative basal area: 0.44%

Species	Frequency std	cop	tot	Relative frequency (total) %	Basal area m^2	Relative dominance %
Acer campestre	2	0	2	2	0.03	0.3
Acer pseudoplatanus	30	6	36	35	0.24	2.1
Betula pendula	1	0	1	1	0.16	1.5
Corylus avellana	1	8	9	9	0.07	0.6
Crataegus monogyna	0	1	1	1	0.06	0.5
Fagus sylvatica	1	0	1	1	0.003	0.03
Ilex aquifolium	1	0	1	1	0.003	0.02
Prunus avium	1	0	1	1	0.002	0.02
Quercus petraea	9	0	9	9	2.92	26.5
Quercus hybrids	1	1	2	2	0.44	4.0
Tilia cordata	41	0	41	39	7.08	64.4

Table 7.8. Density and species composition of compartment 11.

Number of trees measured: 100 — Date surveyed: 4 Sep 1983

Density: 578 trees/hectare — Total basal area: 7.55 m^2

Relative basal area: 0.44%

Species	Frequency std	cop	tot	Relative frequency (total) %	Basal area m^2	Relative dominance %
Acer pseudoplatanus	47	2	49	49	3.77	50.0
Betula pendula	16	0	16	16	1.25	16.6
Castanea sativa	2	0	2	2	0.45	6.0
Corylus avellana	1	11	12	12	0.16	2.1
Fraxinus excelsior	1	0	1	1	0.09	1.2
Quercus petraea	3	1	4	4	0.33	4.4
Tilia cordata	10	0	10	10	1.09	14.5
Tilia hybrids	2	1	3	3	0.25	3.3
Ulmus glabra	2	1	3	3	0.15	1.9

Table 7.9. Density and species composition of compartment 20.

Number of trees measured: 100 — Date surveyed: 9 Sep 1984

Density: 241 trees/hectare — Total basal area: 13.67 m^2

Relative basal area: 0.33%

Species	Frequency std	cop	tot	Relative frequency (total) %	Basal area m^2	Relative dominance %
Acer pseudoplatanus	2	0	2	2	0.03	0.2
Betula pendula	8	3	11	11	0.58	4.2
Corylus avellana	0	42	42	42	0.48	3.5
Crataegus monogyna	1	0	1	1	0.06	0.4
Fraxinus excelsior	3	0	3	3	0.47	3.5
Ilex aquifolium	0	1	1	1	0.02	0.2
Quercus robur	7	0	7	7	1.44	10.6
Quercus petraea	28	1	29	29	9.82	71.8
Quercus hybrids	1	0	1	1	0.06	0.5
Sorbus aucuparia	0	1	1	1	0.003	0.02
Tilia cordata	2	0	2	2	0.71	5.2

Table 7.10. Density and species composition of compartment 80.

Number of trees measured: 100 — Date surveyed: 9 Aug 1984

Density: 198 trees/hectare — Total basal area: 17.85 m²

Relative basal area: 0.35%

Species	Frequency std	cop	tot	Relative frequency (total) %	Basal area m²	Relative dominance %
Acer pseudoplatanus	1	0	1	1	0.01	0.03
Betula pendula	14	0	14	14	0.49	2.7
Corylus avellana	1	13	14	14	0.13	0.7
Crataegus monogyna	1	0	1	1	0.002	0.01
Ilex aquifolium	2	6	8	8	0.30	1.7
Quercus robur	1	0	1	1	0.04	0.2
Quercus petraea	48	4	52	52	14.33	80.3
Quercus hybrids	9	0	9	9	2.56	14.3

Table 7.11. Density and species composition of compartment 81.

Number of trees measured: 100 — Date surveyed: 6 Nov 1983

Density: 305 trees/hectare — Total basal area: 14.80 m²

Relative basal area: 0.45%

Species	Frequency std	cop	tot	Relative frequency (total) %	Basal area m²	Relative dominance %
Betula pendula	14	1	15	15	0.36	2.5
Corylus avellana	2	14	16	16	0.08	0.6
Crataegus monogyna	2	2	4	4	0.12	0.8
Populus tremula	1	0	1	1	0.003	0.02
Quercus petraea	60	1	61	61	13.8	93.0
Quercus hybrids	2	0	2	2	0.43	2.9
Tilia cordata	1	0	1	1	0.03	0.2

Table 7.12. Density and species composition of compartment 82.

Number of trees measured: 100 — Date surveyed: 21 Sep 1985

Density: 226 trees/hectare — Total basal area: 12.13 m^2

Relative basal area: 0.40%

Species	Frequency std	cop	tot	Relative frequency (total) %	Basal area m^2	Relative dominance %
Betula pendula	13	2	15	22	0.94	7.7
Corylus avellana	1	10	11	16	0.09	0.8
Fraxinus excelsior	1	0	1	1	0.22	1.9
Ilex aquifolium	1	1	2	3	0.02	0.2
Quercus robur	1	0	1	1	0.62	5.1
Quercus petraea	25	2	27	40	7.9	65.3
Quercus hybrids	6	2	8	12	1.81	14.9
Sambucus nigra	0	1	1	1	0.002	0.02
Tilia cordata	2	0	2	3	0.50	4.1

Chapter 8

General Conclusions

So far, we have looked at a number of diverse topics - physical geography, landscape and management history, flora and vegetation. Discussions and conclusions pertinent to each of these studies have been included in the respective chapters, but here we shall attempt to pull the threads together and formulate some general conclusions.

8.1 Origins

The historical record

In the course of the documentary research, nothing has come to light which enables us to state with conviction how and when Swithland Wood originated as woodland. Detailed historical records do not go back far enough, and even if they did, the origin of the wood is unlikely to have been an 'event' that warranted an explicit entry in the manorial records. Our study area is surely the culmination of a long series of piecemeal changes that have occurred since the site was occupied by primeval woodland. We might have hoped that at least the later phases of its development were well recorded. Alas, the site has turned out to be very complicated, comprising several woods with confusing names and, at least for some of the time, in more than one ownership. The historical sources, taken in isolation, are simply inadequate to untangle this complex web. However, by calling upon the results of fieldwork, and by preparing ourselves to be satisfied with probabilities rather than certainties, some tentative conclusions may be reached.

Primary or secondary; ancient or recent?

Ridge-and-furrow proclaims much of Swithland Wood to be secondary woodland of medieval or later origin. Although there are no records of this land being ploughed, the general landscape history of the area (section 3.4.3) does suggest a likely period for cultivation. The fact that farmers ever considered tackling such difficult terrain is extraordinary. The acid soil is ridden with chunks of slate and, in many places, lies on steep slopes among awkward outcrops. Its cultivation was surely a desperate response to a shortage of food, at a time when all the good land was already in use. These were the circumstances prevailing in the late thirteenth and early fourteenth centuries. It is surmised that the site of Swithland Wood was cultivated, presumably by farmers based at Hallgates, for a relatively short time prior to the mid fourteenth century, when the Black Death rendered such marginal ploughland redundant. Documentary evidence shows that the part of the wood known as Great Lynns (compartments 3, 4 and 11) had become woodland by the late fifteenth century. This is, in fact, the only part which certainly qualifies as ancient woodland: pre-1600 references to other parts are less explicit, or non-existent, leaving us unsure whether to classify them as ancient or recent. They were definitely wooded in 1677, with the exception of 'Old Slate Pits Hill' (probably part of compartment 5), which was enclosed from the open forest in the mid eighteenth century.

It is conceivable that small parts of Swithland Wood are primary, though impossible to prove. The sole compartment which lacks obvious signs of a previous land-use is compartment 9, yet this cannot even be shown to be ancient. Another possibility is that the outcrops and their immediate surroundings were never completely cleared of trees. At the height of cultivation such places could have been used for little else but growing trees, except perhaps as quarries. Quarrying on a small scale would not have excluded the survival of woodland.

The stimulus for speculating on the existence of primary woodland is the rich flora of Swithland Wood, with many ancient woodland indicator species. If the whole site was completely denuded of woodland then where did these plants of poor colonising ability return from? Perhaps there existed other woodland close by, of which no trace now remains. The two areas of woodland presently adjoining the study area (1 and 2 on figure 2.2) do not appear to be very old. R. Gardner informs me that both contain ridge-and-furrow. The indicator species are by no means concentrated in Great Lynns. They are widespread, hinting that other compartments also are ancient. However, as previously explained (page 80), we must resist the temptation to claim ancient status for the various parts of a single wood, on the basis of their individual species lists. The indicator species technique is not so sensitive as to justify its application in that way. From the viewpoint of landscape history, the most enlightening aspect of the ecological work is the detailed study of one of these indicator species, small-leaved lime.

The significance of small-leaved lime

It is known from pollen evidence that lime became abundant in lowland Britain by the Atlantic period (5500-3100 b.c.), when summer temperatures were higher than at present (Moore 1977, Huntley & Birks 1983). Lime may have been the most important component of the primeval forest (Greig 1982). Now that the climate has cooled, lime only rarely reproduces from seed, but readily propagates itself by vegetative means (Pigott & Huntley 1978, Rackham 1980). This behaviour has rendered the tree particularly vulnerable to clearance. No longer is it an abundant tree because so few places have never been totally cleared of woodland. It was concluded that, during the episode of cultivation, lime was present on the boundary banks, most conspicuously along the boundary to the east of compartments 3, 4 and 20, where massive layered trees (probably the remains of a hedge) are to be found. It also appears to have survived on the outcrops, such as those in compartment 80, lending support to the notion that fragments of woodland persisted there. From these refuges lime has slowly infiltrated the secondary woodland.

Further useful information regarding the status of small-leaved lime at this site is to be found in the very names of the places we have been discussing. The *Lynns* element that recurs in the wood names was spelled *Lyndes* in 1512. Newtown Linford, the parish that contains our study area, was *Lyndeford* in 1290. These names allude to the *linden* or lime tree, and are most unusual in Leicestershire (Bourne 1981, page 25). So too is the tree (Primavesi & Evans 1988). It is surely more than chance that the place-names and the tree coincide here. The correspondence between *lind* place-names and surviving relict populations of small-leaved lime has been observed elsewhere in Britain and Europe (Greig 1982). If this species has been planted here, then it was introduced at a very early phase in the development of Charnwood Forest. Rackham (1980) considers that the practice of planting trees in woodland was commonplace only after medieval times. Planting can never be ruled out, of course, but it seems much more plausible that the trees, from which the settlement and the woods take their names, were remnants of the original natural woodland.

Figure 8.1. The boundary earthwork at the east of compartment 20, viewed from inside the wood, with its ditch apparently on the 'wrong' side (see section AE on figure 2.11). Normally, the ditch would be on the outside of a wood, for better protection against grazing animals. The explanation is that the site of Swithland Wood was formerly common grazing land, and it was farmland belonging to Hallgates, on the far side of the boundary, that was being protected. (SK54051270, September 1981.)

Summary

At this point, we can attempt to summarise the historical development of the site. A complete and coherent story cannot be told on the basis of the facts alone; it has been necessary to incorporate some theories of a more speculative nature in the account that follows.

Before the impact of man, the original natural woodland here consisted mainly of small-leaved lime, oak (principally *Quercus petraea*) and hazel, with holly, birch and alder. Woodland persisted until a relatively late period in Charnwood Forest. Early pioneers found more promising land to clear elsewhere, and by the time of the Domesday survey (1086), there were still very few, if any, people living near the site of Swithland Wood. The extensive tracts of primary woodland were subjected, not only to felling, but also to common grazing from the surrounding settlements, pressures that were to increase through the twelfth and thirteenth centuries. A predominantly wooded landscape degenerated towards heathland with fewer and fewer trees, except in those areas that were deliberately enclosed as woods or quarries. Where farmland adjoined the common grazing land, stockproof boundaries were maintained to protect crops. One of these was along the eastern edge of Swithland Wood, an earthwork which now marks the parish boundary (figure 8.1). Its ditch was towards part of the common grazing land to the west, destined to become Swithland Wood. The bank was surmounted by a hedge, made from whatever suitable trees were to hand - including small-leaved lime. The settlement of Hallgates, whose farmland this boundary would have secured, was established before 1268. Apart from this hedge, and the immediate surroundings of the outcrops, the study area, like the rest of the open forest, was more or less treeless, and probably best described as heathy grassland.

In about 1300, the threat of famine obliged the farmers of Hallgates to bring extra acres into cultivation. Part of the common grazing land to the west of the old boundary was ploughed up, as far as the present western edge of Swithland Wood. This new boundary was marked, not by an earthwork, but probably by a hedge or stone wall; the slate quarries may have been working at this time. Following the local custom, the assart was known as a 'hay'. When the Black Death struck in 1349, the newly won ploughland dropped out of cultivation and reverted to rough grazing. Evidently, the intensity of grazing over the following 200 years was insufficient to prevent the re-establishment of trees. Whether or not natural regeneration was later encouraged by the exclusion animals, or even supplemented by planting, we do not know, but by 1512 Great Lynns had become woodland and was managed as coppice. It seems likely that other parts too had become woodland, but that the records have been lost. Slate Pit Hay was still grazed, but trees were also present there as pollards. Finally, Old Slate Pits Hill, which also had huge pollards, was enclosed as woodland in the mid 1700s, leaving only the Wood Meadows as grassland. Apart from the expansion of the quarries through the nineteenth century, the only further significant change has been the planting up of part of the Wood Meadows in about 1968.

8.2 Management

Wood-pasture and coppice

Prior to the late 1600s there are few clues to the management of the wood, except that some parts were treated as wood-pasture: the sale of bark in 1540 suggests that oak pollards were present. This is supported by the account of massive oak pollards growing around the slate pits in about 1760. The regular coppice cycle, which was clearly well-established by 1761, appears to have been operating at least one hundred years earlier. Coppicing on a strict rotation continued until 1859, when sales of timber suddenly start. The old names for the various parts of Swithland Wood seem to have been abandoned along with the regular coppicing regime. No longer was felling conducted on the basis of these compartments, so their names fell out of use, and were forgotten. The exact timing of the first major timber sale was probably connected with Stamford's financial predicament, but the decision to grow standards among the coppice was clearly made many years previously, perhaps as far back as the early 1700s (we do not know the age of the timber). The shade cast by standard trees would have retarded the growth of the underwood, which might explain the extension of the coppice cycle from 19 to 20 and then 21 years. Eventually, the density of timber trees was allowed to suppress the underwood completely. Considering the long tradition of coppicing in Swithland Wood, there are very few ancient stools to be found today, not even the rotting remains of any. The stools were evidently killed off, or perhaps even grubbed out, a long while ago.

Felling and restocking of timber

Major timber fellings occurred in the late nineteenth and early twentieth centuries, although the records do not specify whereabouts in the wood. Compartment 11 lacks large trees and must have been clear-felled, but this compartment alone could not have produced the total number of trees involved. What little information exists on the timber sales implies that the normal practice was to select individuals or groups of trees which would be 'blazed and numbered', rather than to clear-fell a large block or compartment. This is why fellings do not show up in the compartment girth histograms. There are even fewer indications of how replanting was carried out; we cannot even be sure that it was a regular part of management. In Swithland Wood now, there are no well-defined blocks of 100 year old trees, such as we might expect if substantial areas were replanted at the turn of the century. In fact, trees of this age are scattered around the various compartments.

This accords with our deductions about felling, for planting would surely have taken place in the areas that had just been felled, in small rather than large units. Whatever long term plan the estate manager had for restocking the wood, it did not come to fruition, for young trees are now uncommon. Perhaps the imminent break-up of the estate cut short a felling and replanting scheme, or at least quelled any enthusiasm for tending the 12,187 (or more) saplings planted in 1909. From the forestry point of view, many of the canopy oaks are of poor growth-form, with epicormic burrs, distorted trunks, low branches, and so on. These characters are, to a great extent, genetic traits which we would not expect in planted trees from a nursery (Rackham 1980). Autumn visitors to the wood will have noticed how the leaves of some oaks persist for weeks after others have fallen. The genetic miscellany of the oaks in Swithland Wood suggests that, in the past, natural regeneration has been at least as important as planting.

Had not commercial interest in the wood ceased in 1925, it is most likely that Swithland Wood would have been converted to conifers. Indeed, it is surprising that conifers had not already been introduced by that date, in view of what we know about other estate woods. Subsequent owners appear to have had little impact on the semi-natural woodland.

The present structure

The present high forest structure, with far fewer young timber trees than old, results from the lapse of commercial woodland management, and the reluctance of the principal species to regenerate naturally, other than in very limited areas. If oak, ash and lime have not been recruited into the canopy, then what has taken their place? We have already noted the dominance of sycamore locally, but generally, only birch has been able to fill some of the gaps. This first generation of birch is reaching the end of its lifespan, its demise being hastened by recent droughts such as that of 1976. Many parts of the wood have not developed a closed canopy, despite the spreading crowns of the canopy trees. Of all the light that falls through the gaps in the canopy, very little reaches the seedlings of trees because most is intercepted by bramble or bracken. When the last major fellings took place, much extra light was admitted to the woodland floor, which stimulated the growth of these species. Subsequent owners did not control them, allowing these aggressive plants to spread and suppress all beneath them.

The structure of the lime population in compartment 10 requires further comment. In respect of the density, spatial distribution and growth form of the trees, this compartment is peculiar. It has the appearance of an even-aged stand, and the ring counts tend to corroborate this view. Even-aged monospecific stands can arise naturally if, for example, the previous stand is destroyed by a storm or disease, then conditions happen to favour the establishment of one particular species. Pigott (1975) has observed even-aged stands of small-leaved lime within a natural forest in Poland. Bearing in mind the known history of Swithland Wood, the structure of this compartment is far more likely to be due to management. Evidently, a felling in about 1870 was followed either by (i) singling of existing stools, or (ii) natural regeneration from seed, or (iii) planting. Most trees have straight, clean trunks from the base and show no hint of coppice origin. A flush regeneration from seed cannot be dismissed but in view of the regularity of the stand and the rarity of seedling establishment this seems very unlikely. This forces us to consider the possibility of planting. For what purpose lime may have been planted is not known. It was not regarded as a timber tree, and its special uses were very limited and unlikely to warrant such a long term investment as planting represents (Edlin 1949). Furthermore, lime was already present before 1870. Some of the coppice stools and clusters of interlinked stems are certainly older than this. If the name Little Lynns has been correctly assigned, then continuity of lime is established back to 1512. For reasons unknown, lime coppice seems to have been deliberately converted to lime high forest in this compartment.

8.3 Flora and Vegetation

The paradox of continuity and disturbance

Various reasons have been put forward to account for the unusually rich flora recorded for Swithland Wood. Among them were the popularity of the site with botanists, the wide range of habitats, the shape of the wood and the number of deliberate and accidental introductions. With regard to the long-established woodland and grassland habitats, it has been claimed that ecological continuity has sustained populations of certain sensitive species. Had these habitats been disturbed in recent times, they would have lost these 'indicator' plants and, we might suppose, be correspondingly poorer in species. But there is more to disturbance than this. Two properties of long-established plant communities help to explain what happens when they are disturbed. Firstly, the species present are the ultimate winners of the long, competitive struggle to secure the limited resources of the particular environment in question. Less aggressive plants, which may once have occurred, have been ousted by competitive exclusion. Secondly, it is unlikely that any ecological niches remain unoccupied - suitable plants would have established themselves long ago. Communities that are approaching their climax state are more or less closed to potential colonists. It takes some kind of environmental disruption, such as storm damage, to dislodge climax species from their dominant position, at least temporarily. Plants that were previously suppressed may then seize the opportunity to spread. New habitats may be created, such as bare soil on which the seeds of a random selection of new species may germinate. Thus, by delaying or setting back the process of competitive exclusion, disturbance allows more species to co-exist.

Natural catastrophes, such as climatic extremes or disease, are only one facet of disturbance. On a smaller scale, the collapse of a moribund tree may be equally disruptive to the field layer vegetation below it. Similarly, the total defoliation by caterpillars of a small group of saplings could alter the development of vegetation there for many decades to come. Events such as these must be regarded as part of, and not exceptions to, the natural course of events in woodlands. Indeed, disturbance is gaining recognition among ecologists as a key factor in sustaining the diversity of natural communities (Begon, Harper & Townsend 1986, page 700). Our study area is far from being a natural community, however. Coppicing, grazing, felling, mowing, quarrying, horse riding, etc. are, of course, other kinds of disturbance.

The extraordinary richness of Swithland Wood now begins to make sense. When allowed to proceed too far, quarrying is obviously very destructive, but in Swithland Wood the inheritance of the slate industry is, almost certainly, a greater richness of plant species than we would otherwise have. The new habitats have provided homes for specialised non-woodland species. Were it not for these quarries, the flora would probably lack *Umbilicus rupestris, Polygonum amphibium, Cytisus scoparius, Polypodium interjectum, Ulex gallii, Asplenium* spp., *Phyllitis scolopendrium, Teesdalia nudicaulis,* and so on. It is very doubtful whether as many woodland species became locally extinct due to the destruction by quarrying of the corresponding areas of woodland. Excavations for the water main have added at least four species to the list, as related in section 6.4.7. Trampling by visitors and the maintenance of horse and vehicle tracks probably keeps conditions locally suitable for weedy species such as *Plantago major, Poa annua, Polygonum lapathifolium, Aethusa cynapium* and *Veronica hederifolia.* In the Wood Meadows, grazing and mowing have set back what would otherwise have been a succession to scrub. Without this disturbance to the natural course of events, many of the 'old grassland' specialities would have been shaded out. Similarly, woodland management, in the form of coppicing and felling, has (until recent decades) ensured that shade-intolerant species have been able to find well-lit refuges.

Ecological continuity may be perceived as the antithesis of disturbance, but Swithland Wood illustrates how both may work in the same direction, to enhance species richness.

Future trends

The structure of the shrub and canopy layers was discussed in chapter 7, where attention was drawn to the lack of regeneration in most species. The girth histograms for oak and small-leaved lime show very clearly that there are too few middle-aged trees to replace the old ones. Furthermore, there are not nearly enough young trees to succeed the middle-aged ones; virtually none in the case of lime. There is no doubt that the present distribution of ages cannot be maintained. The wood will present a very different appearance in fifty to a hundred years time, because the number of large trees is bound to decrease. As old trees die, more light will be made available to seedlings and saplings, whose numbers will therefore increase. It is questionable, however, whether sufficient numbers of young trees will survive to be recruited into the canopy, unless steps are taken to control bracken, bramble, sycamore, and the Leicestershire public.

The prospects for small-leaved lime are not as bleak as its girth histograms may suggest. The scarcity of single-stemmed trees of small girth is faithfully illustrated, but those charts do not show the numerous young stems attached to multi-stemmed trees (because only the largest stems were included). Since lime propagates more effectively by vegetative means than by seed, it is the small stems that spring from coppice stools and damaged trees that are crucial for the future of this species. Although lime presently fails to reproduce from seed, there are hints in the distribution map that this has occurred in the past (page 200). The potential for sexual regeneration in the future looks good (figure 8.2). Now that coppicing is no longer practised, many lime trees flower profusely. If, as the climatologists predict, summer temperatures will rise, then a greater proportion of seed will be viable. Perhaps all that will be needed to initiate a new generation of lime trees is a year or two of low rodent populations.

Figure 8.2. Flowers of small-leaved lime. In July, the crowns of mature trees turn pale yellow on account of the masses of sweet scented flowers. Most of these fail to be fertilised, and are aborted together with their bracteoles, which shower to the ground in August like autumn leaves. (Swithland Wood, July 1987).

8.4 Further research

This project set out to answer questions about the history and vegetation of Swithland Wood. Such investigations tend to raise at least as many problems as they solve, and this one is no exception. Some of the questions that arose during the course of the work tempted the writer to inquire further, but, recognising the danger that the project might never finish, have not been pursued. Some ideas for further research are listed below. In addition, an account of the biological groups not addressed by this report, i.e. fungi, algae and all the animal groups, would be most welcome as a companion volume!

Soils and land-use history. Much of the site has been ploughed, and whatever soil profile existed previously would have been largely destroyed. The discovery of a profile, tentatively identified as a podzol (a type characteristic of heathland), raises an interesting question. Has this profile survived the episode of cultivation (by being situated at its margin, perhaps), or did it develop during a later heathland phase, between the arable and the present woodland phase? In general, to what extent do soils bear an imprint of past land-uses?

What are the small pits? They are mostly unconvincing as quarries, yet they are not accompanied by spoil heaps. The writer has been been puzzled by similar pits in other woods.

Previous names for Swithland Wood. If further historical documents can be located, ideally an early map, it might be possible to resolve the confusion over the old compartment names. The Danvers family (Earls of Lanesborough), owners of the adjacent woodland, and previously in possession of parts of the study area, might have left some relevant historical records.

What was the market for the coppice wood? Suggestions have been made, but no evidence is available to explain how such a regular coppicing cycle could be sustained.

Small-leaved lime in compartment 10. Why was lime coppice converted into high forest, apparently by planting, in the late nineteenth century?

The genetics of the small-leaved lime population would make a fascinating study. It might be used to test the hypothesis that the clumped distribution pattern of this species is attributable to vegetative reproduction.

Finally, the importance of Swithland Wood for ***nature conservation*** needs to be properly evaluated, the objectives of management set out, and appropriate actions prescribed. The level of public interest in the site is very high, especially in the wake of the recent dispute between the owners and the Nature Conservancy Council. The timely publication of a mutually agreed management plan would be a welcome reassurance that the unquestioned ecological interest of Swithland Wood will, in the future, be given due regard.

Acknowledgements

I would like to extend my thanks to the following organisations and individuals, for help of various kinds during the course of this work: Loughborough Naturalists' Club; Groby Archaeology Society; Leicestershire Libraries and Information Service; University of Leicester, especially Dr D. Ratcliffe (Department of Botany) and Dr D. M. Harper (Department of Zoology) and the University Library. Leicestershire Museums, Arts and Records Service, especially Mr I. M. Evans, Mr J. G. Martin, Mr J. Mathias, Mrs M. E. Ball, Mrs P. Drinkall, Dr A. Fletcher, Mr P. Liddle and the staff of Leicestershire Record Office. Mr M. Harrison (Bradgate Park Trust), Professor C. D. Pigott and Dr O. Rackham (University of Cambridge), Dr R. A. D. Cameron (University of Birmingham), Dr G. F. Peterken (Nature Conservancy Council) and Mr M. Ainley (Severn Trent Water). Many friends kindly supplied information or advice, notably Mr M. T. Ball, Mrs P. A. Evans, Mr M. Gamble, Mr P. H. Gamble, Mr R. Gardner, Mr C. Green, Mrs E. Hesselgreaves, Dr P. E. Jackson, Mr M. B. Jeeves, Mr D. A. Ramsey, Mr P. B. Smith, Mr A. E. Squires and Mr R. W. Tobin. I am especially grateful for the invaluable assistance so generously given by Mr & Mrs D. W. Ballard, who spent countless hours in the wood with the author, laying out tapes and quadrats, counting hundreds of saplings and measuring thousands of tree-trunks.

Most of the maps are based upon Ordnance Survey material with the permission of the Controller of Her Majesty's Stationery Office, Crown copyright reserved. Drawings and photographs are by the author unless otherwise credited.

References

Published books and papers

Allin, C. E., 1981. *The Medieval Leather Industry in Leicester*. Leicestershire Museums.

Aston, M. and Rowley, T., 1974. *Landscape Archaeology: An Introduction to Fieldwork Techniques on Post-Roman Landscapes*. David and Charles.

Baker, D. W., 1983. *Coalville: the first 75 years 1833-1908*. Leicestershire Libraries and Information Service.

Ball, M. E. and Jones, M. D., 1976. *The Extractive Industries*. *In* Evans 1976.

Bateman, J., 1883. *The Great Landowners of Great Britain and Ireland*. Harrison/Leicester University Press.

Bates, J. W., 1989. Growth of *Leucobryum glaucum* in a Berkshire oakwood. *Journal of Bryology* **15**, 785-791.

Begon, M., Harper, J. L. and Townsend, C. R., 1986. *Ecology: Individuals, Populations and Communities*. Blackwell.

Bell, M. and Limbrey, S. (eds), 1982. Archaeological Aspects of Woodland Ecology. *British Archaeological Reports* **S146**.

Best, J. A., 1983. *King's Wood Corby: Description, History, Explanation of Habitats & Wildlife*. Nene College Publications.

Bloxam, A., 1831. Plants found in Charnwood Forest. *Natural History in the English Counties* **4**, 163.

Bourne, J., 1981. *Place Names of Leicestershire and Rutland*. Leicestershire Libraries and Information Service.

Brown, D. H., Hawksworth, D. L. and Bailey, R. H., 1976. *Lichenology: Progress and Problems*. Academic Press.

Brown, E. H. and Hopkins, S. V., 1956. Seven centuries of the prices of consumables, compared with builders' wage-rates. *Economica* **23**, 296-313.

Buchholz, K. and Pickering, J. L., 1978. DBH-distribution analysis: an alternative to stand age analysis. *Bulletin of the Torrey Botanical Club* **105**.

Bunce, R. G. H., 1982 and 1989. *A Field Key for Classifying British Woodland Vegetation*, parts **I** and **II**. NERC/ITE.

Burke's Peerage, 1938.

Burnham, C. P., 1980. The soils of England and Wales. *Field Studies* **5**, 349-363.

Burton, W., 1622. *The Description of Leicestershire; containing matters of Antiquity, History, Armoury and Genealogy*. Lynn.

Busgen, M. and Munch, E., 1929. *Structure and Life of Forest Trees*. Chapman and Hall.

Cameron, R. A. D., 1980. Stand structure, species composition and succession in some Shropshire woods. *Field Studies* **5**, 289-306.

Cannon, P. F., Hawksworth, D. L. and Sherwood-Pike, M. A., 1985. *The British Ascomycotina: An annotated checklist*. Commonwealth Agricultural Bureau.

Capelnor, D., 1968. Forest composition on loessal and non-loessal soils in west central Mississippi. *Ecology* **49**.

Chalmers, N. and Parker, P., 1986. *The OU Project Guide: Fieldwork and Statistics for Ecological Projects*. Open University / Field Studies Council.

Clapham, A. R., Tutin, T. G. and Warburg, E. F., 1962. *Flora of the British Isles.* Cambridge University Press.

Clapham, A. R., Tutin, T. G. and Warburg, E. F., 1981. *Excursion Flora of the British Isles.* Cambridge University Press.

Clarkson, L. A., 1974. The English bark trade 1660-1830. *Agricultural History Review* **22**.

Colebourn, P. and Gibbons, R., 1987. *Britain's natural heritage: reading our countryside's past.* Blandford.

Colinvaux, P., 1978. *Why Big Fierce Animals are Rare.* Princeton University Press.

Corley, M. F. V. and Hill, M. O., 1981. *Distribution of Bryophytes in the British Isles: A Census Catalogue of their Occurrence in Vice-Counties.* British Bryological Society.

Cottam, G. and Curtis, J. T., 1956. The use of distance measures in phytosociological sampling. *Ecology* **37**, 451-460.

Crocker, J. (ed.), 1981. *Charnwood Forest : A Changing Landscape.* Loughborough Naturalists' Club / Sycamore Press.

Darby, H. C. and Terrett, I. B. (eds), 1971. *The Domesday Geography of Midland England.* Cambridge University Press.

Dare, M. P., 1925. *Charnwood Forest and its Environs.* Edgar Backus.

Edees, E. S. and Newton, A., 1988. *Brambles of the British Isles.* The Ray Society.

Edlin, H. L., 1949. *Woodland Crafts in Britain.* Batsford.

Ellis, C. D. B., 1951. *Leicestershire and the Quorn Hunt.* Edgar Backus.

Evans, C. E. and Becker, D., 1988. *Rhododendron* control on RSPB reserves. *RSPB Conservation Review* **2**, 54-56.

Evans, I. M. (ed.), 1976. *Charnwood's Heritage.* Leicestershire Museums.

Evans, I. M. (ed.), 1989. *Burley Wood: Report on a study of its history and ecology.* Leicestershire Museums.

Farnham, G. F., 1930. *Charnwood Forest and its Historians and the Charnwood Manors.* Edgar Backus.

Farnham, G. F., 1933. *Leicestershire Medieval Village Notes*, **6**. W. Thornley and son.

Fitzrandolph, H. E. and Hay, M. D., 1926. *Rural industries of England and Wales. I. Timber and underwood industries and some village workshops.* Clarendon Press.

Fletcher, J. M., 1974. *Annual Rings in Modern and Medieval Times. In* Morris and Perring 1974.

Ford, T. D., 1975. *The Rocks of Bradgate.* Bradgate Park Trust.

Forsyth, M., 1974. *The History of Bradgate.* Bradgate Park Trust.

Gamble, P. H., 1965. Regarding the future of Swithland Wood. *Loughborough Naturalists' Club Bulletin* **18**, 2-12.

Geological Survey of Great Britain (England and Wales), 1982. Sheet **155**; Coalville, solid and drift.

Geological Survey of Great Britain (England and Wales), 1976. Sheet **156**; Leicester, solid and drift.

Goldsmith, F. B., Harrison, C. M. and Morton, A. J., 1986. *Description and analysis of vegetation. In* Moore and Chapman 1986.

Greig, J. R. A., 1982. *Past and present lime woods of Europe. In* Bell and Limbrey 1982.

Greig-Smith, P., 1957. *Quantitative Plant Ecology.* Butterworths Scientific Publications.

Habek, J. R., 1968. Forest succession in the Glacier Park cedar-hemlock forests. *Ecology* **49**, 872.

Hains, B. A. and Horton, A., 1969. *British Regional Geology: Central England.* HMSO.

Harding, P. T. and Rose, F., 1986. *Pasture-woodlands in Lowland Britain.* Natural Environment Research Council.

Hawksworth, D. L., 1969. Leicestershire and Rutland Lichens 1950-1969. *Transactions of the Leicester Literary and Philosophical Society* **63**.

Hawksworth, D. L., 1971. Field meeting at Leicester. *Lichenologist* **5**, 170.

Hawksworth, D. L., 1974. *The Changing Flora and Fauna of Britain.* Academic Press.

Hawksworth, D. L., Coppins, B. J. and Rose, F., 1974. *Changes in the British lichen flora. In* Hawksworth 1974.

Hawksworth, D. L. and Rose, F., 1970. Qualitative scale for estimating SO_2 air pollution in England and Wales using epiphytic lichens. *Nature* **227**, 146.

Herbert, A., 1946. Swithland Slate Headstones. *Transactions of Leicestershire Archaeological Society* **XX**.
Hewett, C. A., 1980. *English Historic Carpentry*. Phillimore.
Horwood, A. R., 1904. Leicestershire lichens 1886-1903. *Journal of Botany* **42**, 47.
Horwood, A. R., 1909. The cryptogamic flora of Leicestershire. *Transactions of the Leicester Literary and Philosophical Society* **13**.
Horwood, A. R. and Gainsborough, Earl of, 1933. *The Flora of Leicestershire and Rutland*. Oxford University Press.
Hoskins, W. G., 1955. *The Making of the English Landscape*. Hodder and Stoughton.
Hoskins, W. G., 1957. *Leicestershire: the history of the landscape*. Hodder and Stoughton.
Hoskins, W. G., 1972. *Local History in England*. Longman (2nd ed.).
Hubbard, C. E., 1968. *Grasses*. Penguin.
Huntley, B. and Birks, H. J. B., 1983. *An Atlas of Past and Present Pollen Maps for Europe: 0-13,000 years ago*. Cambridge University Press.
Hyde, H. A., Wade, A. E. and Harrison, S. G., 1978. *Welsh Ferns, Clubmosses, Quillworts and Horsetails*. National Museum of Wales (6th ed.).
Jackson, A. B., 1905. The Leicestershire mosses. *Journal of Botany* **43**, 225.
Jarman, M., 1984. *Ground Work: Practical Ways of Learning about Soils*. Leicestershire Museums.
Jermy, A. C. and Tutin, T. G., 1968. *British Sedges*. Botanical Society of the British Isles.
Jones, E. W., 1945. The structure and reproduction of the virgin forest of the north temperate zone. *New Phytologist* **44**, 130-148.
Jones, E. W., 1961. British Forestry in 1790-1813. *Quarterly Journal of Forestry* **55**, 136.
Keble Martin, W., 1978. *The Concise British Flora in Colour*. Sphere Books (4th ed.).
Kershaw, K. A., 1964. *Quantitative and Dynamic Ecology*. Arnold.
Kirby, K. J., Bines, T., Burn, A., Mackintosh, J., Pitkin, P. and Smith, I., 1986. Seasonal and observer differences in vascular plant records from British woodlands. *Journal of Ecology* **74**, 123.
Krebs, C. J., 1978. *Ecology: The experimental analysis of distribution and abundance*. Harper (2nd ed.).
Liddle, P., 1982. *Leicestershire Archaeology - The Present State of Knowledge*. **1**: *to the End of the Roman Period*. Leicestershire Museums.
Locke, G. M. L., 1987. *Census of Woodlands and Trees 1979-82*. Forestry Commission Bulletin **63**. HMSO.
Loughborough Naturalists' Club, 1962. *Bulletin* No. **6**, 7.
Loughborough Naturalists' Club, 1963. *Bulletin* No. **12**, 6.
Loughborough Naturalists' Club, 1970. *Swithland Wood, a Preliminary Survey*. LNC.
Marshall, W., 1790. *Rural Economy of the Midland Counties*. G. Nichol. (2 vols)
Martin, J. G., 1988. *Geology and Soils*. *In* Primavesi and Evans 1988.
McWhirr, A., 1988. The Roman Swithland Slate Industry. *Transactions of the Leicestershire Archaeological and Historical Society* **LXII**, 1-8.
Megaw, J. V. S. and Simpson, D. D. A. (eds), 1979. *Introduction to British Prehistory*. Leicester University Press.
Meteorological Office, 1960-1983. *Monthly weather report summaries*.
Mitchell, A., 1974. *A Field Guide to the Trees of Britain and Northern Europe*. Collins.
Moore, N. W., 1987. *Bird of time: the science and politics of nature conservation*. Cambridge University Press.
Moore, P. D., 1977. Ancient distribution of lime trees in Britain. *Nature* **268**, 13.
Moore, P. D. and Chapman, S. B. (eds), 1986. *Methods in Plant Ecology*. Blackwell (2nd ed.).
Morgan, P. (ed.), 1979. *Domesday Book: 22. Leicestershire*. Phillimore.
Morris, M. G. and Perring, F. H. (eds), 1974. *The British Oak*. Botanical Society of the British Isles/Classey.
Mott, F. T., 1868. *Charnwood Forest*. W. Kent and Co.
Mott, F. T., *et al.*, 1886. *The Flora of Leicestershire*. Williams and Norgate.
Mueller-Dombois, D. and Ellenberg, H., 1974. *Aims and Methods of Vegetation Ecology*. John Wiley.

Nature Conservancy Council, 1975. *Wildlife Conservation in Charnwood Forest: Report by a working party.* Nature Conservancy Council, Midlands Region.
Nature Conservancy Council, 1983. *Leicestershire Inventory of Ancient Woodlands.* NCC.
Neal, E. G., 1958. *Woodland Ecology.* Heinemann.
Newton, A., 1983. The Hallgates Story. *Transactions of the Leicester Literary and Philosophical Society* **77**.
Nichols, J., 1811. *History and Antiquities of the County of Leicester.* **4 (2)**.
Packham, J. R. and Harding, J. L., 1982. *Ecology of Woodland Processes.* Edward Arnold.
Parker, L. A., 1976. *The Large Estates. In* Evans 1976.
Pearsall, W. H., 1971. *Mountains and Moorlands.* Collins New Naturalist.
Pennington, W., 1969. *The History of British Vegetation.* English Universities Press.
Perring, F. H. and Walters, S. M., 1962. *Atlas of the British Flora.* Nelson.
Peterken, G. F., 1969. Development of Vegetation in Staverton Park, Suffolk. *Field Studies* **3**, 1-39.
Peterken, G. F., 1974. A Method for assessing woodland flora for conservation using indicator species. *Biological Conservation* **6**, 239-245.
Peterken, G. F., 1981. *Woodland Conservation and Management.* Chapman and Hall.
Peterken, G. F. and Welch, R. C. (eds), 1975. *Bedford Pulieus : its history, ecology and management.* Institute of Terrestrial Ecology.
Phythian-Adams, C. (ed.), 1986. *The Norman Conquest of Leicestershire and Rutland: A regional introduction to Domesday Book.* Leicestershire Museums.
Pigott, C. D., 1969. The status of *Tilia cordata* and *T. platyphyllos* on the Derbyshire limestone. *Journal of Ecology* **57**, 491-504.
Pigott, C. D., 1975. Natural regeneration of *Tilia cordata* in relation to forest structure in the forest of Bialoweiza, Poland. *Philosophical Transactions of the Royal Society* series **B**, volume **270**, 151-179.
Pigott, C. D., 1985. Selective damage to tree seedlings by bank voles (*Clethrionomys glareolus*). *Oecologia* **67**, 367-371.
Pigott, C. D. and Huntley, J. P., 1978. Factors controlling the distribution of *Tilia cordata* at the northern limits of its geographical range. *New Phytologist* **81**, 429-441.
Pigott, C. D. and Taylor, K., 1964. The distribution of woodland herbs in relation to the supply of nitrogen and phosphorus in the soil. *Journal of Ecology* **52**, 175-185.
Pitt, W., 1809. *A General View of the Agriculture of the County of Leicester with observations on the means of its improvement.* Board of Agriculture and Internal Improvement.
Pollard, E., 1973. Hedges VII. Woodland relic hedges in Huntingdon and Peterborough. *Journal of Ecology* **61**.
Potter, T. R., 1842. *The History and Antiquities of Charnwood Forest.*
Primavesi, A. L. and Evans, P. A., 1988. *Flora of Leicestershire.* Leicestershire Museums.
Prince, S. D., 1986. *Data analysis. In* Moore and Chapman 1986.
Rackham, O., 1975. *Hayley Wood: Its History and Ecology.* CAMBIENT.
Rackham, O., 1976. *Trees and Woodland in the British Landscape.* Dent.
Rackham, O., 1980. *Ancient Woodland: Its history, vegetation and uses in England.* Arnold.
Ramsey, D. A., 1986. Leicestershire Slate. *Bulletin of the Leicestershire Industrial History Society* **9**, 4-29.
Ramsey, D. A., 1987. Bradgate brick kiln or clamp sites. *Transactions of the Leicestershire Archaeological and Historical Society* **LXI**, 92-93.
Ratcliffe, D. A., 1977. *A Nature Conservation Review.* Cambridge University Press.
Richards, J., 1988. The Greys of Bradgate in the English Civil War: A Study of Henry Grey, First Earl of Stamford and his Son and Heir Thomas, Lord Grey of Groby. *Transactions of the Leicestershire Archaeological and Historical Society* **LXII**, 33-52.
Robinson, J. M., 1988. *The English Country Estate.* The National Trust.
Rose, F., 1976. *Lichenological indicators of age and environmental continuity in woodlands. In* Brown, Hawksworth and Bailey 1976.
Rose, F., 1981. *The Wild Flower Key.* Warne.
Sage, B. L. (ed.), 1966. *Northaw Great Wood: its history and natural history.* Education Dept. of Hertfordshire County Council.

Seaward, M. R. D. and Hitch, C. J. B., 1982. *Atlas of the lichens of the British Isles.* Institute of Terrestrial Ecology.

Shaw, M. W., 1974. *The reproductive characteristics of oak. In* Morris & Perring 1974.

Shotton, F. W., 1959. New petrological groups based on axes from the West Midlands. *Proceedings of the Prehistoric Society* **25**, 135-143.

Smith, A. J. E., 1978. *The Moss Flora of Britain and Ireland.* Cambridge University Press.

Sowter, F. A., 1941. *The Cryptogamic Flora of Leicestershire and Rutland : Bryophytes.* Edgar Backus.

Sowter, F. A., 1945. Notes on and additions to the bryophytes of Leicestershire and Rutland. *North Western Naturalist* **20**.

Sowter, F. A., 1969. Leicestershire and Rutland Bryophytes 1945-1969. *Transactions of the Leicester Literary and Philosophical Society* **LXIII**.

Sowter, F. A., 1972. Leicestershire and Rutland Cryptogamic notes, 2. *Transactions of the Leicester Literary and Philosophical Society* **LXVI**, 21-25.

Sowter, F. A. and Hawksworth, D. L., 1970. Leicestershire and Rutland Cryptogamic Notes, I. *Transactions of the Leicester Literary and Philosophical Society* **LXIV**, 89-100.

Squires, A. E., 1981. *History of the Charnwood Forest Landscape. In* Crocker 1981.

Squires, A. E., 1990. Leicestershire's Woodland Heritage. *Heritage* **9**, 8.

Squires, A. E. and Humphrey, W., 1986. *The medieval parks of Charnwood Forest.* Sycamore Press.

Steele, R. C. and Welch, R. C. (eds), 1973. *Monks Wood : A Nature Reserve Record.* Nature Conservancy Council.

Stevenson, J., 1974. *The Greys of Bradgate.* Bradgate Park Trust.

Stewart, G. H., 1986. Population dynamics of a montane conifer forest, Western Cascade Range, Oregon, USA. *Ecology* **67 (2)**, 534-544.

Sutherland, D. S., Boynton, H. H., Ford, T. D., Le Bas, M. J. and Moseley, J., 1987. A Guide to the Geology and Precambrian Rocks of Bradgate Park in Charnwood Forest, Leicestershire. *Transactions of the Leicester Literary and Philosophical Society* **81**, 47-83.

Sykes, J. M., Horrill, A. D. and Mountford, M. D., 1983. Use of visual cover assessments as quantitative estimators of some British woodland taxa. *Journal of Ecology* **71**, 437-450.

Tansley, A. G., 1939. *The British Islands and their Vegetation.* Cambridge University Press.

Taylor, C. C., 1975. *Fields in the English Landscape.* Dent.

Taylor, C. C., 1983. *Village and Farmstead: A History of Rural Settlement in England.* George Philip.

Trudgill, S., 1989. Soil types: a Field Identification Guide. *Field Studies* **7**, 337-363.

Turner, E., 1985. *Robert Martin of The Brand.* Leicestershire Libraries and Information Service.

Turner, J., 1962. The *Tilia* decline, an anthropogenic interpretation. *New Phytologist* **61**, 328.

Usher, M. B., 1983. Species Diversity - a comment on a paper by W. B. Yapp. *Field Studies* **5**, 825-832.

Victoria History of the Counties of England, 1907-64. A History of Leicestershire. Oxford University Press.

Walpole, M. W., 1971. Field meeting to Swithland Wood; Bryophyte report. *Annual Report of Loughborough Naturalists' Club.*

Watson, E. V., 1981. *British Mosses and Liverworts.* Cambridge University Press (3rd ed.).

Watt, A. S., 1919. On the causes of failure of natural regeneration in British oakwoods. *Journal of Ecology* **7**, 173.

Webb, D. A., 1985. What are the criteria for presuming native status? *Watsonia* **15**, 231-236.

Willis, A. J., 1973. *Introduction to Plant Ecology.* George Allen and Unwin.

Woodward, S. F., 1984. *The Landscape of a Leicestershire Parish.* Leicestershire Museums.

Woodward, S. F., 1988. *The status of* Tilia cordata *in Swithland Wood, Leicestershire.* Dissertation submitted for University of Leicester Advanced Certificate in Ecology and Environmental Management.

References

Archival material

N. B. LRO = Leicestershire Record Office

1. De Banco Roll 688. Hilary, 11 Hen VI, 1433, m464. Leyc. Public Record Office; translation published in Farnham 1930.
2. Ministers Accounts. Henry VIII No 1824, 1512. Groby and its members. Public Record Office; translation published in Farnham 1930.
3. Passage describing the need for pollarding, Ulverscroft lands. Translation published in Farnham 1930.
4. Chancery *inquisition post mortem* Edw. III, file 70, No. 6, 1343. Public Record Office; translation published in Farnham 1933.
5. Court Roll, Groby manor, 1350. Public Record Office; translation published in Farnham 1933.
6. 'Plotting of Swithland Wood', April 1858, 4 chains to 1 inch. LRO DG20/2/196.
7. Swithland Enclosure Award and map, 1799. LRO QS47/1/44.
8. Charnwood Forest enclosure award. LRO QS42 and map (1828) LRO QS47/2.
9. Mortgage agreements, 1859. Private collection of Mark Gamble.
10. 'Spring woods in the manor of Groby', c. 1772. Stamford (Grey) papers, Enville Hall, Staffordshire.
11. Volume containing copies of surveys of the manor of Groby, 1658 and 1677, including schedule of woods, 1677. LRO DE1982/181.
12. Estate manager's notebook, 1887. LRO DE1982/191.
13. 'Valuation of estates in Leicestershire belonging to the Rt. Hon. the Earl of Stamford and Warrington', 1857, including report on slate quarry. LRO DG20/2/89 page 220.
14. Account compiled by William Cheselden 1539-40 (in Latin). Northamptonshire Record Office T(S)40/4.
15. Bradgate Estate sale catalogue and plan, 1921. LRO DE1982/241.
16. Bradgate Estate labour books, 1897-1913. LRO DG20/2/81-84.
17. Bradgate Estate 'B' day books, 1896-1910. LRO DG20/2/77-79.
18. Bradgate Estate, Mrs K. H. V. Grey 'B' day book, 1911-14. LRO DG20/2/80.
19. Bradgate Estate ledger, 1915-26. LRO DG20/2/75.
20. Bradgate Estate map, 1838. LRO DG20/2/170.
21. Bradgate Estate valuations, inventories, 1861-1929. LRO DG20/2/90.
22. Bradgate Estate, valuations, tenancies, 1877-1905. LRO DG20/2/93.
23. Bradgate Estate timber sale catalogues. LRO DG20/2/119-127.
24. Bradgate Estate receipts and expenditure account book for half year ending 30 June 1884. LRO DE1982/185.
25. Lancashire, Cheshire, Staffordshire and Leicestershire income and expenditure accounts, 1883. LRO DE1982/195.
26. Hunting Surveys, aerial photos 4 July 1969, run 18 photo 2039.
27. Deed and plans relating to water main, 27 July 1907 (private collection of Mr Mark Gamble).
28. Minutes of Swithland Wood Committee. Leicester Rotary Club papers, LRO 21D69/20.
29. Appeal pamphlet. Leicester Rotary Club papers, LRO 21D69/21/69.
30. Letter from Ferrers dated 21 February 1924 (but actually 1925). Leicester Rotary Club papers, LRO 21D69/21/1.
31. List of donations over £10, 8 July 1925. Leicester Rotary Club papers, LRO 21D69/21/5.
32. Notes on a visit by the Forestry Commission, 6 January 1926. Leicester Rotary Club papers, LRO 21D69/21/9.
33. Letter from Ironside (solicitors), 14 November 1927. Leicester Rotary Club papers, LRO 21D69/21/12.
34. Letter from Leicestershire County Council, 14 May 1931. Leicester Rotary Club papers, LRO 21D69/21/12.

35. Letter from land agents of Swithland Hall Estate regarding boundary, 23 May 1947. Leicester Rotary Club papers, LRO 21D69.
36. Ordnance Survey, 25 inch first edition, sheets XXIV.8, XXIV.12, XXV.5, XXV.9. Surveyed 1883-4.
37. Marriage settlement, Sir John Danvers Bt., to Mary Watson, 1752. LRO DE311/7/1.
38. Lease and release, 8 and 9 September 1819. LRO DE311/7/7/1 and 2.
39. 'Perambulation 'round Charnwood Forrest', Samuel Wylde, 1754. LRO DG9/66/Ma/1 and 1a.
40. Stamford (Grey) Papers, Enville Hall, Staffordshire.
41. Bradgate Estate rental, eighteenth century. Includes schedule of woods of about 1765. LRO DE1982/182.
42. Grant of Manor of Groby to Henry Grey, 1574-5. Enville Hall papers, Staffordshire Record Office.
43. Lease book, 1795. Stamford (Grey) papers, Enville Hall, Staffordshire.
44. Lease book, 1767-69. Stamford (Grey) papers, Enville Hall, Staffordshire.
45. Wood sales accounts. Stamford (Grey) papers, Enville Hall, Staffordshire.
46. Lease book, 1768-1774. Stamford (Grey) papers, Enville Hall, Staffordshire.
47. Bradgate Estate papers. LRO DE453/89.
48. Bradgate Estate rentals, 1851. LRO DE311/68, 69.
49. *Leicester Evening Mail*, 28 July 1921.
50. *Leicester Chronicle*, 30 July 1921.
51. Letter from S. J. Pick, *Leicester Mercury*, 10 May 1965.
52. 'A map of the Manor of Ulverscroft' by Leo Bell, 1796. LRO DE3/48/Ma/340/1.
53. Estate map of Newtown Linford, 1773. LRO DG20/236/1.
54. 'Part of Newtown adjoining the lordship of Swithland and some lands therein' [shows Swithland Wood]; undated, c. 1800. LRO DG20/Ma/236/2.
55. *Leicester Journal*, 26 December 1845.
56. *Leicester Journal*, 1 February 1850.
57. 'A map of the tract of country surrounding Belvoir Castle ...', W. King, 1806.
58. 'A plan of the manor of Groby', Bailey, undated [c. 1800]. LRO DG20/Ma/132/1.
59. *Leicester Journal*, 15 January 1796.
60. *Leicester Journal*, 16 January 1766.
61. Bradgate Estate map, 1859. LRO DG20/Ma/42/3.
62. Correspondence in *Leicester Mercury*, 30 March; 1, 7, 14 and 23 April; 10, 15 and 25 May 1965.
63. Letter from I. M. Evans, *Leicester Mercury*, 6 September 1965.
64. *Leicester Chronicle*, 29 February 1896.
65. Richard Pulteney, 1747. Ms. *Flora of Loughborough district*. LRO FY10, box 9.
66. Ordnance Survey, six inch first edition, sheets XXIV NE, XXIV SE, XXV NW, XXVSW. Surveyed 1883-4.
67. *Leicester Mercury*, 7 May; 1, 6 October 1988.
68. *Leicester Mercury*, September 1984.